CONCORDIA UNIVERSITY
BF39.5.U85
REAL TIME COMPUTERS NEW YORK
3 4211 000004329
W9-ACH-969

Real-Time Computers

Under the Editorship of Wayne Holtzman

HARPER & ROW, PUBLISHERS

REAL-TIME COMPUTERS

Technique and Applications in the Psychological Sciences

WILLIAM R. UTTAL
THE UNIVERSITY OF MICHIGAN

KLINCK MEMORIAL LIBRA
Concordia Teachers College
River Forest, Illinois

NEW YORK, EVANSTON, AND LONDON

To Mi-chan

Real-Time Computers: Technique and Applications in the Psychological Sciences
Copyright © 1967, 1968 by William R. Uttal

Printed in the United States of America. All rights reserved. No part of this book may be used or reproduced in any manner whatsoever without written permission except in the case of brief quotations embodied in critical articles and reviews. For information address Harper & Row, Publishers, Incorporated, 49 East 33rd Street, New York, N.Y. 10016.

Library of Congress Catalog Card Number: 68-10809

90457

CONTENTS

PREFACE

The range of potential applications for stored-program digital computers in research in the life and behavioral sciences has recently been radically increased, owing to two major technological developments. The first development is the availability of the "baby-sized" digital computer, which now sells for less than a single component of previous generations of computer hardware. The second development is time sharing, a process that enables a large number of users to avail themselves of a single computer simultaneously. Both of these developments enable digital computers to be utilized economically, and computers are now being used directly in a wide variety of experimental applications. A few years ago such widespread use of computers would have been impossible, except for those applications, like national defense, in which cost was not significant.

The small-computer idea has developed rapidly into the current concept of a punched paper tape oriented machine with a very small instruction repertoire and very easy connectibility to input-output devices. Modern transistor technology permits systems to be physically small yet have the general-purpose capability of larger systems. It is surprising to realize that some of these small machines are as powerful as the most powerful machines of any cost or size of only a decade ago.

Furthermore, elaborate time-sharing systems have been developed that make it possible for a large number of users to share the capability of a single computer while each apparently has its total powers exclusively available to himself. Behavioral scientists can now implement and experiment with unexpectedly great advances in their methodology, hitherto impossible because of the complexity of the required sequential decision processes. New psychophysical, neuropsychological, and educational techniques are rapidly evolving, specifically because of the availability of this new technology.

Thus, the methodology of experimentation in the behavioral sciences is changing fast. This book is aimed at that methodological set of problems. The audience to whom the book is directed consists of graduate and advanced undergraduate students. In addition, the more seasoned investigator who wishes to update research methods to include these new viewpoints may find it of value. Part I of the book is an introduction to the technological construction of modern digital computers. The attempt to explain the "guts" of digital computers to behavioral scientists is undertaken with full realization that they will be encountering a strange language, but it is, I believe, an absolute necessity that the active and creative investigator understand these devices thoroughly in order to put them to their fullest possible use. The material presented is intended to be self-contained and should allow the reader to design simple logical circuits and integrate them with commercially available general-purpose computer devices. The history of science has shown repeatedly that the technology available to the investigator is a major influence in determining not only the empirical questions he asks but also the theoretical framework within which he labors.

The strategy used in Part I is to build a computer starting at the most basic level of logical organization theory and develop the ideas through the functional units to a discussion of the full complexity of a modern digital computer system with multiple processors and memory units. This proved to be a useful integrating scheme when the course out of which the book developed was taught at the University of Michigan.

Part II is not intended to be exhaustive. It discusses some areas of psychological research that have especially benefited from computer application and in which the author has been particularly interested. To acknowledge all of the influences leading to this particular choice would be impossible and even if it were not would only deceive the reader. The emphasis is on the methodology, and it is assumed that the reader is well acquainted with the theoretical constructs underlying the reasons for a strategy of attack on a given problem.

There is an obvious and intended gap in the coverage of this book. No discussion of the many specific aspects of computer programming beyond the general nature of on-line programming has been included. The reasons for this omission are two. First, there are many fine recent books which do introduce computer programming as such; furthermore, the differences in programming languages are often special unto themselves. Second, in the next few years we shall probably see a continued development of automatic programming systems, so that the programmer will find it increasingly easy to communicate in a language which is more and more like the one he would use in a conversation with a colleague. The extreme stylization of the past is rapidly being replaced by computer languages appropriate to the needs of a particular problem. A knowledge of computer programming is still necessary, but it is left to other sources to convey this special aspect of the general computer problem to the potential computer user.

It is hoped that this text will serve in the same tradition as that initiated by the pioneering publication of Bert F. Green's book, *Digital Computers in Research,* which introduced the digital computer as a particularly important development in the behavioral sciences. The subject matter in this book receives a different emphasis, but that overall message remains the same.

The present book is not a profound one. However, it does introduce the reader, in a practical fashion, to a major new methodological trend in modern psychological research: real-time control by digital computers. Materials have come from many sources, so no claim to originality, other than expression, can be made. To the students of Psychology 724 at the University of Michigan I owe one kind of debt; to teachers and colleagues who have influenced the choice of content, another. I must specifically, however, acknowledge the help in preparing this book which I received from my colleague Mrs. Madelon Krissoff. Without her energetic advice and effort it might never have come into being. I would also like to express my appreciation to Miss Marilyn Millikin, Miss Alice Hecht, and Miss Ann Oliver, whose typing and editorial advice were of constant value. Dr. D. A. Norman was kind enough to read and advise me on ways to improve Chapter 9. Dr. L. Uhr did the same for Chapter 10.

The advice and many helpful comments of Wayne Holtzman, editor of the Harper & Row series on *Psychology,* and of George A. Middendorf, editor of the Harper & Row College Series, were also important factors in the completion of the book. I am grateful for the time and effort both took to make it a better book than it might otherwise have been.

Part of this book was written while I held a USPHS special postdoctoral fellowship at the Kyoto (Japan) Prefectural University of Medicine. I want also, therefore, to express my appreciation to Hisato Yoshimura, professor of the first Department of Physiology, for his cordial hospitality and to the National Institute of Neurological Diseases and Blindness, which made that rewarding experience possible.

July, 1967 *William R. Uttal*

I: TECHNOLOGICAL FOUNDATIONS OF REAL-TIME COMPUTERS

1: INTRODUCTION

It is a truism that the tools available to any generation of scientists in large part determine the nature of their experiments and thus the nature of the descriptive and explanatory theories that evolve, for not only does the availability of tools regulate the availability of alternatives for rational decision making, but science itself is not entirely a rational process! The explorations into the unknown that constitute a large part of the scientific adventure often move forward without the guidance of a comprehensive statement of the expected results or of the problems faced. The nature of such exploration frequently specifies that some protrusions of the frontier of our knowledge shall be guided not by premeditated decision making but by heuristic, serendipitous, or chance forces that are not as well organized as the usual scientific report might suggest. The availability of new measuring tools constitutes one alternative path to discovery other than "hard inference." Certainly the inventions of the telescope, the microscope, and the electrophysiological microelectrode all substantially altered the directions taken by physical and biological scientists in ways that could not have been anticipated.

It is the thesis of this book that psychologists and other experimental behavioral scientists stand at the threshold of an equally great disruption of their currently accepted standards of research methodology as a result of the new availability of computing and control tools in their laboratories. There is a fundamental reason for the extraordinary influence of computers on behavioral scientists. This reason derives from the basic similarity in operation or process that behaving organisms and behaving machines actually exhibit. Make no mistake: we do not propose that computers are equivalent in any sense to brain tissue on a microscopic level or that (unless very specially and intentionally programmed) the underlying logical processes are even similar. Rather, with the development of modern computers, we are now dealing with machines in which the overall behavior can be made adaptive and contingent in much the same molar fashion as is shown in human behavior.

It is this similarity on the most molar behavioral level that makes the computer especially significant to scientists who deal with the behavior of organisms. It has long been appreciated that among the very first users to line up at a newly opened computer center have been the behavioral scientists. Now we are witnessing what might be even more extensive activity on their part to acquire real-time computer capability.

A great many small computers have been integrated into laboratories that are oriented toward experimental psychological or neurophysiological research. The development of the notion of time-shared program preparation at remote consoles also promises to make a substantial change in those behavioral science applications which need not be directly connected to the computer. The work in computer modeling of cognitive processes is an important example of the latter category.

For all these reasons there seemed to be a strong need for a textbook emphasizing the technological and methodological aspects of real-time computer applications. We cannot begin to discuss the substantive subject matter of each of the applications described in later chapters. Nevertheless, the method itself represents a coherent and integrated set of subject matters that are of increasing concern to the behavioral science community. Simply put, the full use of the real-time control capabilities of a computer, like the use of any tool, demands that the user understand its operation at all levels. It is not conceivable that one can fully utilize a computer in an experiment if one's knowledge is limited to programming or some other single restricted aspect of computers. The great strides in advancing methodology will come out of intimate interactions between machine and user. The nature of these interactions is dictated by the computer's electronic and logical nature, as well as by its instruction repertoire.

Plan of the book

The organization of this book is based upon what we believe to be a necessary set of fundamentals for optimum use of real-time computer capability in the laboratory. We begin with an analysis of the organization of computer systems, starting at a basic logical level. There is, however, a major difficulty in the presentation of this sort of material to nontechnically trained scientists. How far back should one start in supplying foundation material? It is not our purpose to provide an elementary course in electricity and magnetism, yet this material is absolutely essential to any meaningful discussion of the logical functions. We have therefore compromised by appending to the main sections of this text a pair of chapters that present the fundamentals of electricity and magnetism and of passive and active circuit components. The material may be ignored by readers who feel competent in these subjects. But the Appendixes are available to those who agree with the author that they are an important foundation on which to build an understanding of much of the material presented in the ten preceding chapters.

Part I of the book (Chapters 2 through 6) is devoted in the main to constructing a model of a digital computer system from basic concepts. First we introduce the notion of codes and the languages of computers. The arithmetic manipulation of units of information is stressed, although it is also stressed that arithmetic is only one of a wider set of operations that a computer can perform. The reader also begins to become familiar with the vocabulary of computing and information handling, but necessarily this is a process that continues throughout the book.

Those who are not familiar with the basic materials covered in the two appendixes are advised to read these after reading Chapter 2. The appendixes also serve as a practical review for readers who may have studied this material in another context, for we do emphasize aspects that are particularly relevant to computing systems.

With this foundation, Chapter 3 on logical building blocks can be well understood. In this chapter we begin to deal with the operations performed within the computer system. From the fundamental set of operations introduced here the more complex processes described in Chapter 4 are synthesized. Chapter 3 discusses the components an experimenter might need to construct some special device. The set of components presented is that which constitutes all commercially available families of building blocks.

An important point made in Chapter 3 is that the set of logical elements from which a computer is built is very small. What we hope the reader will gain from the emphasis on this notion of the "simplest set" is that computers, though functionally very complex, are made up of a concatenation of a few simple components. The potential user, who might be frightened away from constructing some special-purpose device if he approached the computer from the most complex level, often finds himself capable of a surprisingly high level of performance after being introduced to the simple components involved.

Chapter 3 is also particularly important because it presents the notion of an interface and those units that are especially designed to allow communication between the computer and the outside world. The ability to take advantage of the computer's data-handling capability by direct electrical interconnections is a key difference between this newer idea of real-time computing and the conventional application of computers via some intermediary data communication medium such as a deck of punched cards. Direct electrical connectability is one of the foundation stones on which real-time computer application rests.

Chapter 4 begins our ascent into the more complex organizational principles of computers by introducing the logical functions that can be performed by small groups of the basic building blocks. Each logical function, though representing only a slightly more complicated combination of the capabilities of the building blocks, operates at the level of action that is most descriptive of the computer itself. A computer may be conceived of as a family of subunits that perform their function in a controlled sequence. Chapter 5 elaborates this point by describing the various registers and functional units that make up a typical computing system. Perhaps even more important, it discusses the interrelationships between them. This chapter also describes the characteristics of the hierarchy of memories available for today's computers.

Another topic covered in Chapter 5 is the capacity of modern computers to be interconnected with other units capable of processing or storing information. The ability to add major functional blocks, such as an additional central processor or additional memory, allows one to customize a computer installation to his very own needs. Today this expandability with multiple components has led to a major revision of the notion of computer compatibility. While programming languages are becoming more and more standardized so that they can be used on any computer, it is becoming much more unlikely that a given computer will have the necessary memory and/or input-output components to replicate the exact behavior of a program previously executed on even the same type of computer. This difficulty is particularly noticeable when one considers the special input-output equipment that has to be attached to a real-time computer.

Chapter 6 deals specifically with the notion of a real-time computer. The chapter opens with a few definitions and emphasizes the principle that it is not time-sharing *nor* on-line *nor* multiple-access terminal connections that are really at the heart of the new development in computers; rather it is the need for rapid enough computer responsiveness so that whatever process is being monitored by the computer is not disrupted. Therefore, we are stressing the point that these other techniques are really only mechanisms by means of which the *real-time* needs of the user are satisfied. Of course the engineer or the computer systems specialist may be most concerned with the electronic details of how real-time interaction is provided but such technical issues are not germane to the major force behind these developments. That force is the user's need for quick responsiveness with the degree of quickness being specified by the particular environment in which the problem is embedded.

Next we proceed to a discussion of the technical means by which real-time responsiveness is achieved, hoping that the point of real-time primacy is not lost in the attention to technical and organizational detail.

Part II (Chapters 7 through 10) discusses the current state of the art of real-time computer application. By means of a series of examples and discussion of the detailed mechanisms of some of the standard techniques, the nature of the real-time capability offered by current computer systems is presented. Chapter 7 introduces the general problem of interaction between men and machines, pointing out the different strengths and weaknesses of men and computers. The latter point is important, for there is a crucial set of decisions that must be made early when one begins to consider how to go about automating a particular application. The general trend in the last few years may be summed up thus: Those processes that can be precisely described can be automated, and those in which ambiguities are dominant had better be left to the man. We then discuss a number of the special attributes of men and machines. Some are obvious, but some are not quite so immediately evident and are surprisingly significant in the automation decisions.

The next three chapters (Chapters 8 through 10) discuss applications in three areas of psychology in which real-time computers have already shown their value. Chapter 8 concerns the analysis of bioelectric signals. This chapter will probably be most relevant either to physiological psychologists and others who attempt to reduce behavior to its physiological substrate or to those who use physiological signs as an additional response measure. Obviously the analytical techniques that are chosen for a given application are in each case determined by the nature of the signal. The classification of signal types, therefore, is the basic theme of organization of the chapter. We distinguish among three major classes of bioelectric events, each requiring a different analytical approach. The first category includes those continuous signals, such as the electroencephalograph, that are amenable to frequency analysis techniques (spectrum analysis and correlation, for example). The second class includes those signals that are relatively long transients, such as the evoked brain potential. Long transients can be analyzed by techniques that deal with changes in the shape or microstructure of the signal during the transient. The third class includes those very brief transients in which information about the signal, other than the fact that it has occurred and is of a given amplitude, is of only secondary importance.

Chapter 9 turns to the problem of automating the psychophysical laboratory. The major characteristic of this sort of data is the small amount of it emitted by the subject in a given period. While literally billions of bits a second can be recorded from a physiological preparation, only a few bits a second are typically recorded in even the most complicated psychophysical experiment. This chapter, we must admit, has no major organizing theme. The variety of behavioral experiments is not easily classifiable along a single dimension such as the temporal properties of the response that we used in the previous chapter. We have chosen, therefore, to present a series of examples, each representing a specific area of experimental psychology.

Chapter 10, on the other hand, has a strong theme, built about the different logical processes that might be used in computer teaching machines to accomplish the tutorial function. We emphasize the fact that, although different computer teaching machines might appear to be very similar in external operation, there are vastly different ways in which the internal logical operation might be organized. Unfortunately it is necessary to call attention here to some forms of computer teaching that appear not to have taken advantage of the significant features of computers. We refer to such devices as degenerate computer teaching machines and stress the point that *not all teaching machines that use computers are computer teaching machines.* This point could be stressed too in other application areas, suggesting that not all users of real-time computers exploit fully the enormous potentialities of such machines. Chapter 10 also notes recent developments in programming and language systems that are particularly relevant to computer tutoring.

Basic principles of real-time computer applications

The preceding section has given an outline of the substance of the book. Even at this stage, the book can be seen to be a methodological effort which aims, by discussing methods and applications, to introduce real-time computers to readers who have not yet mastered their use.

There are several important and basic principles that might be drawn from the detailed technical chapters of this book. We shall now briefly discuss what we believe are the major implications of the new methodology. It has been said that the real implications of a new scientific concept do not work their way into the public consciousness for many years. Certainly in terms of today's development, neither the public nor the great majority of the scientific community yet understands the essential significance of the digital computer itself, much less of the even newer concept of real-time computing.

Principle 1—
The social efficiency of the computer

The development of the computer is a major social force. It may be compared directly with other socially effective technological innovations, such as the automobile. Personal machine-powered transportation has certainly altered our way of life, the architecture of our cities and our homes, and even our moral codes. On the other hand, there have been technical developments that have had a surprisingly small effect on our society even though they have profoundly changed our ways of thinking about nature. As an example, consider nuclear power generation (as opposed to the nuclear weapon). No matter how influential theoretically, this change in power source does not directly impinge on the way people live. Printing is another example of a socially effective innovation, while certain recent astronomical discoveries such as the detection of the quasar have no immediate social impact.

Separate from the notion of computers as such, yet often confused with them, are parallel developments in communication. Though both represent socially influential forces and both are based on electronic technology, there is a vast difference between the essential natures of the two. Communication techniques allow information transmission between distant points. All too often, however, as in the case of television, the communication system is a one-way affair, merely extending the distances over which we can communicate without really changing the nature of the process itself. Modern communication techniques are going to change our way of life—of this there is no question—but for different reasons from those that underlie the effect computers will have. For example, it is entirely possible that modern communication techniques will reduce the amount of travel for commercial reasons and make travel more of a recreational activity in the not too distant future.

The effect of computers, however, will be due to their adaptive two-way interaction with men and other complicated systems. Let us state some of the reasons for this social effectiveness of computers by listing and discussing other major technological principles that extend throughout much of Part II of this book.

Principle 2—
The essential nature of the computer

The computer is often popularly confused with an automatic controller, a monstrous desk calculator, or simply an arithmetic machine. The computer is of course capable of performing any of the tasks associated with the three instruments mentioned, but its essence does not lie in any single one of these features. Rather, the digital computer is characterized by the following essential properties:

a. Internal and modifiable storage of instructions.
b. Contingent sequencing of its action on the basis of internal state decisions made at any stage of a program.

From one or another point of view, one or the other of these two subprinciples could be given priority. In either case the adaptive nature of the machine, deriving from its ability to make decisions about its own internal state, is a critical feature not shared with other devices such as an automated machining process. The ability to make contingent decisions is based upon the ability of the computer to deal with instructions in exactly the same way it deals with numbers. For example, the ability to substitute one number for another as the address upon which a given instruction is to act is a feature that allows the program to be branched to any place in the stored program. The effect of this simple notion is evident throughout the gamut of applications. The applications described in Part II of this book are almost entirely dependent on the evolution of this notion.

Principle 3—
The principle of limited anticipation

Another recurrent theme throughout the applications section is what may best be called the limited anticipation principle. Computers are, as we have said, relatively simple mechanisms. Their adaptivity is always limited in the sense that it is not possible to have a completely unconstrained stream of input signals accepted by the computer. In discussing the programming languages and the computer teaching machine application, it is particularly clear that some anticipatory preparation must be made before any particular input can be accepted by the computer. This may be in the form of a simple routine or a complicated algorithm, but the important point is that all input to a computer must be anticipated and prepared for by the *people* who put the system together. The practical effects of this principle can be seen in the specific requirements for standardized communication routines and highly stereotyped programming languages. Even though we must keep in mind the ongoing development of programs capable of processing larger classes of inputs, the limitation on generalized unanticipated inputs is fundamental and can be expected to constrain computer applications for many years to come.

Principles 2 and 3 are general to any application of computers in any environment. Let us now consider three principles basic to our understanding of real-time computers in particular.

Principle 4—
The primacy of real time

Principle 4 explicitly states a notion we have already mentioned. There is, in the current literature, a lack of appreciation that the most significant issue in time-shared, real-time, on-line computing is the real-time nature of the environment into which the computer has been inserted. In other words, all of the other issues, as we have said, are merely technical means of achieving real-time responsiveness. It is to the problem environment that we must ultimately turn, rather than to the available technology, when we decide between a time-shared large computer system and a collection of small independent computers.

Principle 5—
Adaptive interaction

Throughout the chapters that discuss the automation of the psychophysical laboratory and computer teaching machines, we emphasize the contingent or adaptive behavior of the computer. On a more microscopic process level the same emphasis is also made in the other chapters. Licklider's (1960) discussion of the intelligent assistant or the symbiotic relationship is another way of stressing this point. The principle of adaptive interaction is the direct descendant of the notion described in principle 2, which is a statement of the organization of the mechanism itself. But now we are talking about the gross behavior of the total computer-environment complex. Adaptive interaction is the feature that distinguishes, in the most significant way, between the computer teaching machine and the conventional programmed textbook—or, for that matter, the conventional lecture room. It is what optimizes and makes unique the new psychophysical traditions, such as the contingent psychophysical techniques and more elaborate decision-making processes that are gaining in popularity as they become realizable with the new real-time computer-controlled laboratories.

Principle 6—
Electrical connectability

The final principle—and it may seem to some readers to be one of lesser importance—is that of electrical connectibility. Computers are electrical machines, operated by substantial amounts of power but on information content represented by negligible amounts of power. The notion of using a computer directly attached to a teaching machine or a neurophysiological preparation is a new idea. Not too many years ago it would have been considered impossible or unnecessarily extravagant, if considered at all. Even today some of the largest manufacturers of computers have not yet completely accepted it, for many still turn out computer systems that are relatively difficult to interconnect with the real world.

Nevertheless, real-time responsiveness and adaptive interaction both imply direct electrical connectibility between external equipment and the internal workings of the computer. Conversely, once direct electrical connections are obtained, the need for real-time responsiveness and adaptive interaction is immediately apparent. All of the examples talked about in this book are electrically connected to the computer through either a keyboard device or some more direct electronic interface. In this sense electrical connectibility is also a basic principle and a distinguishing feature of the new real-time applications of computers.

Another persisting problem in the same context is the confusion still existing between the electrical connectibility of low data rate keyboard-like devices and that of the higher data rates obtained from, say, physiological experiments. The computing requirements of each are quite different, and misunderstandings frequently occur because the two are confused.

This brief chapter has introduced a large number of concepts and terms. The reader may find some of them perplexing and too divorced from concrete situations with which he is familiar to be fully understood in all their implications. The rest of the book is dedicated not only to the presentation of special details but also to an elucidation of the general nature of the computer adventure upon which experimental psychologists are now embarking.

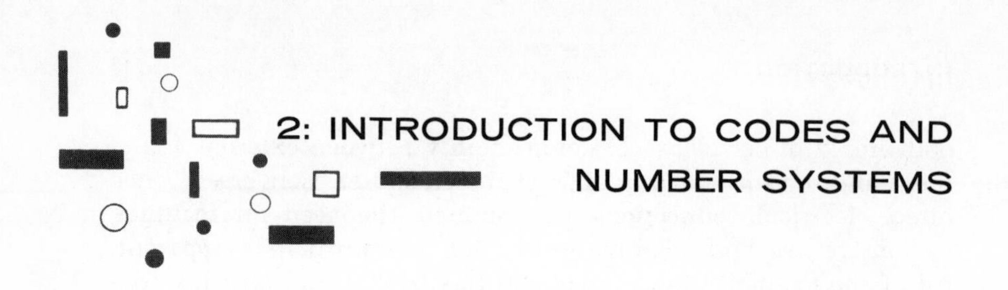

2: INTRODUCTION TO CODES AND NUMBER SYSTEMS

The purpose of this chapter is to present the basic ideas of codes and the various number systems one encounters when dealing with computers.

The idea of a code

It is well known that computers are designed to perform arithmetic functions rapidly and accurately, and that an agreed-upon arithmetic system is necessary with which to make these calculations. In addition, computers have other functions of a logical nature that are fundamentally different from arithmetic operations. In both instances, the computer is called upon to perform a sequence of operations such as "counting," "subtracting," or "anding," all of which must be executed by specifically designed units of the computer electronics. To accomplish these functions in the required orderly fashion, a system of communication is necessary. A system of communication involves the use of a *language,* which is composed of *words*. The words are made up of the members of some sort of *alphabet*. It is important to remember that the language of a computer is only a special case of the general problem of language *coding*. Specifically, a code may be defined as a group of symbols and transformation rules which are used to represent more complex patterns in an economical fashion.

Almost all societies, as they developed awareness of numbers of objects, have adopted a coded form of counting to avoid the difficulties of a system in which a different symbol is used for each number. Similarly, nonnumerical languages, spoken or written, no matter how complex, are always found to have rules of combination that are used to produce compound forms by means of an assemblage of a basic set of symbols. In each case, many considerations have dictated the development of coding systems so that each concept does not have to be represented by a unique symbol. All languages, written or oral, numerical or nonnumerical, can be considered examples of representational systems, employing identifying tags to convey the essential idea of an object without the complete reconstruction of the object itself. The earliest of the representational systems utilized pictographic or diagrammatic symbols for objects and ideas. Even the most primitive languages quickly evolved a stylization of the pictographs to a form which is more of an abstraction of the concept or object. Figure 2-1, for example, shows the evolution of an ancient Near Eastern pictograph representing a cow from its very objective form to a more abstract Assyrian cuneiform.

Original pictograph	Pictograph in position of later cuneiform	Early cuneiform	Classic Assyrian	Meaning
				cow

Fig. 2-1. *A series of progressively less pictorial symbolic representations of the concept of a "cow," showing the evolution from the crude pictorial to the relatively sophisticated coded cuneiform. (From David Diringer,* Writing, *London, Thames & Hudson and New York, F. A. Praeger, 1962, p. 38.)*

Even highly stylized pictographs, however, suffer from the difficulty mentioned above. A very large number of symbols is required, each more or less unique in its designation. Although many modern languages, particularly those of the Orient, have taken the route of multisymbol pictographic forms, others have found it more convenient to evolve in the direction of a small set of symbols—an alphabet—which are grouped together in combinations to form words.

It should be emphasized that there is no single optimum alphabet for representing any given set of concepts. Codes with small sets of characters have the advantage of mnemonic ease and may adapt themselves better to certain sorts of mechanical implementation, but usually languages evolve in complex fashions based upon historical, social, and esthetic considerations that are difficult to trace. In recent times, this evolutionary process has been modified by the presence of coded machines in which a given component technology more or less constrains the most appropriate alphabet. Thus in the modern digital computer, the difficulty in manufacturing electronic components more precise than 1/10 of 1 percent of their stated value has led to components that are used either fully turned on or fully turned off—that is, in either of two possible states. As another example, in Japan the current need for mechanical printing devices has proved an important force pressuring that country toward the adoption of a sort of alphabetic-phonetic system called hiragana.

Alphabetic coding

Our alphabet is, of course, an obvious example of a code in which a small number of symbols is conjoined to encode a large number of concepts. The history of our alphabet is still a vigorous area of inquiry, but it is becoming increasingly clear that the interconnections between the Greek and Roman alphabets may be only part of the total story and that direct evolutionary linguistic influences from the ancient Semitic languages exist, as well as from the Greco-Latin sources.

Composed of twenty-six characters, our alphabet represents an effective compromise between the problems encountered in teaching the enormously elongated alphabet of a pictographically written language and the extreme word length that develops when the symbol set is too small. An estimate of the size of our vocabulary can be made from the number of entries in an unabridged dictionary—calculated, by various means, to be about 450,000 words. A pictographic vocabulary of such magnitude is, of course, patently impossible. This vocabulary has evolved on the basis of a twenty-six-character alphabet, the members of which are used on an average of six or seven at a time. If implemented in terms of a two-character alphabet, a comparable vocabulary would have an average word length of about nineteen characters ($2^{19} = 524{,}288$). Such an alphabet would lead to the disadvantage of excessive word length and the attendant psychological difficulties of having to deal with words differing only very slightly in the critical cues for discrimination. If any second-grade teacher thinks spelling is hard to teach with an alphabet of twenty-six characters, he would be overwhelmed by the difficulties of a two-character alphabet.

The general pressures toward the evolution of an appropriate alphabet for a given application become more specific when we deal with the electronic or electrical circuitry from which modern-day computers are constructed. On a microscopic level within a computer, the decoding of each character is done independently of what has happened before.[1] The computer, therefore, is insensitive to the confusions prevalent in human observations of an alphabet composed of only a few characters. More significantly, as we have said, electronic digital computer circuitry is more reliably implemented by means of two-state devices. For this reason the two-character alphabet, consisting of *0* and *1*, has proved to be a most appropriate choice for the internal workings of a computer. It must be noted, though, that there is no particular advantage to such a scheme other than this technological one.

How then are the alphabetic codes people use encoded in this two-character language? Fortunately, there is no prior restriction on what combination of 1's and 0's are used to represent any given alphabetic character. In the computer, alphabetic materials are only stored or manipulated in indirect ways in the sense that no arithmetic calculations are performed upon them. Thus, computer designers are free to use any coding scheme they choose, although the choice may be dictated by some other criterion of convenience. Since we do have twenty-six alphabetic characters, at least twenty-six different combinations of 0's and 1's must be used to distinguish each of the characters uniquely. Furthermore, there are other *quasi*-alphabetic characters such as the slash (/) or the dollar sign ($) that one may desire to encode. Often as many as forty, fifty, or even sixty alphabetic and *quasi*-alphabetic characters must be included. Let us assume (with some premeditation) that sixty-four distinct characters must be encoded with sixty-four different distinct combinations of 1's and 0's. In this case, six 1's and 0's are required to define each of the sixty-four different characters ($2^6 = 64$).

Table 2-1 is an example of the newly adopted standard ASCII[2]

[1] This is the case, of course, *only* on the microscopic level. On a more macroscopic scale, what words we choose to decode and what the contents of the words are depend upon programmed instructions and previous calculations.

[2] American Standard Code for Information Interchange.

scheme for coding alphanumeric characters. Numerical characters are included in this scheme because they are often stored in a computer as noncomputable symbols, just as are the rest of the alphabetic and special characters. In Table 2-1, not all of the sixty-four possible combinations are assigned to given characters; some are either available for future designations or simply excluded as nonvalid combinations.

Character	Code	Character	Code
A	000 001	5	110 101
B	000 010	6	110 110
C	000 011	7	110 011
D	000 100	8	111 000
E	000 101	9	111 001
F	000 110		
G	000 111	!	100 001
H	001 000	"	100 010
I	001 001	#	100 011
J	001 010	$	100 100
K	001 011	%	100 101
L	001 100	&	100 110
M	001 101	'	100 111
N	001 110	(	101 000
O	001 111	)	101 001
P	010 000	*	101 010
Q	010 001	+	101 011
R	010 010	,	101 100
S	010 011	–	101 101
T	010 100	.	101 110
U	010 101	/	101 111
V	010 110	:	111 010
W	010 111	;	111 011
X	011 000	<	111 100
Y	011 001	=	111 101
Z	011 010	>	111 110
		?	111 111
0	110 000	@	000 000
1	110 001	[	011 011
2	110 010	]	011 101
3	110 011		
4	110 100		

Table 2-1. *A listing of the newly agreed upon ASCII (American Standard Code for Information Interchange) code for alphabetic, numeric, and special characters. This table is presented in the trimmed six-bit form.*

Such a coding scheme is very economical because only a few of the available combinations are wasted, and also because a minimum number of positions are used. As we have noted, the coding of sixty-four different characters requires only six bit positions. The ASCII code is actually defined for eight bits, but the two extra bits on the left are not required and may be omitted or *trimmed* to the form shown in Table 2-1. Occasionally a seventh position is used, however. The latter position is said to be a *redundancy check* and is used to prevent undetected errors in the manipulation of data. The convention is often made that the seventh position has a 1 in it if the number of 1's in all the other six positions is equal to 0 or an even number (2 or 4 or 6). A 0 is placed in the seventh position when there is an odd total number of 1's in the six other positions.

Other codes for the storage of alphabetic and numerical (*alphanumeric*) data have been devised to meet special requirements. The

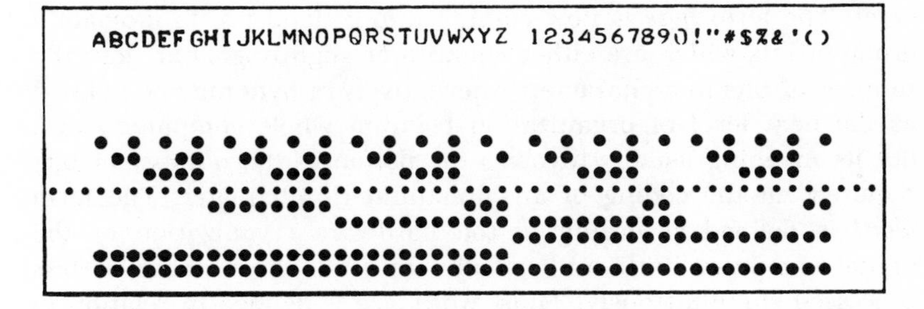

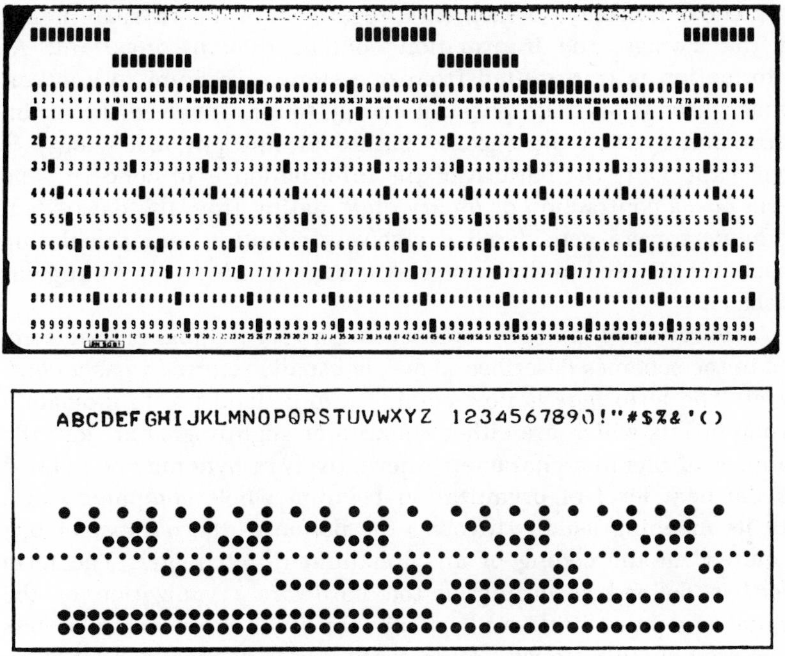

Fig. 2-2. (a) *A punched card showing one form of code for alphabetic and numeric characters. (Courtesy of International Business Machines Corporation.)* (b) *A punched paper tape showing the coding of the same alphabetic and numeric symbols (and some additional special characters) in a quite different scheme.*

Hollerith coding system used on the common punched card and the code used on a punched paper tape are examples of alternative forms of coding. Figure 2-2 presents pictures of a typical Hollerith punched card and a punched paper tape and shows their coding schemes.

Some definitions

So far we have used a number of terms without rigorous definitions. Let us now try to be more specific. The character repertoire of a given alphabet is composed of a number of *letters*. In the Roman alphabet, each letter has a name. In the two-character alphabet dictated by the two-state technology of modern digital computers, the utilized letters 0 and 1, are called *bits*. Although the type of physical implementation which represents a bit varies from one device to another (e.g., a hole versus no hole in a punched card, or a north-to-south versus a south-to-north magnetization in a magnetic core), in each case, regardless of the physical nature of the storage, the information content remains invariant. As information is transmitted from one storage medium to another, what varies is only the physical energy that is involved. In an information system, the specific nature of this physical energy is irrelevant. Only the pattern of the information is of concern. The term *bit* (a contraction of *b*inary dig*it*, dating from the days when computers were considered exclusively counting and calculating machines) is used in the same way as the term *letter* in the regular alphabet.

A collection of six bits, representing a given alphanumeric symbol in the schemes described above, is usually referred to as a *character*. The term *byte* is now coming into general use to indicate a group of bits which are either equal to or slightly greater than the number of bits in a character. Alternatively, a byte may be defined as the next level of organization below a whole computer word, but its meaning usually involves the notion of the number of bits required for the coding of an alphanumeric character. The term *word* is defined according to the hardware organization of the digital computer itself and usually refers to the number of bits processed simultaneously. Thus, word size is defined in relation to the number of bits in the various arithmetic registers of the computer. Further, some coding schemes have one or more additional bits associated with each character, byte, or word, to be used either for error checking or for determining the beginning or end of a group of characters.

The coding of numbers

Codes, as we have seen, are a means of reducing the number of distinct symbols necessary to designate a larger number of concepts. One of the largest classes of codable concepts, of course, is that of number itself. Thus, in the simplest uncoded number systems there is a specific character or symbol for each given count up to some upper limit. Beyond this limit the system breaks down, and larger numbers are often considered indistinguishable within the general concept of "many." The Australian aborigines have just such an uncoded form of counting with their fingers and other body positions, but any number greater then 27 is considered "many."

Coded systems, on the other hand, have developed in several different ways and with more or less advantageous or disadvantageous features associated with any given system. The most efficient modern coded number systems are *based, positional,* and *exponential.* Perhaps the best way to explain the meaning of these three concepts is to discuss in detail both an abstract system and a few of the real number systems used today.

Figure 2-3 is an example of a general number system showing how modern number systems are designed. It is founded upon a base number that we shall call B.

$$N = aB^{\alpha} + bB^{\alpha-1} + cB^{\alpha-2} + \cdots + mB^{0} + nB^{-1} + oB^{-2} + \cdots + yB^{-\alpha}$$

Fig. 2-3. *The general equation for the exponential positional number system described in the text.*

The important things to note concerning this generalized number system are as follows:

1. The system works by exponential expansion of the base as a function of its position relative to the point.
2. The most significant or largest digit (the highest exponential value of B) is on the extreme left. As we move right toward and past the point, the number represented gets smaller or less significant by integral powers.
3. The point represents the demarcation between whole numbers and fractional parts.
4. The coefficients a, b, etc. specify how many of each of the B^n's are to be counted for the representation of any number.

5. Although the original choice of B is arbitrary, once it is chosen, the coefficients a, b, etc. can only vary downward from $B-1$.
6. Exponential values may get as large as you please (to $+\infty$).

Here, then, is the master plan for all number systems of this type regardless of their base. The choice of a specific base depends upon the requirements of the various technologies with which one is dealing. For example, the evolutionary accident of our having ten fingers is probably the reason that the base 10 (the decimal number system) is so strongly a part of our current use of numbers. The base 12 (duodecimal number system) has been used occasionally and bears the advantage of having halves, quarters, thirds, and sixths—fractional components that cannot be constructed from whole numbers in the base 10. The base 16 (hexadecimal number system) and the base 8 (octal number system) have the advantage of being directly convertible to the binary system.

To make these notions clearer, consider the decimal number system, the one with which we are most familiar. Let us see how the positional notation of Figure 2-3 can be used to represent a number. The decimal number 164.75 signifies: 1 each of 10^2 plus 6 each of 10^1 plus 4 each of 10^0 plus 7 each of 10^{-1} plus 5 each of 10^{-2}. Thus the number is formed by summing the various counts represented by each of the positions.

All other positional exponential number systems, regardless of their base, are formed in the same way. This book, being concerned with digital computers, has a special interest in the binary number system, which is specified by the nature of the two-state technology used in computer hardware. The binary number system is organized in the same fashion as the decimal example given above. The differences between the two are few. Instead of powers of 10 and a ten-character repertoire, powers of 2 are used, and thus there can be only two characters used as coefficients—1 and 0. The numerical example (164.75) cited above to illustrate the decimal number system would be encoded in the binary number system as follows: 10100100.11, which can be interpreted as: 1 each of 2^7 plus none of 2^6 plus 1 each of 2^5 plus none of 2^4 plus none of 2^3 plus 1 of 2^2 plus none of 2^1 plus none of 2^0 plus 1 of 2^{-1} plus 1 of 2^{-2}. It can be seen that this system shares a common organization with the decimal number system, with which the reader may be more familiar.

Table 2-2 shows the decimal values of both positive and negative powers of 2.

Obviously the representation of numbers in positional systems

2^n	n	2^{-n}
1	0	1.0
2	1	0.5
4	2	0.25
8	3	0.125
16	4	0.062 5
32	5	0.031 25
64	6	0.015 625
128	7	0.007 812 5
256	8	0.003 906 25
512	9	0.001 953 125
1 024	10	0.000 976 562 5
2 048	11	0.000 488 281 25
4 096	12	0.000 244 140 625
8 192	13	0.000 122 070 312 5
16 384	14	0.000 061 035 156 25
32 768	15	0.000 030 517 578 125
65 536	16	0.000 015 258 789 062 5
131 072	17	0.000 007 629 394 531 25
262 144	18	0.000 003 814 697 265 625
524 288	19	0.000 001 907 348 632 812 5
1 048 576	20	0.000 000 953 674 316 406 25
2 097 152	21	0.000 000 476 837 158 203 125
4 194 304	22	0.000 000 238 418 579 101 562 5
8 388 608	23	0.000 000 119 209 289 550 781 25
16 777 216	24	0.000 000 059 604 644 775 390 625
33 554 432	25	0.000 000 029 802 322 387 695 312 5
67 108 864	26	0.000 000 014 901 161 193 847 656 25
134 217 728	27	0.000 000 007 450 580 596 923 828 125
268 435 456	28	0.000 000 003 725 290 298 461 914 062 5
536 870 912	29	0.000 000 001 862 645 149 230 957 031 25
1 073 741 824	30	0.000 000 000 931 322 574 615 478 515 625

Table 2-2. *The decimal values of positive and negative powers of 2.*

such as these can be accomplished with fewer positions when the base is larger, but a larger quantity of distinguishable characters is then required. In the duodecimal system, based upon the number 12, it was therefore necessary to invent special characters for the numbers 10 and 11 (decimal). Usually, the characters *a* and *b* are used. But these new numbers, when one becomes familiar with them, are found to be no more "unnatural" than any of the other ten characters even though at first one may have trouble subtracting 7 from *a*.

Because of the variety of bases that can be used to represent a given number, unless the context is absolutely clear, it is usually desirable to define the base by means of a following subscript: 7777_8, a number in the octal number system, is equal to 4096_{10} and $111\ 111\ 111\ 111_2$.

As mentioned above, the octal number system is widely used in association with the binary number system because of its direct convertibility from and to the binary system. Convertibility is possible in this and other special cases when the two bases are related to each other in such a way that the first is either an integral power or a root of the other. Since 2^3 equals 8, the conversion may be executed simply by dividing the binary number into groups of three bits and converting each group to its respective octal equivalent. This is a frequently used process in digital computing, since

Binary	Octal	Decimal	Duodecimal
1	1	1	1
10	2	2	2
11	3	3	3
100	4	4	4
101	5	5	5
110	6	6	6
111	7	7	7
1000	10	8	8
1001	11	9	9
1010	12	10	*a**
1011	13	11	*b**
1100	14	12	10
1101	15	13	11
1110	16	14	12
1111	17	15	13
10000	20	16	14
10001	21	17	15
10010	22	18	16
10011	23	19	17
10100	24	20	18
10101	25	21	19
10110	26	22	1*a**
10111	27	23	1*b**
11000	30	24	20
11001	31	25	21

Table 2-3. *A comparison of the various number systems for numbers up to decimal 25. The characters marked with an asterisk are surrogates for the numerals that would represent* 10_{10} *and* 11_{10}, *since we have no usual numeral for those numbers in the duodecimal system.*

the resulting octal numbers are much easier to remember and deal with than their binary equivalents.

Table 2-3 is a comparison of the codes of the various number systems for numbers up to 25.

Arithmetic in the binary number system

Since modern computers have developed around a two-state electronic technology, the binary number system, either directly or in the form of the binary coded decimal number system (BCD), is used in all current computers. Knowledge of how arithmetic is performed in the binary number system is, therefore, fundamental to an understanding of the internal arithmetic manipulations performed by the computer. Although binary arithmetic, at first sight, seems to be a mysterious and complex process, it is indeed a special and simplified case of much more involved arithmetics, just as the binary number system is a special case of the general algorithm for number systems with larger bases.

ADDITION

In decimal arithmetic, we have a familiar table of rules for addition, as is shown in Table 2-4. The sum of any two digits is found at the intersection of the appropriate horizontal and vertical coor-

	0	1	2	3	4	5	6	7	8	9
0	0	1	2	3	4	5	6	7	8	9
1	1	2	3	4	5	6	7	8	9	0*
2	2	3	4	5	6	7	8	9	0*	1*
3	3	4	5	6	7	8	9	0*	1*	2*
4	4	5	6	7	8	9	0*	1*	2*	3*
5	5	6	7	8	9	0*	1*	2*	3*	4*
6	6	7	8	9	0*	1*	2*	3*	4*	5*
7	7	8	9	0*	1*	2*	3*	4*	5*	6*
8	8	9	0*	1*	2*	3*	4*	5*	6*	7*
9	9	0*	1*	2*	3*	4*	5*	6*	7*	8*

Table 2-4. *The addition table for decimal numbers. An asterisk means that a 1 must be carried to the next most significant digit position.*

dinates. Sums that exceed the value of the largest single digit in the decimal number system (9) involve an extra step—a *carry*. A carry is a process indicating that the next highest power should be incremented by one when it is subsequently processed. This addition table can be expanded to include all possible sums. It is usually presented to youngsters as a series of subrules, such as $2+2=4$, etc.

The binary addition table has exactly the same format except that it is much smaller, having only two characters and requiring a carry for the sum of 1 and 1. Table 2-5 shows the binary addition

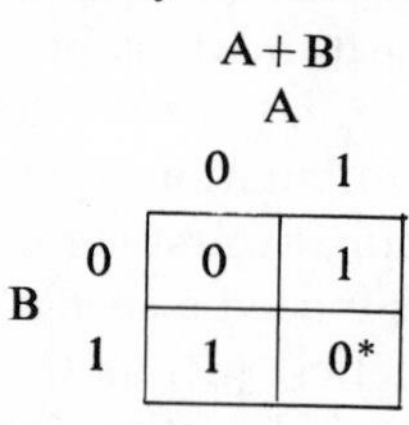

A+B

B \ A	0	1
0	0	1
1	1	0*

Table 2-5. *The addition table for the binary number system. The asterisk also means that a 1 must be carried to the next most significant digit.*

rules. It also contains the general rules for all binary addition, no matter how many digits are included in each number. All other rules hold as they do in decimal arithmetic. As examples of binary addition, consider the following sums:

$$\begin{array}{r} 1011 \\ +\ 0101 \\ \hline 10000 \end{array} \qquad \begin{array}{r} 1111 \\ +\ 1001 \\ \hline 11000 \end{array}$$

Upon careful inspection, the reader will see that the rules defined in the Table 2-5 have been followed. Addition is carried out from right to left as in ordinary decimal addition, with carries performed as necessary.

SUBTRACTION

Decimal subtraction has a table similar to that for addition. It also can be reduced to the special binary form indicated in Table 2-6. Once again, there is a complete analogy between the two number systems. In this case, however, we borrow, as necessary, rather

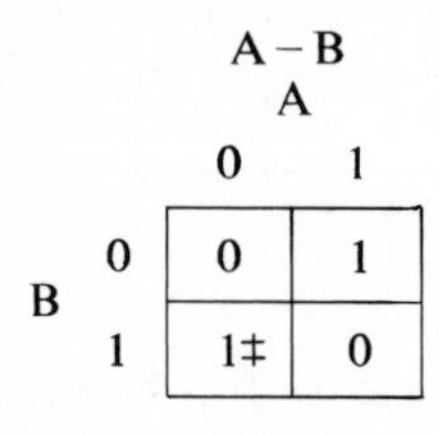

A−B

B \ A	0	1
0	0	1
1	1‡	0

Table 2-6. *The subtraction table for the binary number system. The # in this case means that a 1 must be borrowed from the next most significant digit.*

than carry. The following problems are examples of binary subtraction:

$$\begin{array}{r} 1010 \\ -\quad 11 \\ \hline 111 \end{array} \qquad\qquad \begin{array}{r} 1101 \\ -\quad 111 \\ \hline 110 \end{array}$$

MULTIPLICATION

The table for binary multiplication is illustrated in Table 2-7. Multiplication of binary numbers is carried out very simply by using this table and the same shifting operation used in decimal

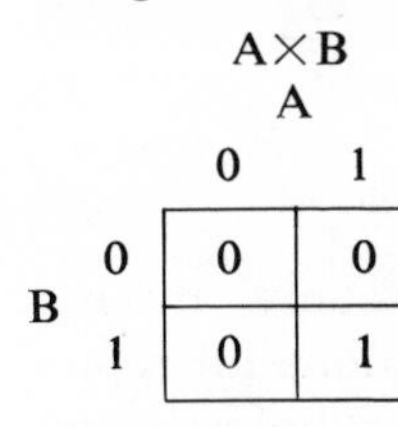

A×B

		A: 0	A: 1
B	0	0	0
	1	0	1

Table 2-7. *The multiplication table for the binary number system.*

arithmetic. Since we are multiplying only by 1 or 0, the partial sums in each case can be either equal to the multiplicand or equal to zero. Thus, multiplication is really a matter of shifting and adding successive values of the multiplicand and can be implemented in the computer in a relatively simple fashion. The following are examples of binary multiplication:

$$\begin{array}{r} 1010 \\ \times\ 1010 \\ \hline 0000 \\ 1010 \\ 0000 \\ 1010 \\ \hline 1100100 \end{array} \qquad\qquad \begin{array}{r} 1100 \\ \times\quad 11 \\ \hline 1100 \\ 1100 \\ \hline 100100 \end{array}$$

DIVISION

Table 2-8 is the division table for binary arithmetic. As in any other number system, division by zero is excluded since it would lead to an indeterminate number. Just as binary addition can be

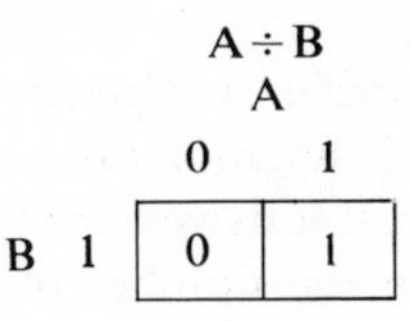

A÷B

		A: 0	A: 1
B	1	0	1

Table 2-8. *The division table for the binary number system. Division by zero is not allowed just as in all other number systems.*

seen to be a series of successive additions of the shifted multiplicand, binary division can be implemented by a series of successive subtractions of the divisor from the dividend. The following examples illustrate this process:

```
      1100
10 | 11000
     10
     ----
      10
      10
     ----
       000
```

```
      111
11 | 10101
     11
     ----
     100
      11
     ----
       11
       11
       --
       00
```

OTHER ARITHMETIC OPERATIONS

The tables for arithmetic operations presented above are not complete guides. It is also necessary to have conventions for representing the sign as well as the magnitude of the number being manipulated. Some computers have a sign bit (usually a 0 for a positive number and a 1 for a negative number) associated with the other bit positions. Other computers take advantage of the fact that negative numbers may be represented as the complement of a positive number with respect to some other number—usually the base raised to some power. In the binary number system, complements are particularly easy to compute since this process only involves switching 1's and 0's for each other. Thus each 1 is replaced by a 0, and each 0 is replaced by a 1. To arrive at the true complement with respect to 2, it is further necessary to add 1 to the sum. Thus, the complement with respect to 2 (the so-called 2's complement) of 1010 is 0101 + 1, or 0110. The reason for adding the 1 arises from the necessity for removing the ambiguity of the two different coded representations for $+0$ and -0. The value of complements lies in the ease with which subtraction can be performed. It can be shown that $A-B$ is equal *to* A + the 2's complement of B. Doing subtraction in this manner makes it unnecessary to have the electronic circuitry for implementing the subtract instruction—an economy that can be significant in very small computers in which a duplication of major portions of the control circuitry would otherwise be required.

Another arithmetic operation to be accounted for is a convention for handling the overflow situation. In any of the four arithmetic operations, it is possible to arrive at a final answer that involves too many bits to be fully accommodated in the number of

90457

assigned bit positions. To handle these exceptional cases, usually another bit is assigned to the arithmetic element of a computer which indicates that an overflow has occurred. Once set to a 1, this bit position would direct the computer program to some routine that could correct for this occurrence.

Computers then, can be seen in the light of this chapter as machines for coded information transmission and processing. The internal workings that allow them to perform these functions will be the subject of the remainder of Part I.

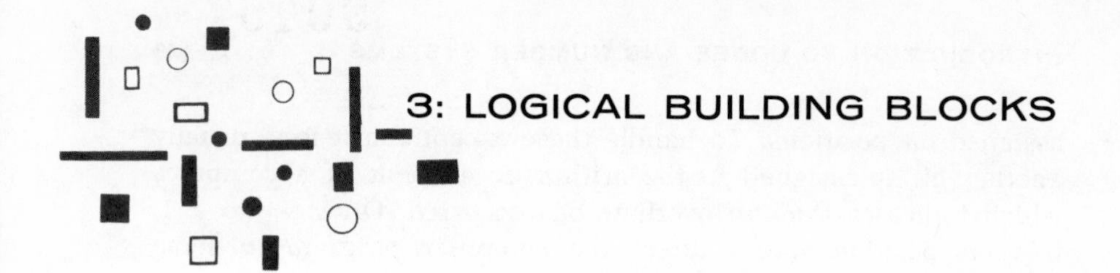

3: LOGICAL BUILDING BLOCKS

Introduction

The purpose of this chapter is to define the basic logical operations and to discuss some of the possible sets of logical units that can be used to design and construct a digital computer. The user of real-time, on-line computing systems must understand this level of computer terminology in order to utilize the capabilities of his system fully. Many manufacturers have offered commercial lines of logical units such as are described here. It is, however, necessary to integrate these basic building blocks into operational devices to perform a given experimental function. The present chapter, it is hoped, will provide the background necessary to allow the user to perform this integration when needed. The reader who is not adequately up to date on the principles of electricity and magnetism and component technology should read the Appendixes before continuing on in this chapter.

THE SIMPLEST SET OF LOGICAL UNITS

It is not well appreciated, when one looks at the great variety and number of logical units used in modern computers, that it is actually possible to design the logical portions of a computer from only two basic building blocks. The first of these two blocks must be able to produce an output if either or both of its inputs are activated (the *or* function). The second should be able to change a positive voltage level into a negative voltage level (the inverter or *nulling* function). The design of a computer from such a minimal set would be cumbersome, however, since so many of the units would have to be interconnected in so many different ways. It would also add enormously to the detailed work required of the logical designer and would probably make repair work rather difficult. For these reasons, computers are usually constructed of more complete sets of logical units capable of an increased number of logical functions. The small size of the simplest set of devices theoretically capable of performing all computer operations does, however, accentuate an important point: computers are constructed of relatively simple devices. Many of these simple devices are wired together into a complex net to achieve the total system capability.

VOLTAGES, LOGICAL SIGNIFICANCE, AND ASSERTION

The novice to logical design frequently has difficulty in appreciating the differences between the *polarity* of a voltage and its *logical value*. Consider first the polarity of signals. Each computer system has an arbitrarily chosen pair of significant voltage levels. This pair is composed of voltages that correspond to the saturated state and the cutoff state of the transistors making up the computer. For example, the two logical voltage levels inside a given computer will be equal to some more positive voltage and some more negative voltage. Wide varieties of voltage levels are found in various machines, since there are no a priori reasons to choose one particular level over another. The type of transistor used, the design power levels, and other considerations may lead to the choice of a given set of voltage levels. One computer might use +6 and −6 volts, while another might use 0 and −6 volts, or even −1 and −2 volts. The only requirement is that the circuitry be able to distinguish easily between the two levels, even when some slight variation is present. For the purpose of standardizing our discussion, let us assume the convention of 0 volts as our more positive level and −5 volts as our more negative level. The same convention will be used in discussing the circuits in this chapter and the functional units described in the next chapter.

Each of the two voltages represents, at one time or another, either a 1 or a 0 in the binary language of the computer. This is the difficulty encountered by the novice—understanding that the more positive voltage may represent either a 1 or a 0 at different times, either because of some operation performed by a previous logical unit or because the voltage has been intentionally reversed in polarity to meet the input requirement of some subsequent logical unit. The input and output voltage requirements are set for each logical unit and depend only upon its basic design and what function it serves in the logical system.

The logical quantities, 1 and 0, represented by these voltages are equivalent to the answer to some question that can be answered with a *yes* or a *no*. Thus, if a logical unit operating only when certain input conditions are met has a *yes* output, that output is said to be equal to 1 or *yes* regardless of the voltage polarity. Such an output is equivalent to a *yes* answer for example, to the question "Are the input conditions met?" If, on the other hand, the input conditions are not met, the output is considered to be a 0 or *no* answer. The *no* or 0 may also be represented by either the more negative or the more positive polarity, depending upon the design of the particular circuit. If this distinction between polarity and logical meaning is understood, many of the ambiguities of logical circuit design will automatically be clarified.

A clarifying vocabulary often used to elucidate these concepts includes the terms *assertion* and *negation*. If an input line to a logical unit is of a polarity such that it meets its part of the requirements for the emission of the 1 answer from the logical unit, the line has asserted its logical value. On the other hand, if the line is of a polarity that prevents the input conditions from being met, it has negated its logical value.

THE BASIC LOGICAL UNITS

Even though a minimal set of logical components may have only two functions, they must be combined into at least four different *logical operators* to build a computer. Almost all logical devices belong to one of these four classifications:

1. The *or* circuit.
2. The *and* circuit.
3. The memory or storage circuit.
4. The inverter.

The *or* circuit is designed to produce a 1 output whenever any one or more of its input conditions are in the 1 state. The *and* circuit will produce a 1 output only if all of its inputs are in the 1 state. The memory function is designed to store information about the occurrence or nonoccurrence of some event in the past. The inverter is used to reverse the polarity of a signal.

We will now introduce another useful diagrammatic technique

called the truth table to describe the functions more completely. A truth table is a chart of all the possible input conditions and the resulting output conditions for a given logical unit. Table 3-1*a* illustrates a truth table for an *or* circuit with two inputs. Since there are two inputs, there are four possible combinations of input

Input 1	Input 2	Output
0	0	0
0	1	1
1	0	1
1	1	1

(*a*)

Input 1	Input 2	Output
0	0	0
0	1	0
1	0	0
1	1	1

(*b*)

Table 3-1. (a) *A truth table for a two input "or" circuit.* (b) *A truth table for a two input "and" circuit.*

conditions. The truth table indicates that there is a 1 output for an *or* circuit whenever any one of its inputs is 1. Table 3-1*b* is the truth table for the *and* functions. We see that the output of an *and* circuit is equal to 1 only if all of its inputs are equal to 1. Although we have illustrated these circuits with logical units having two inputs, it should be understood that an *or* or an *and* circuit can have as many inputs as desired. A multiple-input device doubles the truth table each time a new input is added, but the new truth table will remain similar in form to our examples.

It is important to point out that the logical unit which is an *and* circuit for one polarity is usually an *or* circuit for the other polarity and vice versa. Thus, if a circuit is an *or* circuit for positive inputs, the only way to get a 0 output is to see that all of the inputs are negative. This suggests that the same physical device should be usable in either mode. We shall describe this dual function in detail later in the chapter.

The third logical function, storage or memory, is often accomplished by a device that can exist in one of two states for a specified period of time. One state represents a 0 and the other state a 1. Each two-state device has two outputs, one coded as 1 and the other as 0. The storage function allows the retention of information that some event, however transient, has occurred at a previous time.

The fourth logical function is the inversion function. The inverter is used only to reverse the polarity of a given signal, since it has but a single input line and a single output line. Depending upon its use in the logical circuit, it may or may not also reverse the logical meaning of a given signal.

A standard set of symbols has been agreed upon to represent the four logical functions. Figure 3-1 depicts these standard symbols. Figure 3-1*a* is one of the conventional symbols for a two-

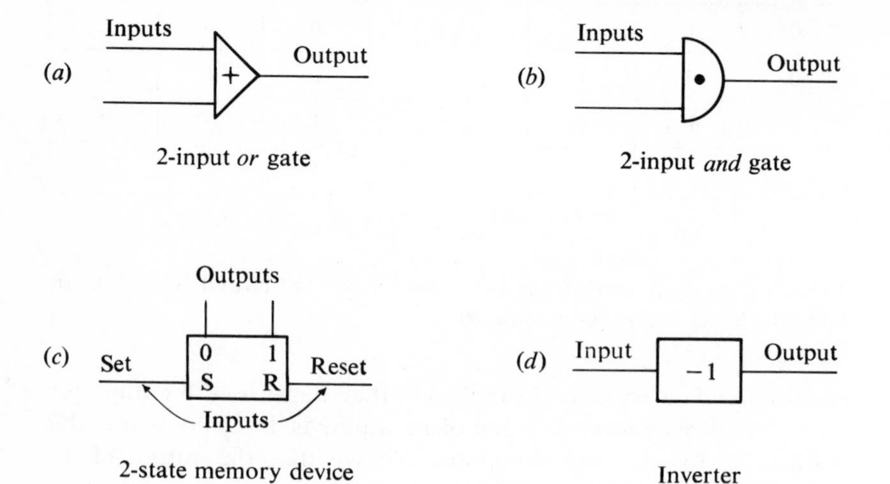

Fig. 3-1. *The standard symbols for the four principal logical units used in the construction of digital computers.* (a) *The symbol for the "or" unit, which will emit an output whenever any one of its input lines is asserted.* (b) *The symbol for the "and" unit, which will emit an output whenever all of its input lines are asserted.* (c) *The storage unit or two-state memory device, which is capable of maintaining information about the past state of some signal.* (d) *The symbol for the "inverter" or polarity-reversing device.*

input *or* gate. The plus sign in this case has a meaning quite different from addition; it indicates the logical *or* function. Figure 3-1*b* is the standard symbol for the *and* function. A dot is the usual symbol indicating this logical operation. Figure 3-1*c* is the symbol for a two-state memory device, with only the outputs indicated. Most two-state devices have many kinds of input lines that allow various input conditions to set the memory device to one or the other state. Figure 3-1*d* is the symbol for an inverter, with the −1 signifying voltage polarity reversal or multiplication by −1.

We shall now consider how such logical operational units are constructed from passive components such as resistors, capacitors, and diodes and from active transistors.

The inverter

It is best to begin our discussion of these logical units by describing the transistor inverter, since it is used as a subunit in the construction of all three of the other devices. As described in Appendix 2,[1] either *NPN* or *PNP* transistors can be used in computer circuits. Again, however, we will choose a convention to standardize the discussion: we will frame our discussion in terms of the *PNP* transistor. It should be understood that an equivalent discussion of a similar family of functional units could be made for the *NPN* transistor.

Figure 3-2*a* is a diagram of a *PNP* transistor in a simple in-

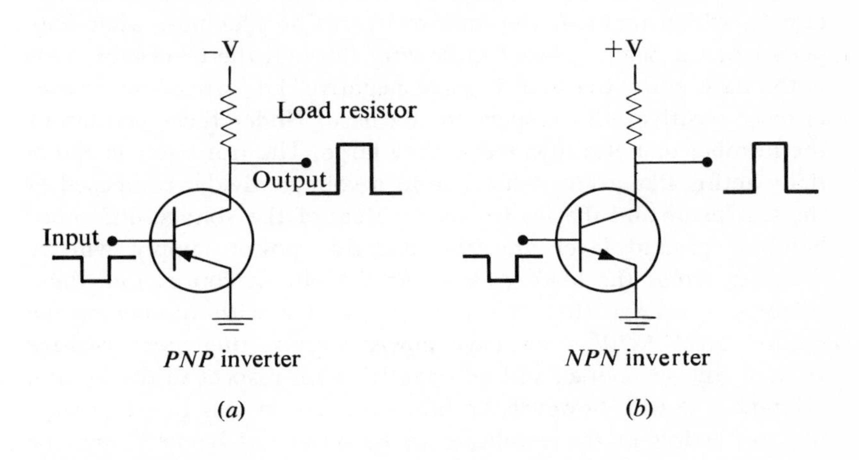

Fig. 3-2. *Two different circuits for implementing the inversion function.* (a) *An inverter constructed from a PNP transistor and a negative power supply.* (b) *An inverter constructed from an NPN transistor and positive power supply.*

verting circuit. This diagram is somewhat simpler than the diagrams in Appendix 2, for here we use just the conventional circuit symbol for the transistor. Similarly, we use the most usual circuit configuration, the common emitter design. Since it is a *PNP* transistor, in order to provide a reverse bias between the collector and the base, we must choose a negative power supply to provide the potential difference. In contemporary computer circuits, the collector voltages typically range between −6 and −15 volts. The

[1] To which the reader is again referred for an elaboration of the technical terms used in the following paragraphs.

forward bias between the base and the emitter is varied to regulate the number of minority carriers (in this case, holes) injected into the base-collector circuit. The more positive the emitter is made with respect to the base, the more holes will be injected into the base. Since the potential of the emitter is fixed at the ground reference, the base must be made more negative in order to develop the proper polarity. This may seem somewhat complex, so it should be emphasized that the potential between two points is the critical factor in specifying the effective voltage. A 0 voltage level is just as much more positive than −6 volts as −6 volts is more positive than −12 volts.

Once minority carriers are injected into the base, they are available to act as carriers for current through the emitter-collector circuit, which includes the load resistor. Consider now what happens when a heavy current is flowing through the transistor. This is the case when the base is most negative, i.e., when the emitter is most positive with respect to the base. Under these conditions the number of holes injected is very large. The transistor is essentially acting like a low resistance in a voltage divider composed of the transistor and the load resistor. Most of the voltage difference between ground level and the negative power supply will be dropped across the load resistor. At the output connection, then, there is a voltage that is relatively positive with respect to the ground level. With a negative power supply, this *more positive* voltage will, of course, still be negative with respect to the ground reference. It will, however, be more positive or less negative than that occurring in the condition to be described below. Thus the injection of a negative going voltage into the base has resulted in a heavy current which caused a positive going voltage swing on the output.

On the other hand, what happens if the base is made more positive, decreasing the voltage difference between the base and the emitter? The minority carrier holes are not injected into the base at the same high rate and therefore are not available for the current flowing into the collector. Owing to the shortage of carriers, the resistance of the transistor in this case seems to be relatively high. The voltage divider is now affected by a component—the transistor—with a relatively high resistance. Consequently, the potential level of the output point will be closer to the voltage of the negative power supply. A positive going signal at the input has thus resulted in a more negative going signal at the output.

Another way to look at this operation is to consider the transistor either an open circuit when it is turned off or a closed circuit when it is turned on to saturation. Then, by Ohm's law, the voltage drop through the load resistor has to vary between no voltage drop (when current flow is nearly zero) and a considerable voltage drop (when there is considerable current flow). A voltage drop in the latter case means a shift from a more negative value to a more positive value. Either way it is interpreted, the important fact is that the polarity of the voltage is reversed when a signal passes through an inverter.

Since the common emitter transistor also amplifies voltages, there is a general tendency for voltages that may have been distorted or loaded down to be restored to their original amplitudes as they pass through a transistor inverter. Sequences of inverters, therefore, tend to keep the voltage levels of the computer circuitry close to the agreed-upon standard. For all practical purposes, however, this restoration takes place without any special planning on the part of the logical designer. It has already been designed in by the circuit designer. A voltage change between the two levels of 0 and -5 on the input of the transistor inverter can be depended upon to produce an equivalent, though opposite, voltage change at the output in all commercial systems of logical units.

Figure 3-2*b* is an equivalent diagram of the *NPN* transistor inverter, and the reader might test his understanding of these processes by following through this same analysis for *PNP* inverters.

The diode gate—for and *and* or *operations*

Now consider the circuit illustrated in Figure 3-3. The action of a diode is such that if it is forward biased it will have a very low resistance while if it is reverse biased it will have a very high resistance. If we apply a positive signal to point *A*, point *C* will be relatively positive. If we apply a negative signal to point *A* (in

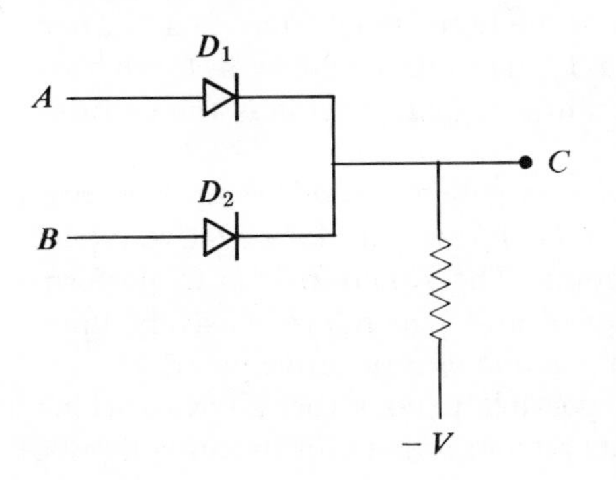

Fig. 3-3. *A diode gate composed of two diodes and a resistor and a negative voltage source. As described in the text, this device may be used as either an "or" gate for positive inputs or an "and" gate for negative inputs.*

both cases with nothing connected to point B), the voltage of point C will also be negative following the input on point A. If, however, there is a positive voltage on A and a negative voltage on B, diode 1 (D_1) will be essentially forward biased (with the consequent low resistance) and diode 2 (D_2) will be reverse biased (with the consequent high resistance). Thus, the voltage on B is isolated from point C by a high resistance while the voltage on A is almost directly connected to point C. In other words, the circuit from A to B through D_1 and D_2 forms a voltage divider with the larger proportion of the resistance represented by the reverse biased D_2. For this reason point C will be positive if a positive voltage is applied to either of the diodes. Point C can become negative only if the voltages applied to both A and B are negative.

Table 3-2 is a truth table for this two-diode device, with the voltage polarities indicated instead of the logical 1's and 0's. If

Input 1	Input 2	Output
+	+	+
+	−	+
−	+	+
−	−	−

Table 3-2. *A truth table for a two input diode gate, showing voltage polarities rather than logical values.*

we compare this truth table to that of Table 3-1*a* or Table 3-1*b*, we see that by having one of the polarities represent a logical 1 and the other a logical 0, our device can perform both the *and* and the *or* functions. Assume that we allow the minus polarity to be equal to logical 1. Then for two 1 inputs we get a 1 output. For all other combinations of the two inputs we would get a plus polarity—a 0. This of course is exactly the *and* function described earlier.

Suppose that we allow the positive input to be equal to a 1. Then if either of the two inputs is a 1, the output will be a 1, whereas both have to be negative to obtain a logical 0. This is the *or* function described earlier.

This diode and resistor device is called a *diode gate*. The particular diode gate presented here is an *and* gate for negative inputs and an *or* gate for positive inputs. The function it is to perform must be selected by the designer and depends exclusively upon whether a 1 is assumed to be a positive or a negative polarity.

By reversing the diodes, it is possible to construct a device which is an *and* gate for positive inputs and an *or* gate for negative inputs, but the functional properties would remain the same. Although the diode gate has been analyzed in this discussion as a two-input element, it should be remembered that there is no theoretical limitation on the number of diodes which can be placed in parallel in the input circuit. Whatever the number, if the circuit is being used as an *and* gate, all of the inputs must be at the voltage level representing a logical 1 to produce a 1 output. If the circuit is being used as an *or* gate, the voltage level representing a logical 1 on any one of the inputs will activate a 1 output.

Diode gates are usually packaged with an inverter. Thus the output voltage level is reconstituted to the system's standard voltage levels, and the polarity is reversed. Such a unit is shown in Figure 3-4. The output voltage that now indicates assertion is reversed in

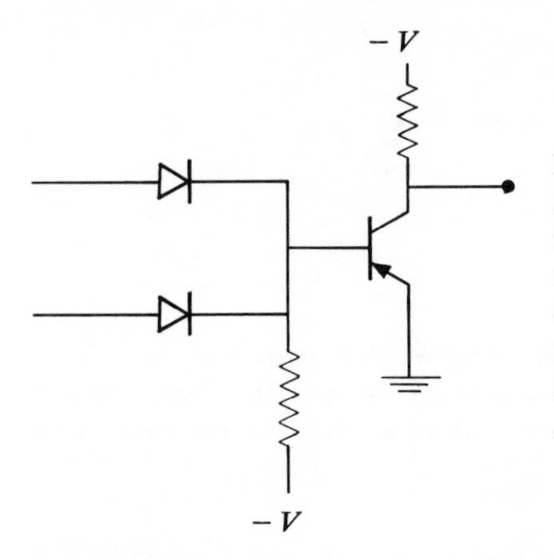

Fig. 3-4. *A diode gate circuit combined with an inverter, which helps to restore voltage levels and rise times. The output of this unit will, of course, be opposite in polarity to that of the simple diode gate of Fig. 3-3.*

polarity. For example, for a negative *and* gate, such as shown in Figure 3-4, a positive output would indicate that both inputs were minus. A negative output would indicate that one of the inputs was positive. This could mean either an asserted *or* gate or an *and* gate in which both inputs were not continuously asserted.

The diode-transistor type of logical element described here is but one of a number of ways *and* and *or* circuits can be constructed. Other circuits involve simple resistor inputs to the transistor or combinations of diodes and capacitors. The diode-transistor logic we have presented is often referred to as NOR logic. It is becoming increasingly popular because of the simplicity with which logical circuits can be implemented. For example, since the 1 output from an *or* circuit is a negative potential, this may be fed directly, without further inversion, into a subsequent *and* circuit, saving one transistor inverter.

Because diodes are inexpensive, their extensive use helps to minimize circuit costs. However, occasionally special versions of the *and* and the *or* functions must be implemented with transistors rather than diodes. Figure 3-5 is a diagram of transistors connected to perform the *or* function. Either transistor can be turned on by

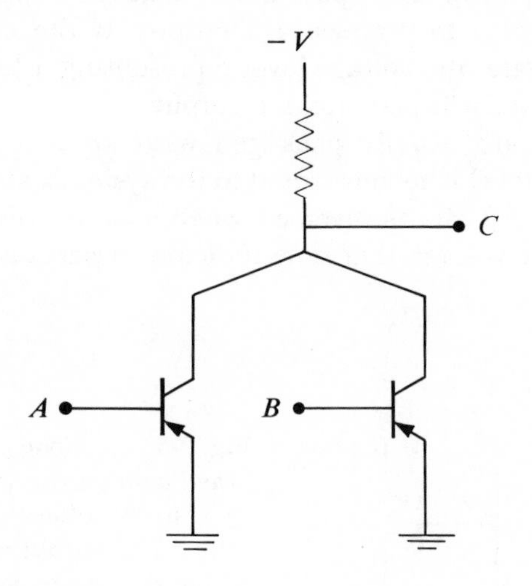

Fig. 3-5. *A logical "or" operation implemented with two paralleled transistors. This circuit is more expensive, in general, than that of Fig. 3-4, but in certain applications it may be a useful means of executing a logical "or" operation.*

means of a negative input to the respective base, thus providing a pathway for current through the single-load resistor. Since either current is sufficient to drop the voltage across the load resistor, the circuit will give a positive output for either of the two negative inputs, thus acting like an *or* logical unit. Figure 3-6 illustrates a series transistor circuit that acts as an *and* circuit for the two inputs *A* and *B*. Both transistors must be turned on to pass a current. The circuit is therefore an *and* logical unit. Similar parallel and series *and* and *or* circuits can be designed from electromagnetic relays in which a closed relay contact corresponds to a conducting transistor.

The multivibrator—the basic memory unit

The memory unit, as we have said, is one that will retain some indication of a previous action. The simple transistor inverter is not able to do so because it was designed to respond rapidly to

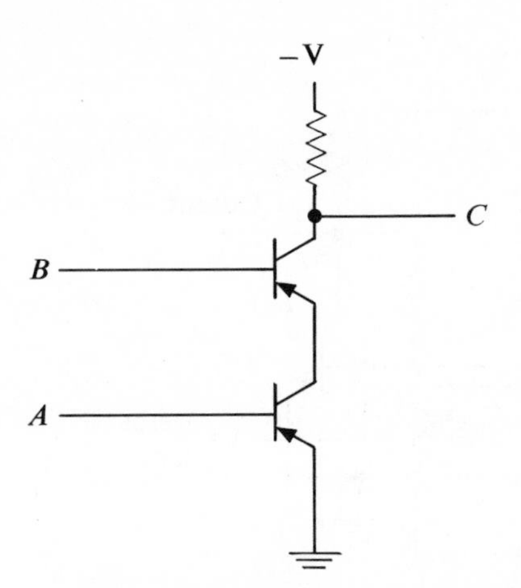

Fig. 3-6. *A logical "and" operation implemented with series transistors.*

variations in its input conditions. The general concept of the *multivibrator,* therefore, has evolved in a number of forms to provide a circuit whose output is dependent upon other factors than simply its input. The basic multivibrator is made up of two transistor inverters, with the collector output of each connected to the base input of the other through some appropriate resistive circuit. This arrangement is depicted in Figure 3-7*a*.

Analyzing the circuit, we see that when one of the transistors is conducting heavily its collector is in the more positive of the two possible states. This positive voltage is connected to the base of the other transistor, which is therefore cut off. The situation is reversed, of course, when the second transistor happens to be the one conducting heavily. The transistorized multivibrator is therefore able to act as a memory device because it can be set by a transient voltage pulse to one of the two states and then can remain in that state for a length of time specified by other conditions than the duration of the input signal.

There are a number of different types of multivibrators used in various applications. The basis for their classification is the length of time that the multivibrator will stay in one or the other state. The classes are as follows:

1. Bistable multivibrators.
2. Monostable multivibrators.
3. Astable multivibrators.

BISTABLE MULTIVIBRATORS

The multivibrator just described and pictured in Figure 3-7*a* is a bistable multivibrator. An input to one of the two transistors will set the device to one of its two possible states. After being

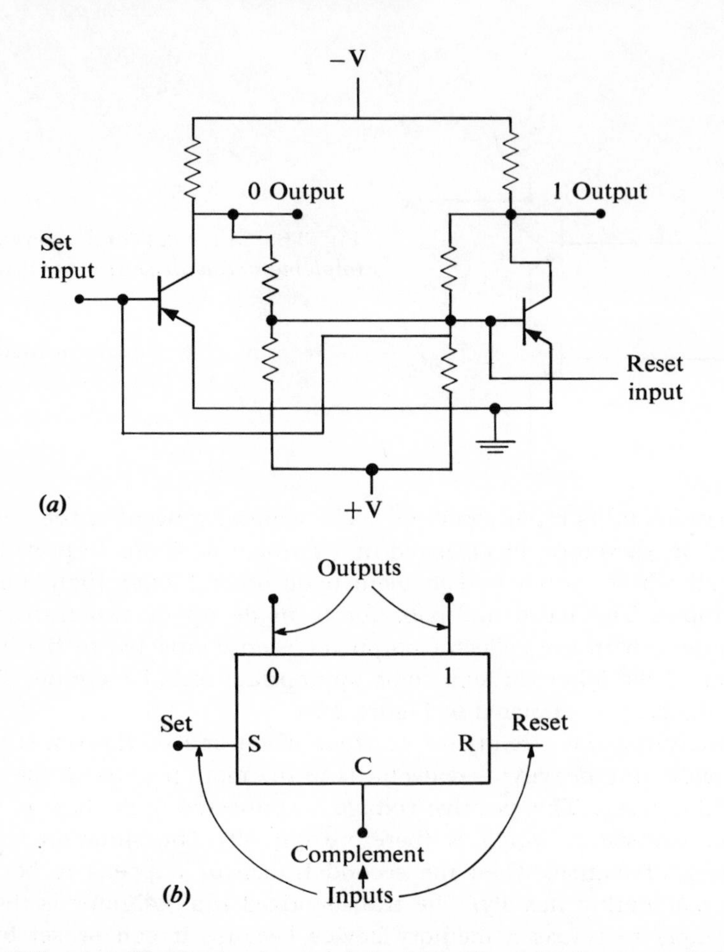

Fig. 3-7. (a) *The basic circuit of the bistable multivibrator, which is the usual one-bit storage medium within the processing and control units of a computer. The circuit shows the emitter-to-base cross coupling between the two transistors. The base circuits of the two transistors are returned to a positive voltage supply so that the voltage divider in the cross coupling circuit can be driven positive enough to fully cut off the transistors.* (b) *The standard symbol for a bistable flip-flop with a complement input (described in text) added.*

set to a given state, the bistable multivibrator will remain in that condition as long as the power supply voltages are maintained and as long as no further inputs occur. It is therefore said to be bistable, for either of the two conditions can be retained indefinitely. Such a multivibrator is called a *flip-flop* because it can flip to one state and flop back to the other on the basis of command signals. Another term for this device is *trigger,* referring to the fact that the state of the device is determined by transient input signals or triggers. Flip-flops can thus be used as buffer memories in various computer operations. In general, whenever information about the prior occurrence of a transient pulse must be retained, a flip-flop is the best device to use. Many different configurations of flip-flops are available. Often some diode gating logic is connected to one of the two inputs, so that the input will be activated only when certain logical conditions are met.

Flip-flops are devices with at least two inputs. They are often referred to as the *set* and *reset* inputs or the 1 and 0 inputs respectively. In each case, a set or a 1 input activates the 1 output of the flip-flop. The reset or 0 input sets the trigger in the opposite state, so that the logical 0 output is activated. Often special triggers are designed with an additional input that can *complement* the state of the flip-flop. The complement input will set the trigger if it is reset, or reset it if it is set. In other words, the complement input is able to change the logical state of the flip-flop to the one opposite to its current state.

Flip-flops often have inverters attached to their outputs so that they can drive a heavy load without interfering with the operation of the flip-flop itself. Such flip-flops are said to be buffered and are capable of driving many units simultaneously. Figure 3-7*b* is the standard schematic symbol of a flip-flop with a complement input line.

Another important consideration is that a simple flip-flop is a scale of two counter. That is to say, if pulses activate the complement input of a flip-flop, it is alternately set into the 1 and the 0 state. This response is a count of the input signal to the base 2 (with truncated rounding since no carry is possible) and as such is the basis of arithmetic computation in the computer. We will deal more thoroughly with counters in the next chapter.

MONOSTABLE MULTIVIBRATORS

If a multivibrator is designed with a resistor-capacitor feedback circuit from the collector of one of the inverters to the base of the other, but with no feedback from the second inverter collector (as illustrated in Figure 3-8*a*), the device will tend to exhibit monostable characteristics. It will, when triggered, change states. The change of state, however, is only transient; once the capacitor charges to a certain value, the multivibrator will switch back to its original state. Such a circuit is said to be monostable since it will not remain indefinitely in the triggered state and has therefore only one stable state.

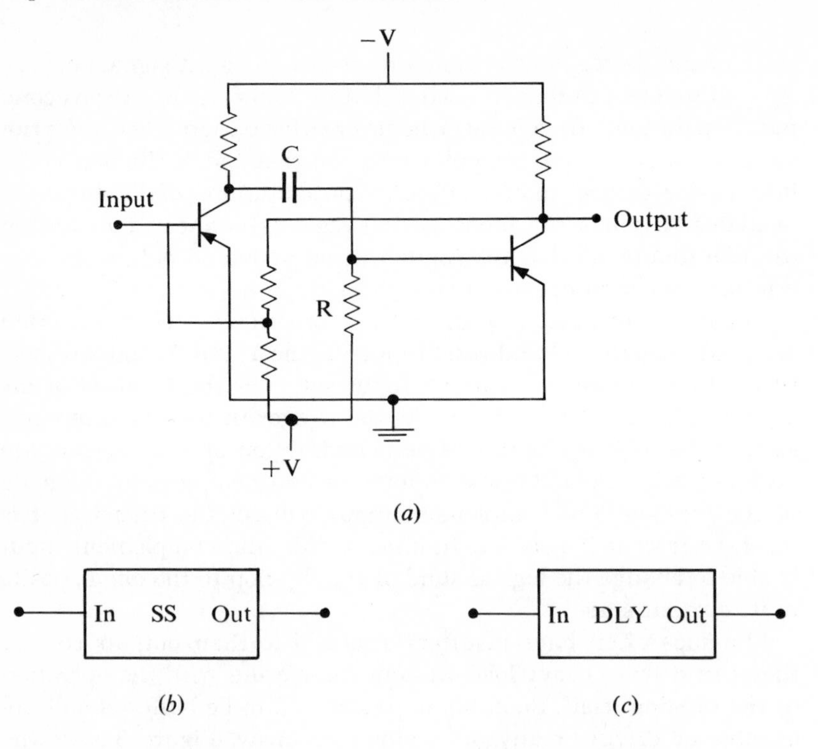

Fig. 3-8. (a) *The basic circuit of the monostable multivibrator, which is typically used as a pulse generator or as a delay circuit. The capacitor in the cross coupling network allows the initial positive cut off voltage impressed on the base of the second transistor to vary toward the more negative saturation voltage of the transistor as a function of the RC time constant. Therefore the duration of the output pulse is exclusively a function of the RC time constant. Once the capacitor has discharged, the voltage on the collector of the second transistor returns to a more positive level, which turns off the first transistor. The positive supply is necessary for the same reason as in Fig. 3-7.* (b) *The standard symbol for the single shot or pulse generating circuit.* (c) *The standard symbol for the delay circuit.*

Monostable multivibrators thus act as generators of long pulses. The duration of the pulses is determined by the RC (resistance-capacitance) time constant of the charging circuit. Either a larger resistor or a larger capacitor may be used to elongate the duration of the output pulse from the monostable multivibrator. In practice, a set of fixed capacitors is used to select the general range of durations, while a variable resistor is used to determine the fine tuning of the duration of the output pulse.

Once the input exceeds certain threshold conditions of amplitude and rise time, monostable multivibrators are, in a sense, independent of the input signal. Thus, they are very often used not only to elongate brief pulses but also to produce standard pulses from level changes that might continue on after the output signal itself. The generally accepted terminology for circuits with these operating properties includes *single shots, start-stop multivibrators,* and *pulse generators*. In addition, a monostable multivibrator is often specially modified so that at the end of its output pulse a briefer pulse is emitted to signify the end of the RC timing period. This device is a *delay* for the length of time between the input pulse and the output pulse and can be used as such in a computer circuit. Figures 3-8*b* and 3-8*c* show the conventional symbols for the single-shot and the delay circuit respectively.

ASTABLE MULTIVIBRATORS

Multivibrators can also be designed so that neither state is a stable one. In such a circuit design, each of the collectors of the two transistors is fed back to the base of the other transistor through resistive and capacitive elements (see Fig. 3-9*a*). Once

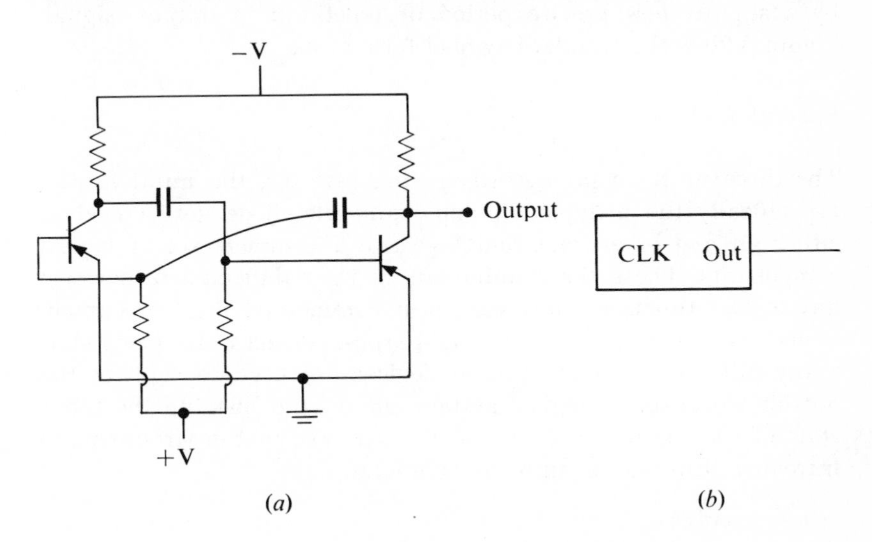

Fig. 3-9. (a) *The basic circuit of the astable multivibrator, which is used for producing a continuous stream of timing or clock pulses. Each of the two collectors is cross coupled to the other transistor's base by RC circuits. The unit thus tends to alternate between one state and the other, the length of each state being a function of the RC time constant in the cross coupling network.* (b) *The standard symbol for a clock such as illustrated in Fig. 3-9a.*

the power is turned on, this circuit tends to transfer back and forth between one state and the other without any input signal. It therefore produces, at either collector, a square wave whose on and off times are determined by the respective RC time constants of the two feedback circuits. The astable multivibrator can be used to generate a standard repetitive signal and is typically used as the master timing signal for more complex systems. An additional application, important for the readers of this book, is its use in the measurement of the timing of external events.

Astable multivibrators are often called *clocks* and usually have their outputs either differentiated (in the mathematical sense) or passed through a pulse transformer to make the output signals conform to the standard pulse duration required by a given logical system. *Crystal oscillators* are often employed instead of astable multivibrators because of their extreme stability, but once a given crystal has been inserted, the output frequency of the circuit is unchangeable. Astable multivibrators, however, can be adjusted over wide ranges by variation of the resistor or capacitor in one of the feedback circuits. This advantage is compensated for by a slightly less precise period of repetition in output signal. Figure 3-9*b* is the standard symbol for a clock.

Special devices

The three units so far described—the inverter, the multivibrator (specifically the bistable flip-flop), and the diode gate (used as either an *and* or an *or* circuit)—make a complete set of logical components. These three units can be interconnected to perform any logical function. However, most commercial lines of components also include other, special-purpose devices. In particular, many different kinds of special devices are used to connect the outside world to the logical system either by displaying the inner state of the computer or by enabling the external environment to introduce information into the computer.

INPUT DEVICES

The special circuits that assist in coupling information from the outside world into a computer include:

1. Switch filters.
2. Pulse generators.
3. Schmitt triggers.
4. Diode clippers.
5. Level amplifiers.

Some circuits are used to make the temporal properties of the external signals compatible with those of the computer. For example, switch filters are circuits composed only of passive components, usually RC circuit elements. The function of a switch filter is to smooth out jagged voltage waveforms, such as those produced by the closing of electromechanical contacts, so that these waveforms may be fed into subsequent stages of the input circuitry without multiple effects. Figure 3-10*a* shows a jagged input voltage

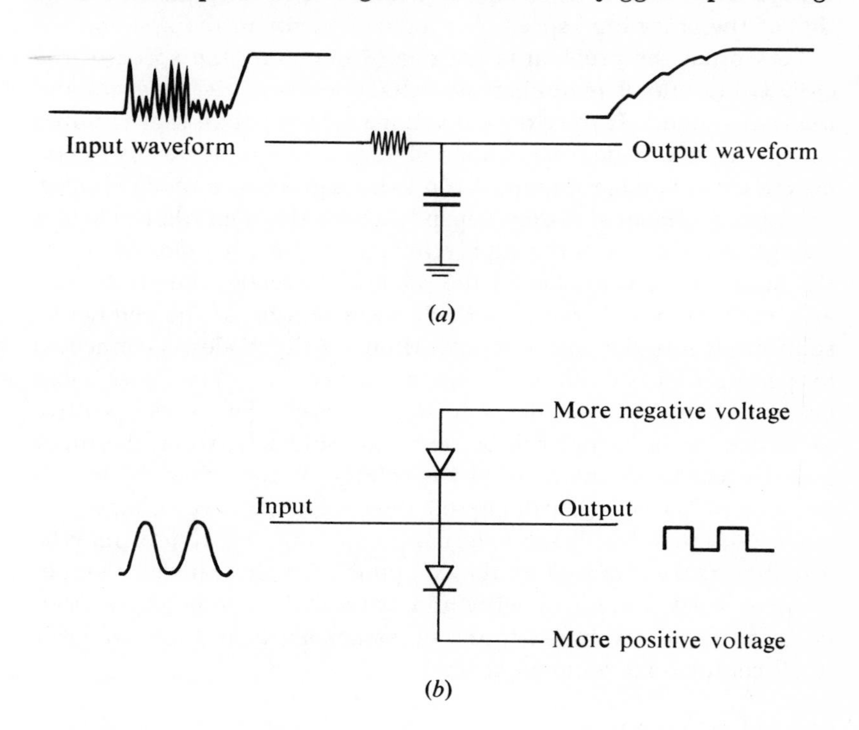

Fig. 3-10. (a) *A diagram of a resistor and capacitor connected as a switch filter showing the very jagged input from a mechanical contact (which could result in erratic computer operation) being smoothed (integrated) to a monotonic waveform.* (b) *A diagram of two diodes being used to clip the amplitude of a large input signal to a lower level.*

being converted into a monotonic waveform by a switch filter. It can be seen that switch filters are simply integrating RC circuits, like those described in the first appendix.

Once smoothed out, the waveforms can be fed into one of two different types of specialized input devices. One, the pulse generator, is designed to emit a standard pulse when a nonstandard input is applied. (Pulse generators are special modifications of the monostable multivibrator described earlier.) The other, the so-called Schmitt trigger, is a special bistable device whose state depends upon the magnitude of the input voltage. This circuit is able to switch its state in fractions of microseconds once a certain threshold voltage is exceeded in either the ascending or the descending direction. Thus, the Schmitt trigger can transform the very slow voltage changes of an integrating switch filter into a voltage level that changes rapidly with a rise or fall time similar to that of the other high-speed electronic elements in the system.

Very often the problem is not one of matching the speed of the circuits but one of matching the voltage levels of the external and internal systems. If the external voltage is larger than that required by the internal logic, one can simply use a couple of diodes to clip off the extra voltage. Figure 3-10*b* is a diagram of a diode clipper. The diode clipper's action depends upon the fact that when a voltage signal exceeds the supply voltage on the other side of one of the diodes it forward biases the diode. The diode, therefore, acts as a short circuit; it removes that excess portion of the voltage by shunting it into the power supply. If one of the diodes is connected to a more positive voltage *B*, so that when the signal goes more positive than *B* the diode is forward biased, the excess positive excursion of the signal will be removed. Similarly, when the input signal exceeds the more negative voltage *A*, the other diode will be forward biased and will clip off the excess negative voltage.

On the other hand, the external voltages of the system may be less than those required by the computer. Simple transistor amplifiers, or level amplifiers with and without inversion, have been designed to raise voltages to the necessary levels and are available in all commercial component lines.

OUTPUT DEVICES

It is often desired to communicate logical states generated within the computer to the external environment or to another electronic device. Sample circuits which accomplish this function are:

1. Relay drivers.
2. Indicator drivers.
3. Bus drivers.
4. Level amplifiers.

All are designed to provide the special current and voltage capabilities required by the external device.

Relay drivers are high-current, high-voltage circuits that can amplify the levels of the logical signal from the computer sufficiently to activate an external electromechanical relay. An *indicator driver* is a similar device, but its output current and voltage are designed only to light a lamp of some sort, which can be used to communicate, by visual means, some information about the internal state of the system to the user. *Bus driver* is a generic term for a high-current amplifier capable of being heavily loaded with many different devices without exceeding its current driving capacities.

In addition to these generally useful devices, each commercial line of components contains others which perform special functions. They often allow the designer to implement difficult operations with a great deal of ease.

All of these circuits are usually available as unit packages. The package may be a fiber glass board with a connector at one end to which connections from the circuits mounted on the board are led. The board can then be plugged into a mounting panel containing a large number of receptacles into which the connectors slip. This type of system can be easily repaired, for circuit boards can be unplugged and replaced without disturbing any of the connecting wiring.

New microelectronic circuits have been designed which are physically so small that an entire logical building block can be fitted into the small case previously housing only a single transistor. These tiny units themselves might be mounted on special subpanels and the latter mounted on wired mounting panels. In any case, whatever the specific technology, the discussion in this chapter holds true because it deals only with the general logical concepts. The future promises even more striking changes, for recent developments in thin-film and molecular techniques have suggested that entire computers can be made by sequentially depositing the semiconductor and passive components on substrates of one or another material. If the interconnections themselves prove to be susceptible to this sort of approach, very tiny and extremely reliable computers can be anticipated. The major problem with such systems will be inserting information into and accessing information from a tiny block of material.

Now that we have discussed the building blocks making up logical systems, let us consider the types of functions these circuits perform. We now turn to a discussion of the fundamental operations performed within computer-like devices.

4: LOGICAL FUNCTIONS

Introduction

A collection of the logical elements described in the previous chapter does not in itself constitute a working computer system. The elements must be combined into more complex functional units to perform all the operations that collectively make up a total computer. This chapter will discuss the operations of the higher functional units and will describe how they are formed from the simpler set of logical elements.

The functional units which are constructed by interconnecting logical building blocks can do a wide variety of things. In many cases, special applications require functional units designed specifically for them. There are, however, a relatively small number of generally applicable functions which we will describe here. But in order to describe them we must have a set of conventions that will allow us to standardize the discussion. It should be remembered that the set of conventions used in this chapter is extremely arbitrary; as many alternative conventions as one can imagine could have been used. Nevertheless, agreeing upon one set of conventions adds a specificity to our discussion that will make it more useful in the long run. The conventions are as follows:

1. The logical voltage levels will be 0 volts (ground potential) for the more positive level and −5 volts for the more negative level.
2. The diode *and* gate used will be asserted by a negative voltage, the diode *or* gate by a positive voltage. In each case an inverter is associated with the diode gate such that a positive output indicates that a diode *and* gate has its input conditions met and a negative output indicates that a diode *or* gate has its input conditions fulfilled.
3. The outputs of a flip-flop will be such that the connection associated with the present state of the flip-flop will be −5 volts. Thus if the flip-flop is in the 1 state, the 1 output will be at −5 volts and the 0 output will be at 0 volts.
4. Pulses produced by some pulse-generating source will be negative going at their point of origin.
5. Flip-flop inputs will be such that they are activated by negative going pulses.

We must introduce a new concept, the *register*, at this time. A register is a set of flip-flops or other storage devices that are functionally joined together to perform a specific job. Most of the logical functions we will describe involve the use or manipulation of the contents of such coordinated groups of flip-flops. As the next chapter will show, computers may be described as organized groups of registers which process, route, and store information. In general, the number of flip-flops in a few critically important registers defines the word size of a given computer system. Each flip-flop can store one bit of information. The number of flip-flops is, therefore, equivalent to the number of bits in a word. In other applications within the computer, however, registers may have other purposes than storing a total computer word. For instance, the computer control circuitry contains registers that sequence, select, count, and transfer information from one location to another. We shall describe this variety of registers in the next chapter. Now let us discuss the fundamental logical processes required to perform these operations.

Logical gating

We have spoken of diode gates and their ability to serve either the *and* or the *or* function. In many instances within computers there is a need for routing control signals through a logical net composed of several sequential *and* or *or* diode gates. Such a signal is said to be *gated* to one or another destination by the logical conditions of the system. Suppose that we wished to gate a pulse to a given point to initiate a certain operation whenever three flip-flops—*A*, *B*, and *C*—were simultaneously in the 1 state, or that we wished to do the same thing when a fourth flip-flop, *D*, was in the 1 state. This verbal statement can be implemented by the circuit shown in Figure 4-1. The output of a three-input *and* gate is fed into a two-

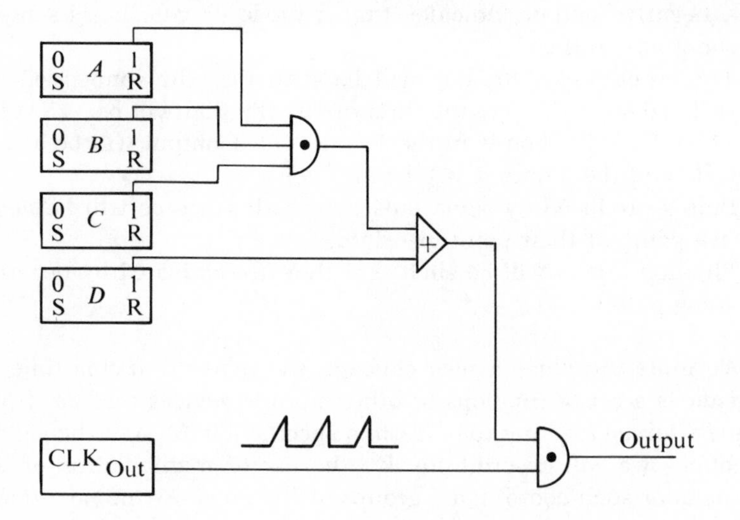

Fig. 4-1. *One possible diode gating circuit, which will allow clock pulses to pass to the output when either flip-flop A, B* and *C are in the "1" state* or *flip-flop D is in the "1" state.*

input *or* gate, which has the output of the *D* flip-flop as its other input. The output of this *or* gate is therefore activated when either of the two input conditions is met. Its output, a negative voltage (by the conventions described above), can be fed directly into the two-input *and* gate, whose other input is the output of the pulse generator. Thus the pulse will be passed or asserted to signal some subsequent actions under the defined logical conditions. This is but one example of the many different gating operations that can be performed. The class of gating operations is a large one, but, since each circumstance is so specialized, it would be of little value to give many examples. The general principles are covered adequately by this single example. The important point to remember is that pulse signals can be gated about in complex, though predetermined, fashions by cascading diode gates appropriately.

It should also be realized that usually several equivalent circuits will perform the same logical functions. Thus, there may be many effective circuits for the same logical operation, each of which is completely satisfactory. Often the criteria for selecting which of the circuits will be used are secondary ones, such as minimization of circuit elements or operating time.

Transferring or copying

It is often necessary to transfer the information contained in one flip-flop register to some other flip-flop register. Figure 4-2 illustrates an arrangement for the transfer of information between two 4-bit flip-flop registers. The assumption in this example

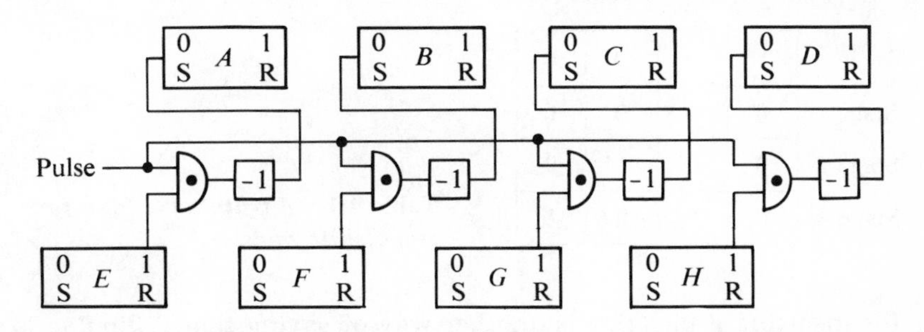

Fig. 4-2. *A system for transferring the contents of one flip-flop register (composed of flip-flops E, F, G and H) to another register (composed of flip-flops A, B, C and D).*

is that the second register (*B*) has been previously cleared so that all of the flip-flops are in the 0 state. The clearing may easily be done by means of a common pulse input to each of the reset inputs of each flip-flop in that register. Each of the 1 outputs of register *A* is connected to one of the inputs of a set of two-input *and* diode gates. The other input of each of the diode gates is connected to a common pulse generator which is activated when certain other logical conditions obtain. Since our convention stated that negative going pulses were required to set or reset the flip-flops, inverters are required to give the proper polarity to the output signal from the *and* gates in this example. In each case, then, if there is a 1 in the *A* register for a given flip-flop position, the circuit will set the corresponding flip-flop in the *B* register to a 1 when it is pulsed. Otherwise, the corresponding flip-flop will remain in the 0 state. Transferring, as illustrated here, is an important operation that occurs whenever information is transferred between various components of a computer system. This example also illustrates the way diode gates can be used to control the input condition of a flip-flop register. The terms *loading* and *copying* are also used frequently to describe this operation.

Shifting

A special kind of register often used for sequencing operations is a *shift register.* In shift registers, only one of the flip-flops in the register can contain a bit at any given time. Another restriction is that this bit is transferred serially down the chain of flip-flops in the register. The truth table for a four-stage shift register is shown in Table 4-1. We can see by inspection that the condition

	ff A	ff B	ff C	ff D
Stage 1	1	0	0	0
Stage 2	0	1	0	0
Stage 3	0	0	1	0
Stage 4	0	0	0	1

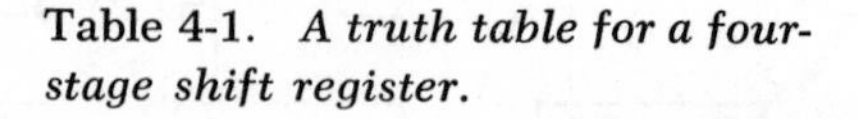

Table 4-1. *A truth table for a four-stage shift register.*

for inserting a bit (this is another way of saying that a flip-flop is set to the 1 state) is that the previous flip-flop in the register is in the 1 state. The shift register function can, therefore, be implemented with the logical units shown in Figure 4-3.

In this case we assume that the initial condition of the register is that specified by state 1 in the truth table. Once again a functional operation is performed by using the states of the flip-flops

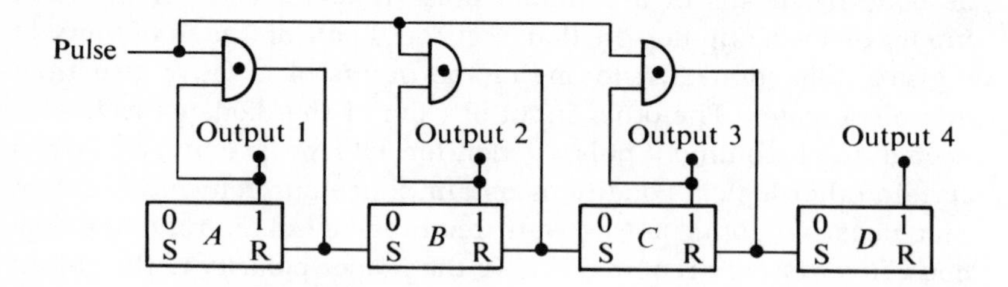

Fig. 4-3. *A shift register.*

in the register to determine, by means of appropriate conditioning of diode gate *and* circuits, what the subsequent state of the entire register will be. In our example a pulse is passed to the set input of a flip-flop if, and only if, the previous flip-flop is set to a 1. This set pulse is also used to reset the previous flip-flop.

The output of a shift register like the one illustrated in Figure

4-3 will be a set of sequential states, available at a rate dependent upon the frequency of occurrence of the shift pulses. It is possible to perform a series of sequential acts such as those required in the execution of a complex instruction in this manner. Shift registers are, therefore, important parts of the control elements of a computer's central processing unit.

Comparing

Another basic computer operation is *comparing* the contents of one flip-flop register with those of another. For example, a question is often asked which has a two-state answer: "Are the two registers equal or are they not equal?" Figure 4-4 illustrates a circuit that performs a "compare for equality" operation on two 2-bit flip-flop registers. The conditions for equality may be ex-

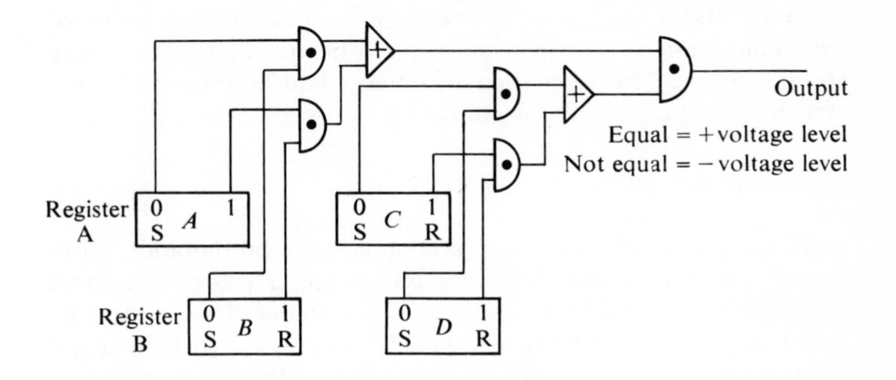

Fig. 4-4. *A circuit for testing the equality of two registers, each composed of two flip-flops.*

pressed verbally: equality exists if in each case corresponding pairs of flip-flops are either both in the 1 state or both in the 0 state. The circuit shown in Figure 4-4 implements this operation by first determining whether either of the two possible conditions, 0 and 0 or 1 and 1, holds for the first pair of flip-flops. To achieve the determination, the 0 ouputs are *anded* together, and the 1 outputs are also *anded* together, both by means of diode gates.

The output of each *and* circuit is then fed into the inputs of an *or* gate to assure that either of the two conditions will be accepted. The outputs of this *or* gate and of all the other *or* gates for *each* pair of flip-flops are then *anded* together to make the final test for equality. The output will be 0 volts if all conditions are met and

−5 volts if any one or more of the pairs of flip-flops are not equal. This basic operation can be expanded to include any number of flip-flops in a register. The only additional requirement is that the number of inputs on the final *and* diode gate must be expanded to equal the number of pairs of flip-flops.

Comparison circuits are useful in many computer applications that involve tests for subsequent contingent operations. For example, circuitry for a computer instruction can be constructed specifying that the next sequential instruction in a computer program is to be skipped when a given state occurs. That given state is loaded into a register, which is then compared with the calculations as they are being made. An affirmative answer to the comparison is used as a signal to alter the address of the next instruction to be executed.

The usefulness of compare circuits is extended by the fact that it is not necessary for both registers being compared to be flip-flop registers. A flip-flop register can be compared with a group of electromechanical switches or even with the input from some storage device. Thus a particular action could be initiated by the arrival of a special word or character.

Decoding and selecting

In Chapter 2 we described the economies of representation introduced into a language that uses an encoding process. A small number of symbols can represent a large number of basic ideas by concatenated combinations of a small basic alphabet. Thus a six-position code in which each position could be either of the members of a two-character alphabet would be able to represent sixty-four different alphanumeric characters ($2^6 = 64$). In a computer, these sixty-four characters could, therefore, be represented by the combined states of a register of six flip-flops. On occasion, however, it is necessary to decode the contents of this flip-flop register by selecting the single character represented by it. The process of translating the coded contents of a register into the specific character or output signal is called *decoding*. Decoding the contents of a six-bit register would therefore result in the selection of one of sixty-four output lines.

Decoding can be simply accomplished by means of diode gates. Figure 4-5 depicts a decoder for a two-bit register that illustrates this idea. A two-bit register, of course, can be decoded into four output lines ($2^2 = 4$). This is accomplished by using *and* diode gates with their inputs connected to the outputs of the two flip-flops. In each case, the diode gate inputs are connected to the combination of flip-flop outputs corresponding to the code for one of the decoded lines. Output line 1 is represented by the binary code 00, and both of its diode gate inputs are therefore connected to the 0 outputs of the two flip-flops. Whenever both flip-flops are in the 0 state, output line 1 will be activated. This output can be used either to initiate another action directly or to control some

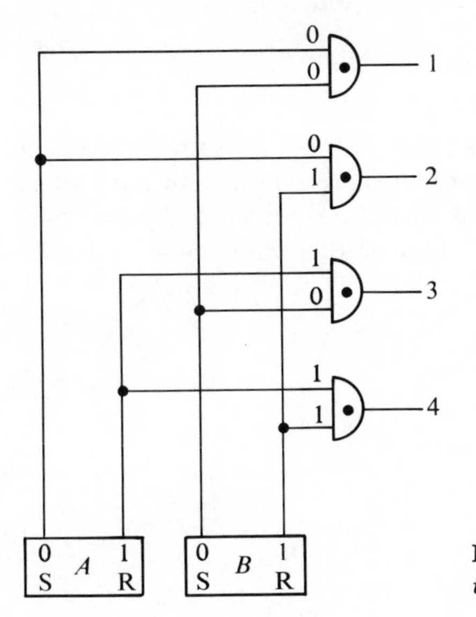

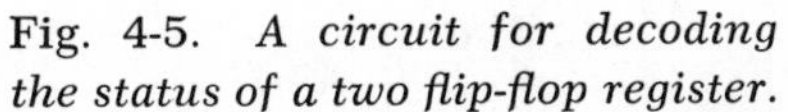
Fig. 4-5. *A circuit for decoding the status of a two flip-flop register.*

subsequent gating operation. Each of the other diode *and* gates acts in essentially the same way except that it is activated by a different state of the register.

Decoding processes like these can be used for as many flip-flops as desired as long as the number of inputs on each diode gate is equal to the number of flip-flops in the register. To have fewer inputs to the diode gate would lead to ambiguous coding situations in which two bit combinations could conceivably activate the same output line. On the other hand, the number of output lines increases as the square of the number of bits in the register if all possibilities are used.

The basic process illustrated here is only a single example of the many decoding processes found in a computer. All computers require extensive decoding for the input or output of information, for the selection of the address to which information is being sent, and for the selection of a given instruction or part of an instruction to be executed. Decoders may also be used to initiate the action of a shift register so that the decoding of a given instruction will cause a specific sequence of actions to be executed.

By now it should be well understood that modern high-speed digital computers are composed of families of registers whose logical and sequential actions are controlled by means of *and* and *or* units. We shall proceed to a consideration of how the logical operations described in the previous chapter can also implement arithmetic functions such as counting and addition.

Counting

Counting in a coded form, of course, is also a more economical process than an uncoded, one-for-one represenation. In particular, the binary counting process up to 7 can be represented by the truth table shown in Table 4-2. Inspection of this truth table and con-

N	4	2	1
1	0	0	1
2	0	1	0
3	0	1	1
4	1	0	0
5	1	0	1
6	1	1	0
7	1	1	1

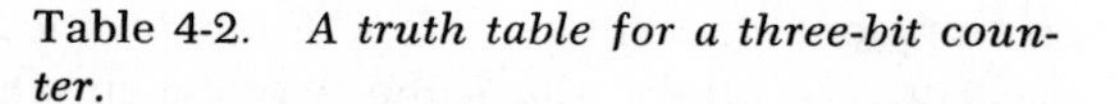

Table 4-2. *A truth table for a three-bit counter.*

sideration of what we have learned about the control of flip-flop registers suggest that it should be possible to specifically construct a binary counter out of a flip-flop register in which sequential states are controlled in a definite way by a specially organized group of diode gates.

Consider, for example, the action of a single flip-flop with its inputs and outputs connected as shown in Figure 4-6. In Chapter 3 we pointed out that a flip-flop so connected is, in fact, a simple binary counter that effectively rounds by truncation every time it is reset to the 0 state.

Inspecting the truth table (Table 4-2) once again, we see that subsequent states in the counting process are also uniquely determined by the preceding states. Thus, as an example, the second least significant bit is set to a 1 whenever a counting pulse is

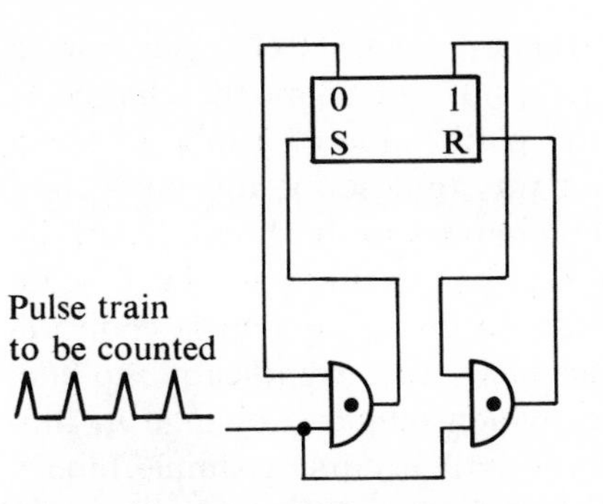

Fig. 4-6. *A single flip-flop wired so that it will alternate between its two states when triggered by a series of pulses.*

applied *and* the least significant bit is in the 1 state. This suggests that a diode gate might be used to set the second flip-flop to a 1 when these appropriate conditions occur. Similarly, the conditions for the setting of the third least significant bit include the presence of the counting pulse and a 1 in each of the two other flip-flops. The conditions for resetting any flip-flop can be deduced in a similar manner. Using a diode gating type of control, we can implement a three-bit counter (which can count to 7) by means of a circuit wired in the form shown in Figure 4-7. Counting to

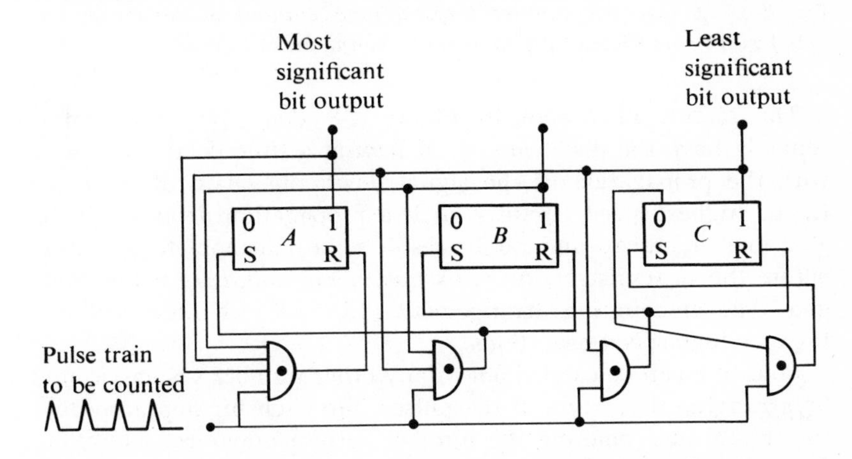

Fig. 4-7. *A three-bit binary counter developed by controlling the inputs to the appropriate set and reset inputs by diode gating so that the operation is in accord with the truth table of Table 4-2.*

higher numbers requires additional flip-flops and the appropriate additional gating circuitry to control the change of state of each flip-flop, according to the rules expressed in an expanded truth table.

The binary counting circuit can be very much simplified if complement inputs are used and the flip-flops are designed so that they will be complemented whenever a level changes from a 1 to a 0 (from −5 volts to 0 volts), but not when the change is from 0 to −5 volts. Inspecting the truth table of Table 4-2 once again, we see that it is but another way to describe the same complementing action. A given flip-flop changes to the 1 state from the 0 state whenever the preceding flip-flop changes to the 0 state from the 1 state. Thus at each stage a given flip-flop is counting half of the pulses counted by the next least significant flip-flop. Using a special complement input which effects a change in flip-flop state only when a positive level shift occurs, a simple binary counter can be constructed without diode gating, as shown in Figure 4-8.

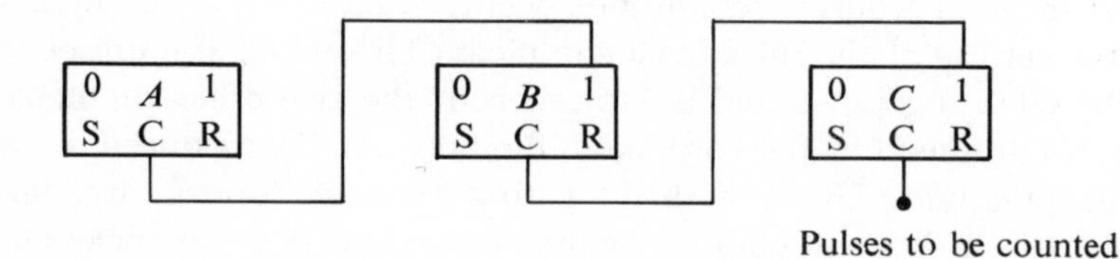

Fig. 4-8. *A three-bit counter implemented without diode gating but using more complicated flip-flops with complement inputs.*

The circuit illustrated in Figure 4-8 does, however, unfortunately have the disadvantage of having a time delay associated with the propagation of the signal down the chain of flip-flops. In the highest-speed circuitry such a propagation delay might be a serious handicap and might result in an incomplete operation before the next instruction is executed. For this reason the diode gate type of counting arrangement (Fig. 4-7) is more desirable for very high-speed operations.

Counting can be carried out in any other number system desired by arranging the gating of the pulses into each flip-flop according to a truth table defining the number system under consideration. Decimal counting is usually accomplished by means of the binary coded decimal scheme so that the two-state flip-flop technology can be used.

It should be obvious that a down or decrementing counter can be constructed in a way similar to that used in the construction of the up or incrementing counter just described. The truth table would be essentially the same, but in the reverse order, and the rules for changing the state of a given flip-flop would be different. The design of such a circuit is left as an exercise for the reader.

Adding

In Chapter 2 we described the addition table for binary arithmetic. It was a simple table stating the rules for addition in the following form:

$$0 + 0 = 0$$
$$0 + 1 = 1$$
$$1 + 0 = 1$$
$$1 + 1 = 0 \text{ carry } 1$$

In other words, if the two bits to be added are the same, the output is 0. In the special case in which the two are each equal to 1, there is an additional output bit called a *carry*—a bit of information to be conveyed to the next stage of the adder. If the two bits are different, the output is equal to 1. A device implementing this table for the addition of two binary bits is called a *half adder*. It is so named because the addition is only half completed. There is still a carry bit that has not yet been added to the next most significant bit position (if there is one).

A typical half adder is shown in Figure 4-9. The 1 outputs of two flip-flops are fed into the circuit. The determination of whether or not there will be a carry is simple. There will be a carry if both of the 1 outputs of the two flip-flops are at -5 volts. The two inverters are used to correct polarities so that an $\bar{A}$ or a $\bar{B}$ will

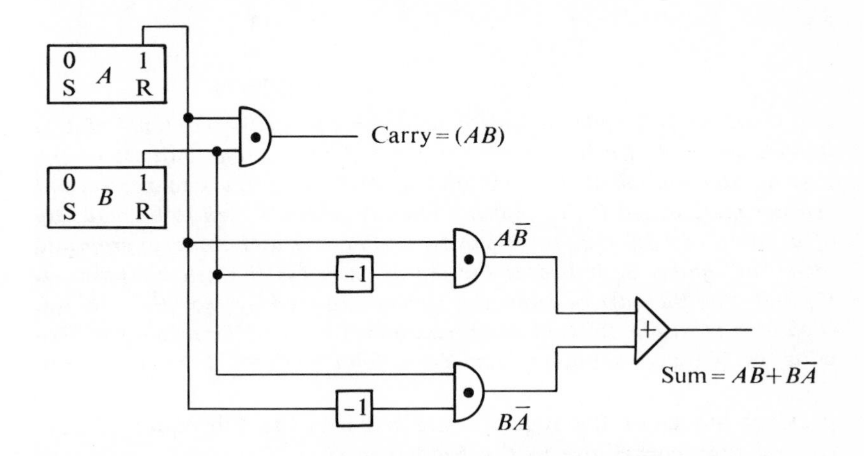

Fig. 4-9. *One possible half adder, showing the carry and the sum outputs. The operation of this important circuit is described in the text. (Redrawn from Fig. 2-19 in A. I. Pressman,* Design of Transistorized Circuits for Digital Computers, *New York, John F. Rider, 1959, p. 2–22.)*

be able to assert the two other *and* diode gates which determine whether A is 1 and B is 0 or A is 0 and B is 1. Either of these two inequalities produces the sum output through the final *or* diode gate. Thus the half adder has two outputs: the *carry output* (which is 1 when both flip-flops are in the 1 state) and the *sum ouput* (which is 1 if the two flip-flops are in opposite states).

In practice, however, one is seldom interested in adding the contents of a single flip-flop to those of another. The more interesting situation is that in which the contents of a multiple-bit register are to be added to the contents of another register of equal size. Figure 4-10 is a diagram of a logical system made up of a group of the half adders described in Figure 4-9 and carries out the full addition process on the contents of two registers, A and B, in a parallel manner. In this circuit the carry outputs from

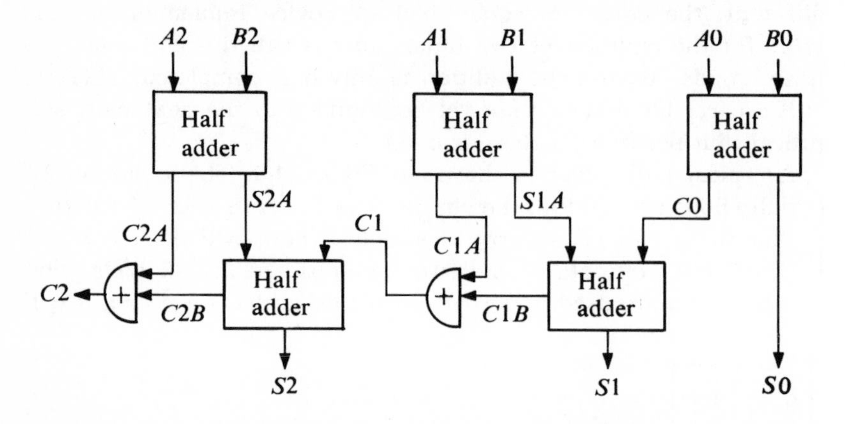

Fig. 4-10. *A full adder circuit capable of adding the contents of two flip-flop registers. Each register has three flip-flops. The outputs of the first register are labelled* A_1, A_2 *and* A_3 *and the outputs of the second register are labelled* B_1, B_2 *and* B_3. *The full adder is seen to be made up of a group of half adders as shown in Fig. 4-9 and some appropriate diode "or" gates.* S_n *indicates the output sum for the* nth *bit position.* C_n *indicates the carries from the various half adders for the* nth *bit. (Redrawn from Fig. 2-21, in A. I. Pressman,* Design of Transistorized Circuits for Digital Computers, *New York, John F. Rider, 1959, p. 21–24.)*

previous stages of the registers are fed into the subsequent stages so that they contribute to the final sum.[1]

[1] In this as in other diagrams we have followed the usually accepted convention of placing the most significant flip-flops on the left. Our discussions, then, generally will proceed from the least significant bit on the right to the most significant on the left.

Thus there is a certain amount of time delay associated with the propagation of the carry down the chain of flip-flops in the register. Each bit is affected by the carrys of all the preceding lower-order stages. The end result of this sequential interaction is that this type of full adder displays a considerable amount of activity as these influences are progressively felt by the more significant stages. The final output of the register is a set of states ($S_0 \ldots S_n$) that might then be used to condition an appropriate network of diode gates to accomplish whatever subsequent operation is required.

Other types of full adders operate on the basis of a two-step cycle. A first half adder operation is designed to occur when an initial pulse occurs. The first pulse is used to set up the half addition of all the pairs of flip-flops in the two registers. A second pulse then triggers the second half of the addition, in which all of the carrys are processed. By using a pulse-controlled system of this kind and carefully timing the occurrence of the pulses, it is possible to make the unstable settling activity incapable of affecting any other circuit functions.

The output of such a full adder circuit is a series of sums and a final carry if it is required. The final carry can be used as an indicator of an *overflow*, which occurs when the sum of the contents of two n-bit registers is greater than the number represented by n bits all set to the 1 state.

Subtracters can be designed in a similar fashion. It is possible to design a half subtracter and a parallel circuit like that shown in Figure 4-10, which accomplished the subtraction operation for two full registers. The reader would find it a useful exercise to repeat the analysis given above for the subtracter capable of determining the difference between two registers.

Starting, stopping, and synchronizing

Another important computer function repeatedly used in computer construction is the ability to start, stop, and otherwise synchronize the operations of various parts of a given device. Very often for this purpose a diode gate and a flip-flop are arranged as shown in Figure 4-11. The 1 output of the flip-flop is used to gate the series of pulses through the *and* diode gate. The flip-flop is turned on by a start pulse and off by a stop pulse generated by some other control circuitry. These other control signals might be, for example, two pulses produced during sequential states of a shift register, which itself is driven by a clock. If it is also used in the stream of gated

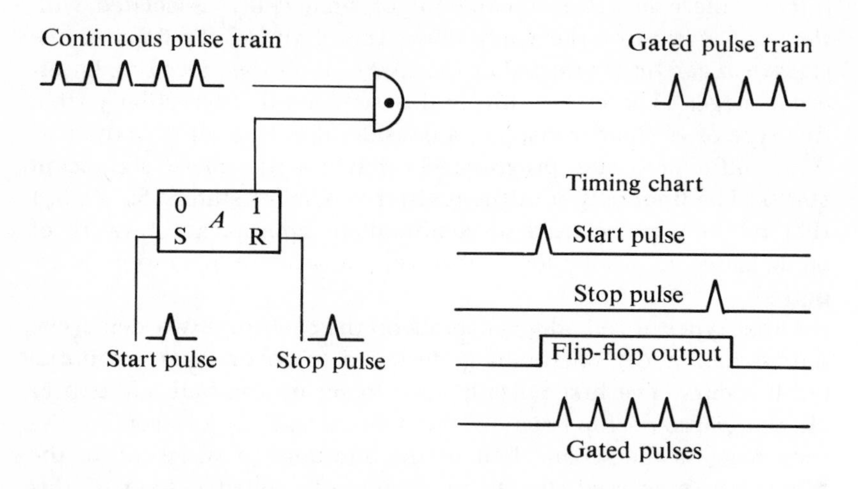

Fig. 4-11. *A flip-flop and an "and" gate used to gate a stream of clock pulses. The pulses are allowed to pass through the gate only when the flip-flop is in the "1" state. During this state the gate is said to be* enabled.

pulses, the clock pulse driving the shift register should be delayed slightly to insure a synchronization such that the first pulse passed through the gate will be the one following the pulse that turned the gate on. Otherwise a pulse of less than the necessary full duration may be passed by the gate, resulting in unstable operation of the circuitry it is driving. The delay can be effected either by a delay unit specifically designed for this function or by designing the flip-flops so that there is a delay in the shift of state greater than the duration of the triggering pulse.

This brief discussion of logical functions, it may be surprising to note, is relatively complete. Although most computers will have many variants of each of these devices (and our examples show only some of the many possible ways to implement each function) there is still a restricted set out of which a total computer is constructed. We have also restricted our discussion to devices that operate in parallel—that is, devices in which the entire contents of a register are processed almost simultaneously. This is the most common technology in modern computers. Parallel operation speeds up the operation of the entire computer system, but it also requires an increased number of the logical components. Serial systems of computer logic are occasionally discussed but are rarely used in commercial computers because of the resulting reduction in operating speed. An example of a serial technique is an adder that actually uses a circulating series of pulses to perform arithmetic. In such a system, addition or subtraction is carried out by adding or removing pulses in the temporal sequence. Frequently, compromises between full parallel operation and serial operation are made by composing arithmetic units of registers capable of handling only a part of a computer word. These character-oriented machines (as opposed to the word-oriented machine) have the advantage of variable word length but usually achieve it at the cost of a lowered operating speed. The result of variable word length is to allow memory to be used in the most efficient fashion for a particular application, so that in character-oriented machines fewer locations are wasted because the basic addressable word length is no longer than the contents desired to be stored in that location.

Boolean algebra and circuit minimization

So far we have dealt descriptively with computer components and logical organization. There is, however, a formal notational system which is often used to represent more complex systems. It is called Boolean algebra, and although it was originally created as a symbolic notation for the two-value Aristotelian logic, it has recently proved to be a useful notation for similar two-value electronic circuits. Boolean algebra is a manipulative system having only two operators, unlike ordinary arithmetic, in which four arithmetic functions can be manipulated. The two Boolean operators may differ from one type of Boolean algebra to another, but we have already met the most familiar pair, consisting of the *and* and the *or* functions.

Since the terms of Boolean algebra have two values, they can conveniently represent the two-state electronic devices discussed so far. Boolean algebra has no way to describe a switch that is "partly open" or a flip-flop that is "halfway between the 0 and the 1 state." Thus the Boolean notational and algebraic system can deal with initial and final states, but not with transitions. It should also be pointed out that a detailed knowledge of Boolean algebra is not necessary for the ordinary experimenter who is customizing a few logical circuits to implement a particular research problem. Yet Boolean algebra is very important for representing logical circuits in larger systems. Methods of minimizing the number of circuits in a large system can often be made obvious when the system is reduced to the symbolic notation of this algebra.

In addition to the two operators, *and* and *or*, it is necessary to include the idea of a complement in the Boolean notation. A complement (otherwise known as the null operator) is simply the inverse of a given statement or term and is usually indicated by a bar ($\overline{\quad}$) across the top of the term. Thus for a given two-state device whose output state is indicated by A,

$$\text{when } A = 1, \text{ then } \bar{A} = 0 \tag{4-1}$$

The Boolean notation is probably best illustrated for the novice in terms of relay circuitry, but it is similarly applicable to diode gates or to transistors that also perform the *and* and the *or* functions.

The Boolean algebra is rigorously defined as a set of constituent units (entities that can be in one or another of two states) which by means of a set of two operators (the *and* and the *or* functions) satisfies a given set of postulates. The postulates of the algebra are a set of reduction laws that can be used in circuit minimization and design. Table 4-3 lists a number of the postulates; some are

$A+0=A$	$A \cdot 0=0$
$A+1=1$	$A \cdot 1=A$
$A+A=A$	$A \cdot A=A$
$A+\overline{A}=1$	$A \cdot \overline{A}=0$
$A+B=B+A$	$A \cdot B=B \cdot A$
$(A+B)+C=A+(B+C)$	$(A \cdot B) \cdot C=A \cdot (B \cdot C)$
$A+(B \cdot C)=(A+B) \cdot (A+C)$	$A \cdot (B+C)=(A \cdot B)+(A \cdot C)$
$\overline{(\overline{A})}=A$	$A+AB=A$
$\overline{A+B}=\overline{A}\,\overline{B}$	$A+\overline{A}B=A+B$
$\overline{A+B+C}=\overline{A}\,\overline{B}\,\overline{C}$	$AB+A\overline{B}=A$
$\overline{AB}=\overline{A}+\overline{B}$	$AB+AC+B\overline{C}=AC+B\overline{C}$
$\overline{ABC}=\overline{A}+\overline{B}+\overline{C}$	

$$(A+B)(A+C)=A+BC$$
$$(A+B)(\overline{A}+C)=AC+\overline{A}B$$
$$\overline{(AB+AC)}=\overline{A}+\overline{B}\,\overline{C}$$
$$\overline{(AB+\bar{A}C)}=A\overline{B}+\bar{A}\bar{C}$$
$$\overline{(A+B)(A+C)}=\overline{A}(\overline{B}+\overline{C})$$
$$\overline{(A+B)(\bar{A}+C)}=(A+\overline{B})(\overline{A}+\overline{C})$$

Table 4-3. *Some of the postulates of Boolean algebra. (From Table 10, in E. M. Grabbe, S. Ramo, and D. E. Wooldridge (eds.),* Handbook of Automation, Computation, and Control, *New York, Wiley, 1958–1961.)*

basic axioms of Boolean algebra, while others are derivable from these basic axioms. Some of the postulates may seem to state the obvious, but it is surprising how frequently logical absurdities and redundancies are built into the simplest circuits, even by experienced designers.

Let us take a sample law and explain it in order to demonstrate how the postulates work. First, however, we will summarize the notational system. The output of a given two-state device is represented by A or B or any other capitalized alphabetic symbol. This device may be in either the 1 or the 0 state. The *and* operation is indicated by a • and the *or* operation is indicated by a +.

Now consider the postulate

$$A + 0 = A \tag{4-2}$$

This is an *or* circuit, illustrated by the relay circuit shown in Figure 4-12*a*. A is the relay contact; it can be either open or closed. On the other hand, the 0 in this equation indicates that there is an open contact which, for the purposes of this postulate, can never

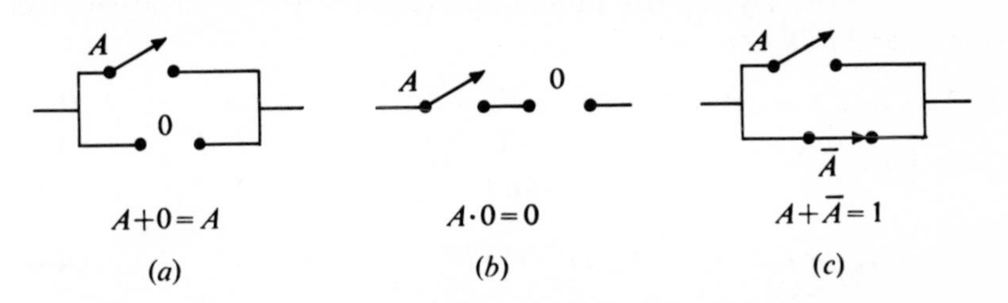

Fig. 4-12. *Relay circuits presented to show the meaning of some terms in the Boolean notation.* (a) *An "or" circuit in which one of the elements is always in the "0" state, illustrating the fact that in such a circuit the operation is completely defined by the state of the other component.* (b) *An "and" circuit in which one of the elements is always in the "0" state, illustrating the fact that in such a circuit the operation of the circuit will always be "0," regardless of the state of the other component.* (c) *An "or" circuit in which one of the circuits is always the inverse of the other, illustrating the fact that this circuit will always be in the "1" state.*

be closed. That is, the 0 represents another contact, B, which is perpetually in the 0 state. This Boolean postulate, therefore, states the obvious fact that the operating characteristics of this circuit depend exclusively on the state of A. If A is closed, the whole circuit will pass current. If A is open, the whole circuit will be open.

The related equation for *and* circuits is

$$A \cdot 0 = 0 \tag{4-3}$$

Figure 4-12*b* illustrates this postulate with a relay circuit. We see that, since one of the circuit elements in the *and* circuit is perpetually in the 0 state, it really makes no difference whether the contact denoted by A is open or closed. For any state of A the circuit can never conduct and is therefore perpetually in the 0 state.

Similarly, circuits composed of complements have certain peculiar properties. Consider the Boolean postulate

$$A + \bar{A} = 1 \tag{4-4}$$

Figure 4-12*c* is an example of an *or* circuit made up of the two functions A and $\bar{A}$. It should immediately be obvious that if one of these circuits is equal to 0 its complement must be equal to 1; the *or* circuit thus shown will always be capable of passing a current, regardless of whether the function A is in the 1 or the 0 state.

The utility of some of the more elaborate postulates can also be easily shown. Two of the most important are the associative laws for *or* and *and* operators:

$$A + B + C + D = A + (B + C + D) = (A + B) + (C + D) \tag{4-5}$$

and

$$A \cdot B \cdot C \cdot D = A \cdot (B \cdot C \cdot D) = (A \cdot B) \cdot (C \cdot D) \tag{4-6}$$

The advantages of Boolean algebra as an aid in designing can be clearly demonstrated by considering the first of these two equations. Let us design a circuit that implements the logical functions described in the three parts of the equality of the associative law for *or* circuits (equation 4-5). Figure 4-13 shows the three implementations derived from the three parts of the equation made up of the standard logical blocks described earlier. One can easily see that a large number of components can be saved by reducing the term on the right to the form of the term on the left. It is very important to point out, though, that the saving is only a practical one and has no logical significance. Each of these three circuits performs the identical logical operation and could be substituted for either of the other two.

The novice enjoying his first experience with logical circuit design should experiment with some of the other postulates shown in Table 4-3 to develop insight into a few of the less obvious wastes that can occur in circuit design.

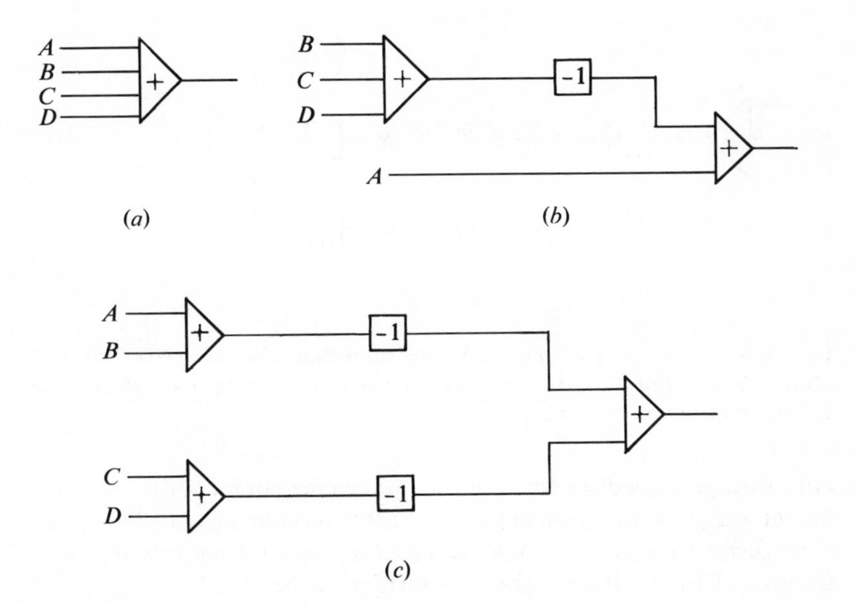

Fig. 4-13 (a, b, c). *Three different logical circuits are presented, each of which implements different parts of the logical equation 4-5.*

Two additional postulates are unusually useful. Known as DeMorgan's laws, they deal (as do a number of other postulates) with the relations of complements. DeMorgan's laws are formally stated as follows:

$$\overline{A + B + C} = \bar{A} \cdot \bar{B} \cdot \bar{C} \tag{4-7}$$

$$\overline{A \cdot B \cdot C} = \bar{A} + \bar{B} + \bar{C} \tag{4-8}$$

The important function of DeMorgan's laws is to relate expressions involving only the *or* operation to equivalent expressions involving only the *and* operation. These equations are, therefore, the formal expression of the fact mentioned earlier that the minimum set of logical elements required to implement computer circuits need not include both the *or* and the *and* operations. It is only for reasons of convenience that both are usually used. DeMorgan's laws also illustrate another way to minimize circuits. For example, we can implement the expression described by the first of DeMorgan's laws above with either of the two circuits shown in Figure 4-14. By doing so in the manner prescribed in Figure 4-14*a* we save two inverters.

In conclusion, we should note that Boolean algebra is not the

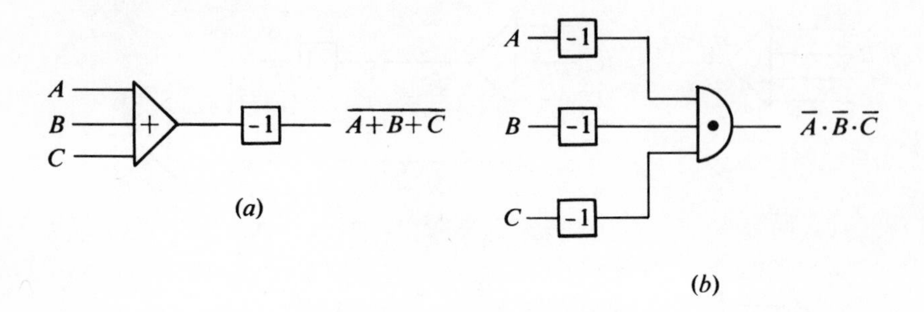

Fig. 4-14 (a, b). *Two circuits implementing the two sides of DeMorgan's first law (Eq. 4-7) and which therefore are equivalent but use different numbers of components.*

only formal procedure for minimizing circuit components. A number of other techniques exist, and they receive an excellent and clear discussion in the *Handbook of Automation, Computation, and Control* (Grabbe, Ramo, and Wooldridge, 1958–1961).

5: COMPUTER SYSTEMS ORGANIZATION

So far we have considered the organization of functional units that perform one or another useful logical process. We are now ready to synthesize these functional units into a total working system able to perform all of the necessary processes making up a computer. Functionally, one may consider a computer to be an organized family of registers among which information is transferred. During the transfer, various kinds of logical or arithmetic manipulations are carried out on this information. In a digital computer the registers and the transfers between them are controlled in such a way that a timed sequence of operations, equivalent to the specific function to which the system has been applied, takes place. In other words, a computer program is actually represented within the computer by a concatenation of the electronic, logical, and arithmetic functions described in the previous chapter.

It is appropriate to mention here that the modern digital computer is distinguished from other forms of automated control devices by two basic organizational properties basic to the major technological revolution occurring during the last two decades. Advances in component technology and electronics, on the other hand, while concomitant, are not the main causes of this revolution, for though transistors are smaller, require less power, and even operate faster than relays or vacuum tubes, they still are logically identical to these more primitive components. Rather, the impact of computers is being felt because of new logical concepts—ideas that can be traced back to such workers as John von Neumann and his colleagues Burks and Goldstine, who among others suggested them in the early 1940s.

The first of these revolutionary concepts is that the instructions or directives which sequence the computer through its series of operations are stored within the computer memory itself. No separate peripheral control sequences the system; the instructions are stored in the computer in exactly the same way as the data being manipulated. There is, therefore, no difference between the instructions and the data as far as storage is concerned. This identity of data and instructions leads directly to the second of the two major concepts: since instructions may be altered or manipulated just as data are, a given instruction in a programmed sequence may do one thing at one time but another thing at some other time, depending upon the state of the system. Therefore a *contingent instruction* can have one effect under condition *A* and another under condition *B*. A related concept is the alteration of the location on which the instruction will act. The reader who is familiar with computer programming may recognize this idea as the precursor of the *branch instruction* and the *indexing operation* —two important tools frequently used in the construction of a computer program.

At a higher level of consideration, this notion of contingency is basic to the most effective utilization of computers as tutors or laboratory control instruments, elaborations that will be discussed in later chapters.

The contents of a given register may thus represent either a datum to be manipulated or an instruction describing which manipulation is to be applied to the contents of some other register. Computers, therefore, must have a number of registers in addition to the storage registers which control the addressing and selection of the sequence of action. When it is determined how a given memory location is to be treated, other registers must be used to decode the contents of a given storage register. Perhaps the best way to illustrate this general idea of a family of registers is to outline the organization of a simple computer.

Systems organization of a simple digital computer

Figure 5-1 depicts the organization of a simple digital computer at the grossest level. The input block indicates all the devices that can be used to introduce information from the user into the computer. Similarly, the output block indicates all the devices that can be used to communicate processed information from the computer to the user.

It is sufficient to say at this time that input-output devices act as sensors and effectors for the central processing components of the system. The term *central processing unit* (CPU) is generally

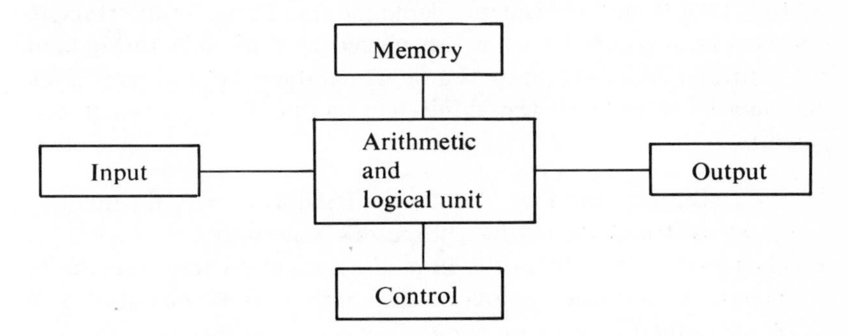

Fig. 5-1. *A block diagram of the major sub-units of a simple digital computer.*

used to describe the control, arithmetic, and logical units of the computer; *memory* is used to describe those parts of the computer system that merely store information, faithfully reproducing on demand whatever has been entered into them.

An ambiguity between the terms *memory* and *input-output unit,* however, may be appropriately mentioned here. Many computer devices have the capacity to store information on files which can be physically removed from the system. The files include, for example, magnetic tapes, cards, and disks. When the contents of these files are read back into the computer, they act essentially as input-output devices—just as a card reader does. In each case the card or the tape represents stored information, or memory, while the device that reads the information into the computer is an input device. Obviously, for these removable storage media, memory and input-output are not clearly distinguishable functions. The exception to this ambiguous definition of memory and input-output is the magnetic core memory, which cannot practically be removed from the system. The magnetic core memory, the working memory of the computer, will be discussed fully later in this chapter.

The arithmetic and logical units of a computer are composed of the registers that actually perform the operations defined by the computer instruction. They may be formed from subgroups of registers that count or compare, add or subtract, or execute any of the other functions within the instruction repertoire of the computer. The control unit, on the other hand, is composed of registers which select and time each of the logical or arithmetic operations that will be called upon to perform its function at a particular stage of the program. Actually, in most computers, control, logical, and arithmetic elements are physically intermixed. Component registers of each are placed side by side throughout the central processing unit. We separate them here in our block diagram to emphasize the difference in the function each one performs:

1. The arithmetic and logical units implement the actual functions of the instructions in the computer's repertoire.
2. The control units direct the flow of information from register to register and select arithmetic and logical functions that will be performed at a given time.

Detailed register organization of a hypothetical small digital computer

To illustrate further the idea of the computer as a system of registers, we present a more detailed breakdown of computer organization and define a number of the specific registers found within a typical small computer.

Figure 5-2 is a diagram of a small computer at this more detailed level of organization. The computer is composed of a number of specific registers interconnected by lines of information transfer. The computer operates by sequencing the flow of information between the various units and the manipulations that are performed within each block. Each of the blocks represents a functional entity implemented by a group of cooperating transistors, diodes, and other electronic components. Most of the blocks can be described as registers composed of appropriately interconnected flip-flops. The number of flip-flops in a given register determines the size of the register and depends upon the specific task performed by that functional block. In addition to the transistor flip-flop register, other functional units are built into some of the blocks of Figure 5-2. In the control circuits responsible for sequencing the operations of the entire system and in the decoding nets, large numbers of *and* and *or* gates are used. The more economical magnetic cores, rather than flip-flop registers, are used in the main memory. But, generally, each block on the diagram may be considered a register for the temporary storage of some portion of the information needed to operate the computer. Let us now discuss the most important of the registers in terms of the specific functions they perform.

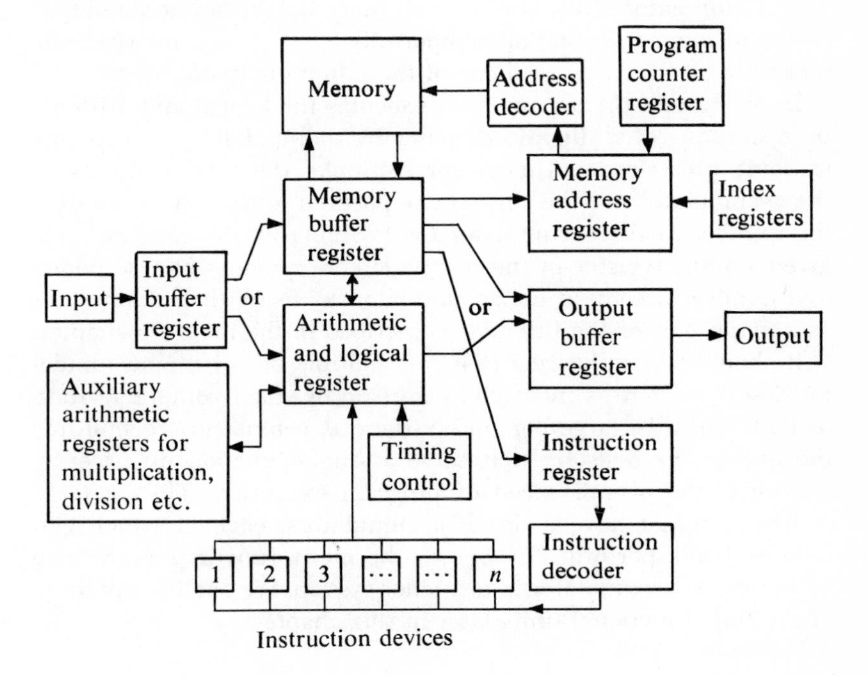

Fig. 5-2. *A detailed block diagram of a simple digital computer showing the various registers making up the system.*

ACCUMULATOR OR ARITHMETIC REGISTER

The basic register of a computer is called the *arithmetic and logical register* or, in most machines, simply the *accumulator*. The operation of all other registers is, in a sense, secondary to that of this register, for it is in the accumulator that the basic functions of the computer actually occur. The accumulator usually contains the same number of bits as the typical storage word of the computer memory. The main function of the accumulator is to act as the basic arithmetic and logical unit in the computer. Numbers may be added or subtracted from its contents, and usually the higher-order results of a multiplication or division are deposited here.[1] Logical tests and other manipulations which do not involve arithmetic transformations are often also performed in this important register. Furthermore, in some small computers the accumulator may actually be used as the major interface to peripheral equipment such as tape readers and printing devices. The accumulator thus alternatively may act as an input-output buffer to store information temporarily as it passes between the magnetic core memory and one of these input-output devices.

In most cases the accumulator executes the logical and arithmetic operations of a digital computer by manipulating its contents in some prescribed manner. For example, the total contents of the accumulator may be shifted one position to the left to multiply the number in the accumulator by 2. Similarly, the contents of a given storage register in the magnetic core memory can be added to a number already in the accumulator, by using the accumulator as a major part of the full adder described in the previous chapter.

It should be emphasized that the multiple use of the accumulator described here is more characteristic of small computers than of large ones. In large computers there is a tendency to multiply the number of registers that serve a single function, in order to maximize the overall speed of program execution. Thus a large computer might have a dozen accumulators, each of which can independently perform any one of the many functions performed by the single accumulator in a smaller system. We shall speak more of multiple functional units later in this chapter.

MEMORY BUFFER REGISTER

The central memory of a computer is a family of registers. It is actually the largest group of registers in any computer, since it must store all the instructions which are to be executed in a given program, as well as all the necessary data. For some computers the size of this group of registers exceeds one million. In order to minimize the cost of each register, magnetic cores are usually used for storage rather than transistor flip-flops.

As we shall see below, the output from a magnetic core is not a voltage maintained for a long period of time. It is, rather, a brief pulse lasting for only a fraction of a microsecond. This duration is far too short for use by most of the computer activities. The information may be required either for a longer period of time or at

[1] Other auxiliary arithmetic and logical registers are frequently associated with the accumulator for the storage of other parts of the multiplication or division process.

a time different from the moment it is emitted from the core memory. To maintain this transient pulse information for a longer time, a *memory buffer register* is used. Composed of a set of flip-flops initially set to 0, it is loaded with the information contained in the pattern of pulses from the core memory. Thereafter, the buffer stores that information in the state of the flip-flops until it is intentionally erased. Any of the registers in the computer memory is able to feed information into the memory buffer register, which temporarily stores the information until it passes on to some other register for interpretation and program execution.

The buffer concept is therefore mainly one of synchronization, in which a time base difference between two different registers is compromised. In many instances the memory buffer register is intermediary between the magnetic core memory and the accumulator, but often there are also auxiliary memory buffer registers that convey information elsewhere in the system. Thus, auxiliary memory buffer registers may provide alternative paths or *channels* into and out of the magnetic core memory that do not pass through the arithmetic or logical parts of the computer.

Such additional channels speed up computer operation by allowing computer arithmetic processing to occur almost simultaneously with input-output transfers to and from the magnetic core memory. This process is called *overlapping*. It is made possible by the fact that not all arithmetic operations require reference to the main computer memory, and therefore the memory is available some significant portion of the time for other uses. This time would be wasted if there were only one memory buffer register.

The memory buffer register performs another useful function. Reading a magnetic core memory register destroys its contents, as we shall see later. The temporary storage of these contents in the memory buffer register allows them to be immediately rewritten in the magnetic core memory, thus simulating a nondestructive memory. We shall elaborate the details of this operation in due time.

MEMORY ADDRESS REGISTER

The memory buffer register, as we have said, may receive information from or send information to any one of the magnetic core registers in the central memory. The *memory address register* selects the core memory register desired. This register contains the address in a coded form; the information is subsequently decoded by a diode matrix which is often intimately associated with the core memory itself. Thus, the contents of the memory buffer register may be sent to the core memory register whose address is in the memory address register.

The memory address register may be used in several different ways. In the mode in which the next sequential instruction is being acquired, the contents of the memory address register are determined by the current status of the program counter register described below. On the other hand, memory references are made as a result of the needs of an acquired instruction. In this case the contents of the memory address register will be determined, not by the program counter register, but by the information contained in the instruction itself.

In some computers the information about the next instruction is not based on the incremented contents of a program counter but is contained in the instruction. Such a multiaddress instruction would typically contain information concerning the nature of the current instruction, the address of the location on which the effects of the instruction are to be felt, and the address of the next instruction. It should be noted that most modern machines do not use this scheme but are designed to use single-address instructions. In the latter case the instruction consists only of the function to be executed and the address of the register on which it is to have its effect. The next instruction to be executed is, unless otherwise specified, the instruction stored in the next sequential register.

PROGRAM COUNTER REGISTER

Since the memory address register in a single-address instruction machine is often diverted to obtain data required by an instruction, a separate register is needed to keep track of the next instruction. This apparent inconvenience actually is a reflection of one of the most important features of a computer—the ability to treat data and instructions identically in storage, a capability well worth the slight engineering inconvenience. This additional register is usually called a *program counter register* and has the property of simply adding 1 to its current contents at the completion of any given instruction execution.

The program counter register is usually the place in which transfer instructions effect their diversion of the program sequence. If a transfer instruction (i.e., an instruction transferring control of the computer program to some other point than the next sequential instruction) is executed, the contents of the program counter register are altered. They are then transferred to the memory address register when the next instruction is called for. Without a transfer instruction, the program counter defines an unbroken string of sequential computer instructions by simply acting as a counter adding 1 to the previous address.

INDEX REGISTERS

Often associated with the memory address register and the program counter are a set of registers usually called *index registers*. The purpose of an index register is to increment a given address each time it is referred to by the computer program, without requiring any additional processing time. For example, to perform a calculation on a list of items, one has only to place the address of the first item on the list in an index register. Subsequently, each time the next item in the list is called for, its new, correctly incremented address is automatically available. Usually this is accomplished by modifying an instruction to indicate that it is associated with a given index register. Each time the index register is so referred to, it is automatically incremented and the new address is placed in the memory address register in order to produce an effective data address.

Decrementing types of index registers are also known which subtract rather than add numbers to the contents of the memory address register. It is interesting to note that in some small computers the index registers and the program counter register are actually core memory locations rather than separate flip-flop registers. Addressing one of these special locations automatically triggers the additional functions for which they are responsible.

So far we have been referring primarily to the registers that are influential in determining the location of core memory from which or to which information is transferred. Now let us turn to the other major section of the central processor of a modern digital computer. The registers of this section hold the various parts of an instruction that have been transferred from the core memory and control their execution.

INSTRUCTION REGISTER

Part of the contents of the memory buffer register may define the nature of the next instruction to be performed, just as part may refer to the address of the register on which its effects are to be directed. We have already spoken of how that part of the contents of the memory buffer register constituting the address is transferred to the memory address register. The other part, indicating the instruction to be performed, would at the same instant be transferred to the *instruction register*. This register is usually small, consisting of only enough bits to encode the various computer instructions. The coded instruction must subsequently be decoded by an *instruction decoding matrix*. The latter is usually a combination of diode gates and timing circuits which sequences the various substeps making up the total instruction. In this manner, the electronic components are directed to operate in an order specific for each individual instruction.

TIMING CONTROL

We have made a number of references to sequences and timing. In all computers, a master electronic clock beats out a rhythm (typically at megacycle rates) with which all operations are in step. A given instruction might require two, three, or more separate master clock cycles to complete its full operation. In any case, the intervals between the separate steps making up an instruction and the pulses that activate them are controlled by the master clock. All computers, even the so-called asynchronous ones, require some master time control. At some point in the system, the signals driving the timing control are produced by a highly periodic crystal-controlled oscillator, without which the entire computer would cease to function. This single oscillator truly deserves the appellation "master" of the computer system.

INPUT-OUTPUT BUFFERS

In order to synchronize the operation of the arithmetic and storage components of the computer system, input-output devices are buffered in much the same manner as the magnetic core memory. Input-output buffers may temporarily store information before it is transferred either into the accumulator or, as we have indicated, directly into the core memory through a separate memory buffer register system.

We have just presented a brief review of the main registers used in the central processing unit of the computer. Now we turn to a discussion of the largest group of registers, the family of core memory storage locations in which instructions and data are stored before transferral into one or another of these special operating registers.

Magnetic core memories

Because of the central importance of the magnetic core memory in most modern digital computers, and the fact that certain peculiarities of its operation limit and determine the actual operating speed of a digital computer, the ferrite core memory and its operations will be taken up in somewhat greater electronic detail than that given in the previous section. Furthermore, there are a number of electromagnetic properties in its operation, in addition to those already introduced, which will also be discussed.

As we have said, it is not feasible to have large amounts of information storage composed of transistor flip-flops; the cost in power, space, and components is too great. Maintaining the state of a transistor flip-flop requires that power be consumed by the involved circuitry. In addition, even though great progress has been made in miniaturization, transistors are still relatively large, and the total circuit for storing one bit is of considerable size. A flip-flop also suffers from the disadvantage of being a multiple-component device that is relatively expensive to construct. What is needed, then, is a component that is small, that will store information passively (i.e., without the active consumption of power), and that is relatively inexpensively produced by automatic fabrication techniques. The additional necessity that the device be able to have information read into or out of it at very high speeds has excluded many possible components. All of the criteria, however, are met by the *ferrite magnetic core,* invented in 1952 by Forrester.

Magnetic cores are manufactured by pressure-forming a complex mixture of powdered metallic oxides into tiny donut shapes. This process can be carried out automatically on special manufacturing machines. Figure 5-3 is a picture of a typical core showing the characteristic dimensions of a unit that might be used in a modern computer.

Each core is capable of storing only one bit of information. Thus,

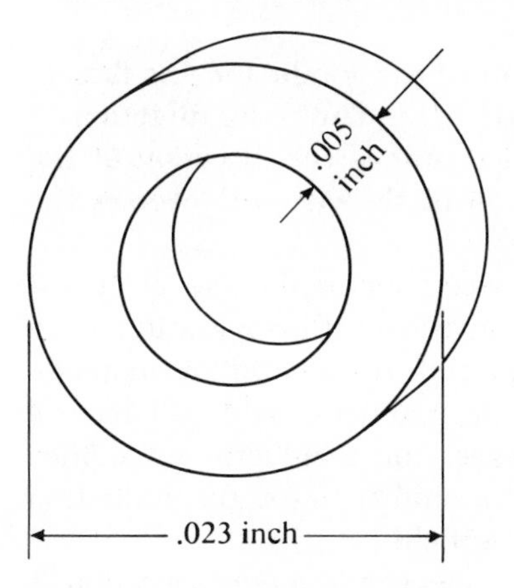

Fig. 5-3. *A single magnetic core showing the dimensions of a typical unit.*

to store whole words, registers must be formed of combinations of individual units. We shall discuss the organization of an entire core memory "matrix" below. For the moment, let us consider the operation of a single core in order to elucidate the physical principles underlying magnetic core memory operations.

The ferrite core is a magnetic device. This means that it must accept information magnetically, store information magnetically, and finally read out information magnetically. There are two distinguishable types of magnetic action involved in these processes.

The first type of magnetic action consists of the electromagnetic fields created around a conductor that is passing a current. This type of magnetism is the basis of electromagnetic induction. A current passing through a linear conductor produces a circular magnetic field around the conductor. Further, this circular magnetic field has a direction determined by the so-called *right-hand rule*. If the hand is held as in Figure 5-4, with the thumb

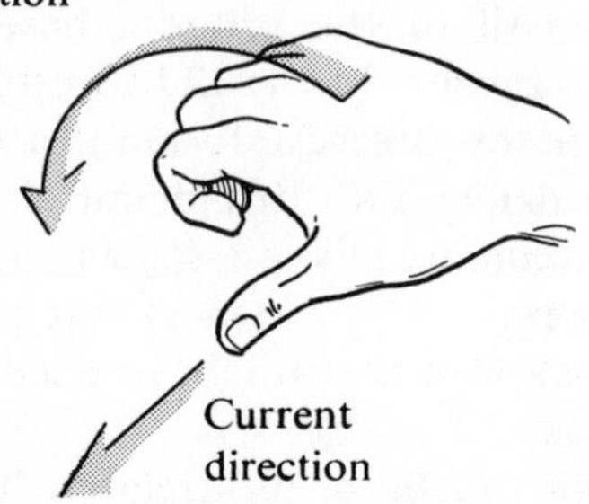

Fig. 5-4. *A graphic illustration of the right-hand rule, showing the relationship between the resultant magnetic field direction and the direction of a current through a conductor. If the thumb points in the direction of the current, then the fingers point in the direction of the magnetic field.*

pointing in the direction of the current in the conductor, the fingers point in the direction of the magnetic field. Thus, the direction of the current through the conductor determines the direction of the magnetic field. Reversing the direction of the current reverses the direction of the magnetic field.

The same type of interaction between magnetic and electrical forces, but in a reverse direction, underlies the operation of a transformer. A conductor which is placed in a changing magnetic field or which moves through a stable magnetic field will have a current "induced" in it. In either case, the conductor cuts lines of magnetic flux. This is the critical condition for the induction of an electrical current by a magnetic field.

It should be noted that this type of electromagnetic operation is the physical principle (at higher power levels) underlying both electrical power generation and motor operation with rotating machinery. At much lower power levels, the principles of electromagnetic interaction also explain the way current generated by logical units in the computer can be converted into magnetic fields for operating the magnetic memory units. It is also important to recognize that this type of magnetic induction ceases to operate when the current ceases or when motion through the external magnetic field is inhibited.

The second kind of magnetic action is the basis of information storage in the magnetic core itself. It is a type of permanent magnetism rather than a temporarily produced electromagnetism dependent upon physical movement or current flow. A permanent magnet, once placed in a certain magnetic state, will remain in that state until its magnetic properties are intentionally altered. This holds true even if the magnet is broken into small pieces; each piece will be a miniature of the original magnet.

An intact and permanent magnetic core may be magnetized in one of two possible directions, by applying a sufficiently strong and properly directed magnetic field to it. The field may run either clockwise or counterclockwise in the donut-shaped core. This difference in direction of the magnetic field of the core is the basic storage medium for one bit of information in the main memory of a computer. Magnetization in one direction is arbitrarily assigned the meaning of a 0 and magnetization in the other direction is arbitrarily assigned the meaning of a 1. Let us now consider the process of controlling the direction of this magnetic field.

Magnetic cores, and indeed also any permanent magnet, display a property called *hysteresis*. Hysteresis is a property of magnets that keeps the magnetic field from instantaneously following the magnetic forces that influence it. The magnetic field of a magnet displaying hysteresis may lag behind the driving force or even prove to be unchangeable until some critical threshold of magnetic force is reached. Each magnet has an associated hysteresis function which may be plotted as shown in Figure 5-5. This figure shows the magnetic field strength (H) of a typical magnet as a function of the current (I) which is generating the magnetic forces acting upon the magnet. Current I is a particularly useful measure in this case because the magnetic field acting on the core memory is produced, as we shall see below, by induction by the current passing through a wire strung through the core itself. Ordinarily, this graph would describe a relation between the magnetic field of an electromagnet and the current passing through the conductor itself. In the case of the core, no current passes through the magnetic core, but it is understood that there is the intervening effect of the magnetic force produced by the current through the conductor on the magnetic field of the core.

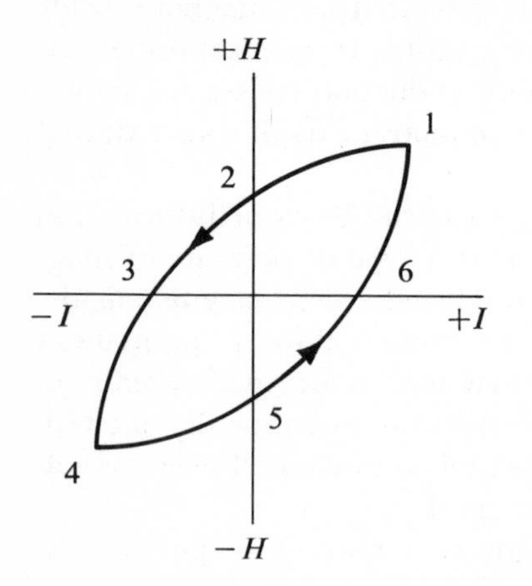

Fig. 5-5. *The hysteresis curve for an electromagnetic material whose magnetic state relatively easily follows the field produced by an applied current. The horizontal coordinate represents the current at any given time and the vertical coordinate, the resulting magnetic strength. The numbered points are described in the text.*

Suppose that we start at (1), the point representing the maximum magnetization in the north-south direction produced by a maximum positive current. Let us observe the magnetic field strength as a function of current. When the current has gone to zero (at the intersection of the coordinates), there is still an appreciable north-south magnetization (2). This is not completely dissipated until a strong reverse current brings the residual magnetization down to 0 at (3). Finally at (4) the magnetic field is completely reversed to a south-north direction but only when a sufficiently strong current has been forced in the opposite direction for an adequate period of time. Reversing the current once again, we can track the magnetic field through points (5) and (6) and see that in this direction the magnetic field lags behind the applied current.

As the hysteresis curve becomes more rectangular, there is an increasing tendency for a *threshold* to develop. In the case of a threshold, there is no change in the magnetic field until a sufficiently strong current is applied. When this critical current is reached, the magnetic device will more or less suddenly switch from one direction of magnetization to the other. This, of course, is analogous to the flip-flop action of a transistor circuit and is the function desired for magnetic core memory operation. Figure 5-6 is a plot of the rectangular type of hysteresis curve. Both the ideal rectangular curve theoretically desired and an actual practically realized hysteresis curve are shown. The flat top and bottom, (1) and (2), of the ideal curve tell us that the magnetization of the core is unchanged until the threshold of applied current is exceeded. Thus, once magnetized in the north-south direction, a given magnetic core with this hysteresis curve will

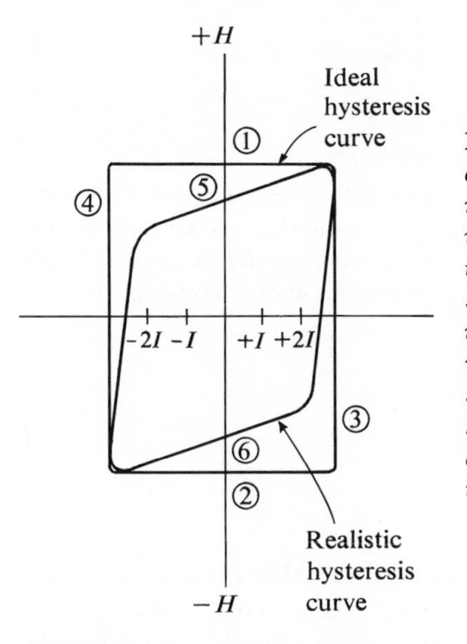

Fig. 5-6. *The hysteresis curve for a magnetic core should be as rectangular as possible, indicating very high thresholds and rapid transition between the two possible states of magnetization. This idealization is represented by the more rectangular of the two curves shown in this figure. Actually the hysteresis curves of most materials are really more like the less rectangular one shown.*

remain in that state until a current ($2I$) occurs sufficient to produce a magnetic force which can switch the core. The steepness of the sides, (3) and (4), indicates that when the threshold is exceeded and the change in field direction occurs, it is a sudden and complete change just like the change of state of a flip-flop. On the other hand, the practically realizable hysterisis curve shows that there is some tendency (5 and 6) for the magnetization to follow the applied current. The change, however, is still slight enough so that it may be considered equivalent to (1) and (2).

The threshold values for this change have been called $+2I$ and $-2I$. A current of $+2I$ must flow to switch a core from a $-H$ state to a $+H$ state. A current of $-2I$, $-I$, 0 or even $+I$ will have no effect on a core initially set to a $+H$ state.

This threshold condition provides the means for addressing a particular set of cores in the large matrix of cores making up the total array of a computer's memory. Figure 5-7 will help us to understand how the addressing is controlled, by showing the wiring which is threaded through a single typical core of a matrix. Two wires carry current from the circuitry of the computer and write information into the magnetic core. These two *write drive lines* are called the x and y write drivers; when activated, each carries a current that is one-half of the magnitude necessary

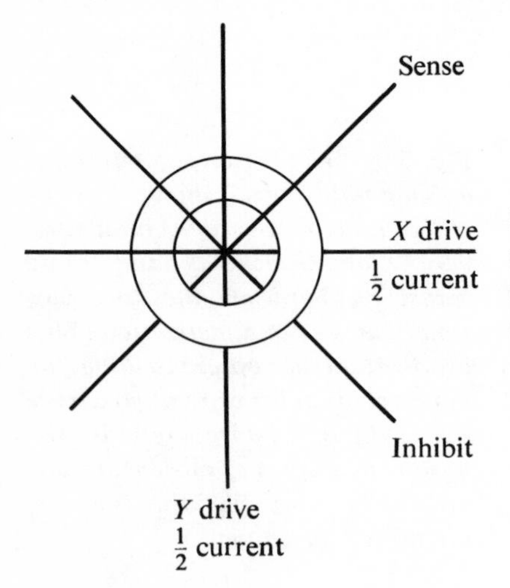

Fig. 5-7. *This diagram shows the four wires that are strung through each core in the most usual kind of magnetic core memory.*

to switch the core from the zero state to the 1 state. It seems appropriate at this point simply to use the binary symbolic notation of 0 and 1, but remember that these really represent the arbitrary assignment of these values to the north-south and south-north directions of magnetization.

If a current flows through only one of the drive lines, the induced magnetic field will not be strong enough to change the magnetic state of the core. This is what was meant by a current of magnitude I. Both lines must be activated with a total current of $2I$ simultaneously for the transfer of state to occur. The system works because the magnetic fields are additive and the current I through each conductor has a relatively constant value. This constancy prevents a large current through a single wire from ever exceeding the threshold $2I$.

But cores are arranged, as we shall see, in a three-dimensional array. To write a message in a given core, it is therefore necessary to have three identifying coordinates. The x and y drive lines serve as two of them. The other wire which is used to select a particular core is called the *inhibit line*. Suppose that the x and y drive lines through a given core are both activated with a total current of $2I$. In addition, assume that the inhibit line is also activated, but that it is passing a current equal to $-I$ (i.e., the current producing a magnetic field in the opposite direction to that produced by the two drive lines). Thus, the total current through the conductors will be $2I - I = I$, which is not sufficient to switch the core from the 0 to the 1 state. The inhibit line has acted to inhibit the loading of a 1 bit into the core, in spite of the fact that this core had been selected by the x and y drive lines.

The x drive, the y drive, and the inhibit line, then, act as the three coordinates of a three-dimensional addressing scheme. Essentially, the x and y drive lines define a single column of cores, while the inhibit line defines which core in that column will be loaded with a 0.

The contents of a core are read by sending a current equal to $-2I$ through the x and y drive lines. That is, each drive line has a current equal to $-I$ in it, but going in the opposite direction to that necessary to set the core to a 1. The effect of this current is to reset each core that is in the 1 state to the 0 state. If the core were in the 0 state, there would be no apparent reaction; if the core were in the 1 state, there would be a transient change in its magnetic field. This change acts just like a tiny change of a magnetic field in a transformer. The core acts as the primary of the transformer, and a *sense wire* also threaded through the core acts as the secondary, so that a current is induced in the sense wire if a 1 had been present in the core. This current appears as a brief pulse that is amplified and used to set a bit in the memory buffer register.

Now we have arrived at a very important point. The reading of a magnetic core is an information-destroying process, since it resets all addressed cores to 0. In order not to lose the information stored in the involved cores, the computer must immediately rewrite the information read out. The memory buffer register acts in this case also as a temporary storage unit, from which the information is regenerated into the cores by means of the same writing process described above. Unfortunately, the rewriting requires an additional cycle of memory operation during which no memory reference can occur. This extra rewrite operation thus reduces the speed of a computer to as little as half of the maximum possible with a given set of electronic components. We shall see later some of the procedures that have been developed to overcome this handicap of magnetic core memories.

Now let us consider the organization of the total array of cores making up the magnetic core memory of a typical computer. Figure 5-8 shows a hypothetical small core memory made up of nine words of three bits each. To present a larger memory would complicate the diagram without adding any new principles. The selection of a given core, as we have said, depends upon the specification of a three-dimensional address by the x and y drive lines and the inhibit line. The x drive line defines one vertical

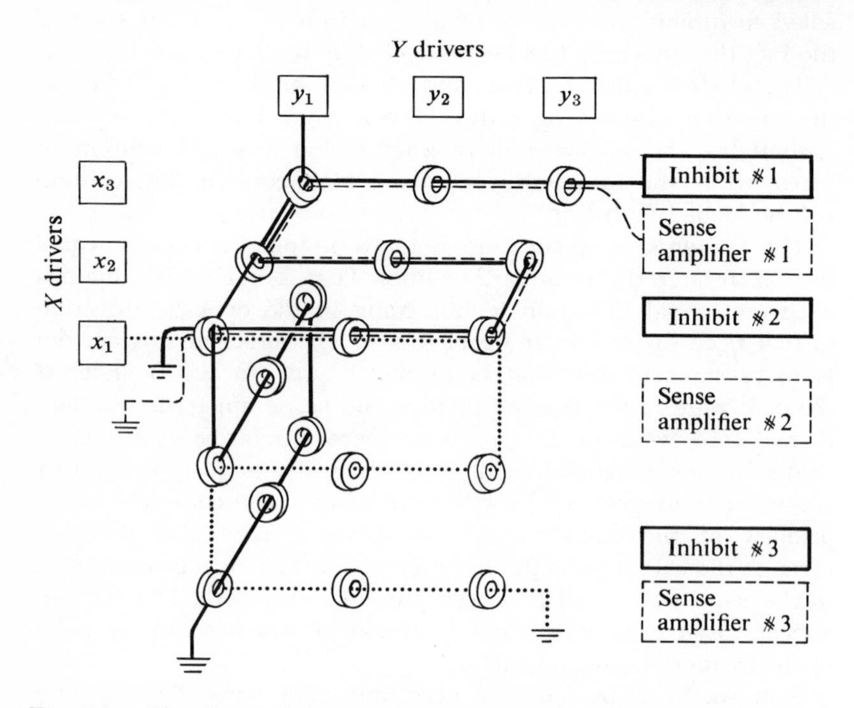

Fig. 5-8. *The three dimensional arrangement of a very small magnetic core memory made up of nine words of three bits each.*

plane, and the y drive line defines a vertical plane perpendicular to that. Together in the matrix they define a column of cores. This column of cores is usually equivalent to a single storage register or word of the memory. The number of cores in a column is therefore equal to the number of bits in the usual computer word. The inhibit line is threaded through all of the cores in each horizontal plane to define the third dimension. Let us look at this in detail with regard to our drawing in Figure 5-8.

As already noted, each x drive line is connected to all the cores in one plane. Thus, in this diagram, the plane closest to the front of the matrix has all of its cores connected to the x_1 driver. Similarly, all the cores in the y plane on the left-hand side of the matrix are connected to the y_1 driver. When the x_1 and y_1

drivers are simultaneously activated, then, all of the cores in the front left-hand column are set to 1's. This is the physical location of the storage word defined by the address x_1y_1. However, this is not the end product desired.

It is also necessary to be able to select which cores are set to the 1 state. This is the task of the *inhibit drive lines,* each of which, as previously stated, is wound through all the cores in a horizontal plane and carries a current opposite to that of the drive lines. Thus, when a given inhibit driver is activated, the core in that level of the column selected by the x and y drivers is not set to 1. For cores that were in the selected xy column the effect of an inhibit line is, therefore, to override the attempt to write a 1 in the core in the plane associated with that inhibit driver. Since the inhibit drivers receive their input from each bit of the data word to be written, the effect is to load a 0 into the core corresponding to each bit of the memory buffer register that has a 0 in it. Otherwise a 1 is written in a core corresponding to each bit of the memory buffer register with a 1 in it.

From our brief discussion it can be seen that a number of x or y drive lines is equal to the square root of the number of words in the memory of the computer. To avoid the necessity of having a single drive amplifier for each x and y drive line, the output of the x and y drive amplifiers is coded. This output is directed to the appropriate drive line after being decoded by a set of diodes. For example, a 4096-word memory would require 64 x drive lines, one for each of the 64 x planes. There are, however, usually only 6 drive amplifiers, which represent in a coded form all 64 of the x drive lines. The outputs of the amplifiers are gated through an addressing decoder to the appropriate one of the 64 planes. Similarly, there are only 6 y drivers. Thus each word of a 4096-word memory can be addressed completely and uniquely with a 12-bit address.

The number of inhibit drivers is equal to the number of bits in the computer word. No decoding process is possible here since each bit of the memory buffer register must be connected to a given plane of the core matrix.

This, then, is the general nature of the high-speed core storage used as the memory of a modern digital computer. Though the device performs magnificent feats of storage at high speed, the principles of operation are relatively simple. Once understood for the unit core, they extrapolate easily to the total core memory matrix. It should be pointed out that, although newer processes of fabricating high-speed magnetic memories are being developed, the basic physical principles underlying their operation remain constant.

Moving-medium magnetic storage devices

One of the advantages of the magnetic core memory is that each element in the storage matrix is electrically addressable. Thus no mechanical movement of any of the components of the drive circuitry or of the core matrix itself is necessary. All operations may, therefore, be carried out at very high speeds, but the capacity of the memory is relatively small. In many computer applications memory requirements are very large and cannot be satisfied by magnetic core capacities. The user, however, is often willing to sacrifice *access* time (the length of time between the decision to acquire a specific piece of information and the instant it arrives at the central processing unit) to gain *capacity* (the number of bits or words that may be stored in a given memory file). Many devices have therefore been developed in which the magnetic medium storing the information is physically moved in relation to some appropriate reading or writing mechanism. Though the variety of these devices is large, the generalization may be made that the larger the capacity of the device, the longer the access time.

All the devices are based upon the same electromagnetic principle. A semipermanent magnetic material is physically moved past a recording or reproducing *head* containing a small electromagnetic coil or ferrite plug. Running a transient pulse current through the coil or plug produces a magnetic field strong enough to alter the direction of magnetization of a small portion of the magnetic material at a specific location. Later, when this magnetized part of the material passes by a similar coil or plug, a transient electrical current will be induced, since it is cutting the lines of magnetic force generated by what is essentially a moving magnet. Magnetization of the material in one direction will produce a current in a given direction which can be associated with the storage of a 1. Magnetization in the other direction will produce an oppositely directed current pulse which can be associated with a 0. Alternatively, in clock-synchronized systems a pulse might equal a 1 and no pulse a 0.

This simple introductory statement, of course, almost completely ignores the two great technological problems that have occupied moving-medium storage engineers for over a decade. The first problem is the mechanical engineering of the machinery which actually moves the magnetic medium past the recording and reproducing head, as well as the system which must in some cases move the head itself.

The second technological problem is the improvement of the physical characteristics of the magnetic recording material. In order to take full advantage of the improvements in the mechanical system and electrical circuitry, it has been necessary to improve the magnetic medium. Specifically, the problem has been one of improving the packing density of the magnetic medium so that more bits may be packed per linear inch. The difficulty is that the storage of one bit of information may affect adjacent areas, and reducing this interaction can greatly increase the storage capacity of moving medium magnetic storage devices.

Great progress has been made on packing density problems; densities as great as 2000 bits per inch have already been achieved. Furthermore, all moving-medium storage devices share the enormous advantage that the medium itself can be produced by a batch process. In contrast, the manufacture of magnetic cores requires that each individual unit be constructed as a separate physical entity.[2] Moving-medium devices allow fabrication techniques in which an entire surface is plated with the magnetic materials. The functional separation of the surfaces into individual storage units is accomplished at a later time by electrical timing control.

The classification of the moving-medium devices is usually carried out on the basis of the mechanical accessing mechanism, since the fundamental techniques of recording and reproducing signals are common to all. The order of the following classification depends upon increasing average access time for a given bit of information.

MAGNETIC STORAGE DRUMS

Magnetic storage drums usually have the smallest capacity of any of the moving-medium devices. In the drum configuration the magnetic material is deposited on the outside surface of a cylinder which is revolving at a high speed underneath a set of permanently fixed recording and reproducing heads. One head may contain a writing mechanism for recording information, or a reading mechanism for reproducing information, or both of these mechanisms, or even a single mechanism that performs both functions.

[2] This generalization is not entirely correct today. Some experimental techniques are now under development for batch fabrication of corelike magnetic memories which are electrically addressable.

A magnetic drum typically has a relatively large number of heads, any of which may be electrically selected to address a particular region of the drum memory. Because of this electrical addressing scheme, the only delay in reading information is the rotation time required to bring the specific location under the appropriate head. Many modern high-speed drums have a rotational delay under ten milliseconds. This represents the fastest access time for any moving-medium device. As we mentioned above, such speed is associated with a rather modest storage capacity; most conventional drums store less than five million computer words of information. Another disadvantage is that the critical alignment and other mounting conditions of the drum itself keep the user from easily interchanging the storage medium and thus further reduce the potential capacity of the system. Interchangeability of magnetic recording surfaces is an important means of increasing storage capacity in all the rest of the devices we shall discuss. Figure 5-9 is a schematic sketch of a magnetic drum storage system.

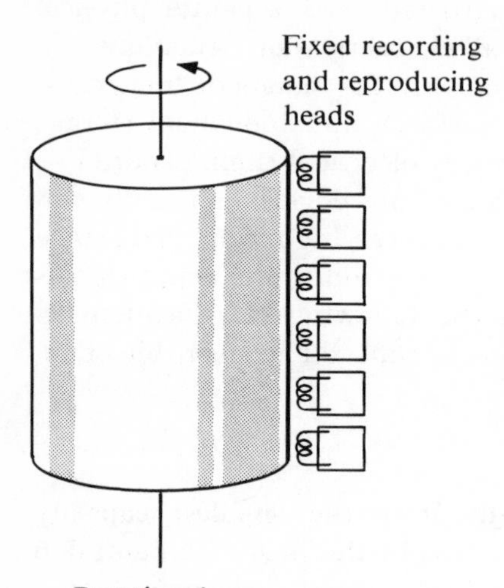

Fig. 5-9. *A schematic drawing of a magnetic drum showing the cylinder on which the magnetic medium is deposited and the set of magnetic recording and reproducing heads.*

MAGNETIC DISK STORAGE DEVICES

A compromise between the virtually unlimited storage capacity of the magnetic tape and the high access speed of the magnetic drum has evolved in the form of the magnetic disk memory unit. The magnetic disk configuration is capable of storing a larger amount of information than the drum. Furthermore, since it uses moving heads which are mechanically addressed to the desired storage region, usually a smaller number of heads is required than is necessary in a magnetic drum. Most large-capacity magnetic disk storage units are composed of a group of disks, and characteristically a single head is associated with each disk surface.

Magnetic disks are mounted on a common rotating shaft with sufficient separation between each pair of disks to allow the head mechanism to slip in and out as necessary. Some of the smaller disk systems have a single head at the end of a few individually addressable access arms; but some of the larger and more modern ones have a family of heads that move together on a comblike mechanism. Although the single-head system reduces the number of heads required because the access mechanism is able to move up and down as well as in and out, it does increase drastically the complexity of the required mechanism. On the other hand, the comb arrangement obviates the necessity for the up-and-down movement because there is a head for each magnetic disk surface. Figure 5-10 is a diagrammatic sketch of a magnetic disk storage

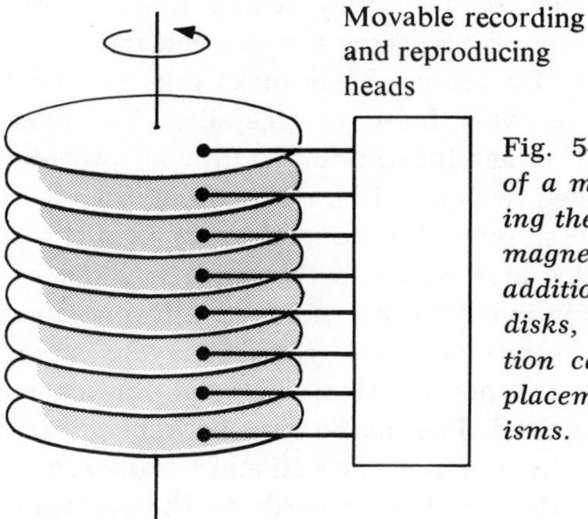

Fig. 5-10. *A schematic drawing of a magnetic disk memory showing the stack of disks on which the magnetic medium is deposited. In addition to the rotation of the disks, access to specific information can be made by mechanical placement of the head mechanisms.*

device, showing the multiple heads and the stack of disks storing the information.

An important recent development in magnetic disk technology is the availability of interchangeable groups of disks. This has allowed a vast increase in the storage capacity of a given disk system since an entire package of disks on the drive mechanism can be bodily removed and replaced with another. Thus information not currently in use could be stored on a shelf until needed without tying up the valuable access mechanism of the disk control itself.

The optimization of information file organization on magnetic disk surfaces to reduce access time and increase capacity has almost become a profession in itself. The special techniques for maximizing the efficiency of these operations depend specifically upon the structure of each individual device and therefore go beyond the scope of this book. But briefly, many systems organize data on *information cylinders*, or families of addresses, on all of the disks in the group at a common radius from the central drive shaft. Thus, since no radial or other mechanical motion of the head mechanism is required, information is available quickly from such a cylinder (if there is a head for each disk surface). These and other similar storage organization procedures can make the difference between full packing of a storage unit and a wasteful use of what might have been many more bits of storage capacity.

MAGNETIC CHIP AND CARD STORAGE UNITS

Groups of disks, though of relatively large storage capacity and interchangeability, often require long access times. When the operator interchanges one disk package for another, the access time may be on the order of minutes. Thus disks may not be a suitable storage medium for very large storage files, like those involved in libraries and other information retrieval projects. Instead, a device is needed which, although it might have a slightly longer average access time, has no such protracted delay. The magnetic storage device best suited to this need is a mechanism that retrieves information recorded magnetically on small chip or card records; thousands of these records may be stored in small receptacles that are not physically moved until their particular contents are required. Pneumatic and hydraulic transport systems of ingenious though not revolutionary nature have been designed to find and deliver these records to the recording and reproducing mechanism. The total storage capacity of systems of this sort may be billions or even trillions of bits of information—sufficient to store the entire contents of large libraries. Since the small receptacles containing the chips are also interchangeable, it is, indeed, virtually unlimited.

MAGNETIC TAPE STORAGE UNITS

Historically, the oldest of the moving-medium magnetic storage devices is the magnetic tape unit. The *magnetic tape unit* or *drive* usually has only one head and its position is fixed. The magnetic medium itself is moved past the head by a drive mechanism. Magnetic tape comes in the form of reels, and the tape drive feeds tape from the storage reel to a take-up reel. Various forms of pneumatic and mechanical drive mechanisms have been developed to handle the movement of the tape. All of them are faced with the problem of accelerating the considerable mass of the loaded tape reel rapidly enough to minimize computer waiting time. In many tape drives there is a pneumatically controlled storage area for a small portion of tape, the only part subject to the severe accelerative forces, so that the acceleration delay has been reduced to a minimal millisecond or two.

More seriously, since a magnetic tape is a linear storage medium, access time for information at the other end of the tape can be as much as minutes, a delay not acceptable under most modern computing conditions. In order partially to overcome this limitation, a number of computers have twenty or more magnetic tapes operating nearly simultaneously. While one tape unit reads information into the computer, for example, another may wind the tape toward some addressed storage area. The actual storage capacity of a magnetic tape unit is also very large because one magnetic tape can be interchanged for another. However, the practical considerations of tape reel storage and, more importantly, the time required for interchanging tape reels limit this seemingly infinite storage capacity.

Many people believe that the utility of the magnetic tape is drawing to an end. Magnetic tapes, the first bulk storage devices added to digital computers, played a leading role in the development of computing, but in spite of their capacity advantages they are being largely supplanted by the new disk and chip magnetic memories, all of which have much shorter access times. Some current installations have systems in which magnetic tape units are used only to communicate with other installations. We will see below that even this function is being taken over rapidly by direct electronic links between distant computers. In other installations, it seems as if the only reason for maintaining magnetic tapes is a sentimental tradition.

A major feature of all these moving-medium magnetic storage devices is that the storage capacity of a system may be enlarged almost endlessly by adding more and more of the individual units to the system. Thus, each computer can be tailored to a special set of applications. This specialization adds a serious burden to programmers who wish to run programs prepared on one system on another.

The expandability of memory is also illustrative of a general feature of modern computing systems: it is now possible to increase capacity and even operating speed by adding additional functional units of all kinds to the computer. For this reason most large systems are now individually tailored to the user's special needs; two computers with the same model number from a given manufacturer may have very different effective capacity.

We now turn to the specific nature of the multiple-component organization of computer systems, for it plays an important role in real-time, on-line computer operation.

Systems organizations with multiple components

Earlier in this chapter we discussed the computer as a coordinated system of registers. Information is routed between and manipulated in the registers in order to accomplish the sequence of operations defined by the computer program. Essentially we were speaking of *serial information processing*,[3] in which events occur sequentially as the various registers are freed from their previous tasks. Therefore, only one instruction could be executed at a time. This limitation was partly due to the nature of the serial logical processes defined by the program. From another point of view, however, the hardware organization of the computer defined the logical possibilities that could be programmed.

From the earliest days of computer design, some engineers have objected to the inefficiency of serial operation. They believe that computers can be improved by organizing them as *parallel information processors*. In such systems many operations might occur simultaneously. One of the first designs of a parallel system organization was that proposed by John Holland (1959). His system was essentially a massed group of accumulators each of which could be simultaneously and independently active. The complexity of computer accumulators has prohibited this sort of fully parallel computer operation, but in the last few years many steps have been taken in the direction of more highly parallel operation. In each case, with additional circuitry, the computer could be made to perform several functions nearly simultaneously and thus to operate much more efficiently.

Let us consider an example. Remember that in the simple computer described earlier all communication with the high-speed

[3] Serial information processing of instructions does not imply, of course, that within the electronics of each instruction, individual bits may not be processed in parallel, as described earlier in this chapter.

core memory was carried out through a single memory buffer register connected directly to the accumulator. A typical computer program, however, has occasional stretches in which the accumulator is being very heavily used, but relatively few references are being made to the core memory. Yet in this simple system there is no possibility of using the "waiting time" of the core memory to advantage. In addition, there are often parts of programs in which information is being transmitted between the core memory and some other peripheral memory such as a magnetic tape unit, and the rest of the computer operation must wait until the transfer is completed. In other situations extreme requirements for reliability demand that two computers be multiplexed to a single memory so that one could take over in the event of a machine breakdown in the other. Airlines reservations and military command and control systems are included in this category. For these and other reasons computer designers developed multiple capabilities. The following sections show how the use of multiple functional units has increased the efficiency of computer systems.

MULTIPLE BLOCKS OF CORE MEMORY

One of the most important problems facing computer designers was the elimination of the information bottleneck created by a single information channel communicating with a monolithic central core memory. Another core memory problem was the halving of effective computer speed because of the requirement for a rewrite cycle after each word was read from the memory. By finding some way to release the central processor during the rewrite cycle, one sweep of the designer's ingenuity could double the speed of a computer.

The second of these two problems was ultimately solved by designing computers in which the core memory had associated with it the circuitry necessary to read, write, and buffer information, as well as the independent capacity to carry out a complete rewrite operation from its own memory buffer register after read information had been transferred to the computer. Thus, the central processor could be released by the memory after the information was read from a given register. The arithmetic and control units could then execute the contained instruction or process the obtained data. The advantage of this system is that the memory rewrite cycle no longer delays the operation of the arithmetic and logical components. To implement such capability fully is difficult, for the program often requires the central processor to obtain further information from the core memory for the next instruction. This was not possible with a single memory unit; once again, the computer would have to wait for the single memory unit to complete its rewrite cycle.

A solution to the problem was devised in which the single block of core memory was separated into several independent units, each with its own rewrite capability and associated memory buffer register. Figure 5-11 depicts a system with a single central proces-

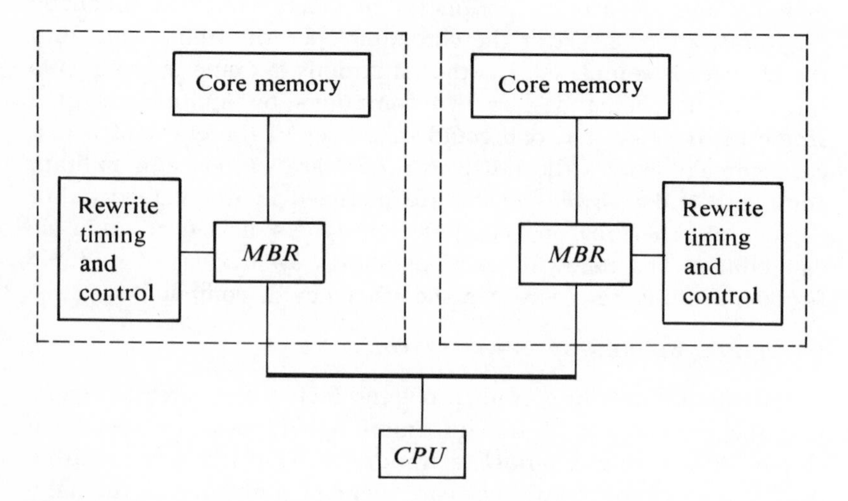

Fig. 5-11. *A digital computer system in which a single central processing unit (CPU) uses two core memory blocks to double its speed of operation.*

sor and two completely independent memory units. For example, if all even number addresses were placed in one block and all odd number addresses in the other, on the average the instructions would be taken alternatively from each memory unit. Sequential memory references would therefore overlap with the rewrite cycle of the previous memory reference, as shown in Figure 5-12*a*, in contrast with the operations of a single memory unit, as illustrated in Figure 5-12*b*.[4] This procedure is theoretically capable of doubling the effective speed of the computer, but any such statement must be carefully qualified because its truth depends upon a program in which every instruction is simply a memory refer-

[4] This system is exemplified in the memory organization of the PDP-6 computer developed by the staff of the Digital Equipment Corporation of Maynard, Mass. However, other manufacturers have developed essentially similar paradigms for multiple-block memories.

ence. When other instructions are interspersed among the memory references, the effective speed is less than doubled.

Figure 5-11 illustrates another basic concept: the "bus" arrangement of the lines carrying information to and from the two memory units. A *bus* is defined as a signal line which can either feed information to more than one destination or acquire informa-

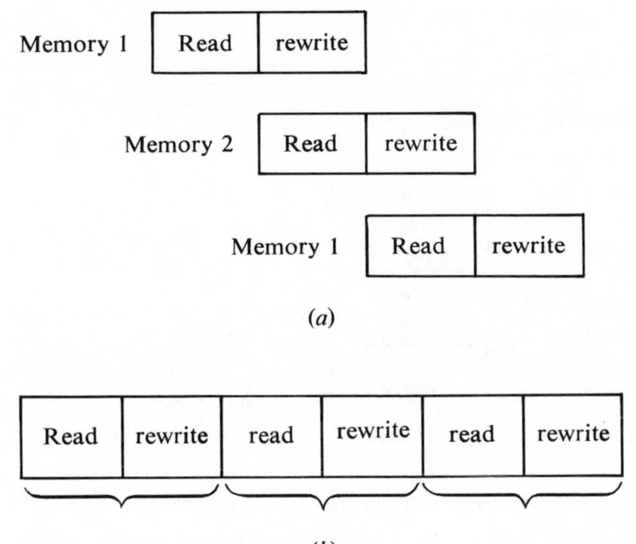

Fig. 5-12. *With a double core memory unit such as that shown in Fig. 5-11, and with separate memory buffer registers, the computer may double its speed of operation by going to the other core memory as soon as the read cycle is completed in one memory unit. The rewrite operation occurs afterwards independently. A timing chart for this mode of operation is shown in* (a). *Compare* (a) *with the non-overlapped operation of a single memory unit computer as shown in* (b).

tion from more than one source. In the case of Figure 5-11, the input to the central processor is said to be on a bus capable of acquiring information from either of the memory units. Similarly, the information outflow to the memories passes through the bus. The bus is then said to have multiple destinations.

MULTIPLE CHANNELS INTO A SINGLE UNIT OF CORE MEMORY

Since the input and output of a central processor can be placed on a bus, it should be possible to do the same with the input and output of a magnetic core memory unit. This would help obviate the first of the two difficulties discussed above—the bottleneck produced by the single channel into a core memory block. More specifically, the central processor would not have to become the single communication link between the core memory and the input-output or other storage media. Figure 5-13 illustrates the organiza-

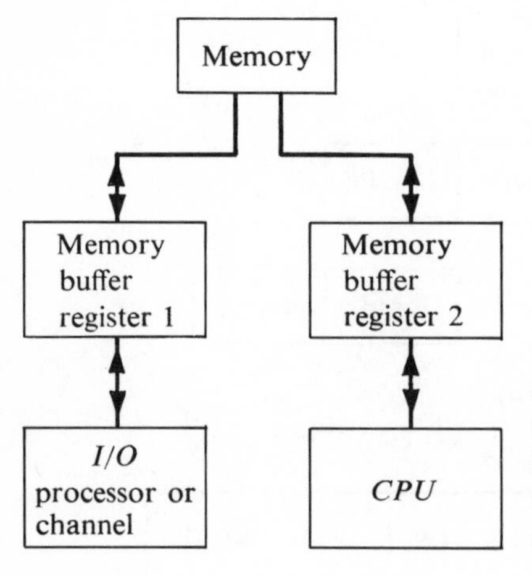

Fig. 5-13. *A computer system with multiple channels into a single block of core memory. Each channel has its own memory buffer unit associated with it.*

tion of a memory unit which has several *portals* of entrance and exit, through which information may flow to other parts of the computer system. The two sources of information are a central processing unit and a special minimal logical control unit, the latter capable only of controlling information transmission between the core memory and other storage or peripheral input-output devices. This special minimal logical control unit is called either an *input-output processor* or a *channel* by different computer manufacturers. Input-output processors are usually controlled by an initiating instruction from the central processor indicating to the unit such information as the starting address and how many words of the data block are to be transferred. The input-output processor continues automatically to transfer sequential words until all desired have been moved. It then signals the central processor that it has completed its job and is available for other assignments.

In this type of system organization, the capacity and temporal characteristics of the memory unit are critical in the determination of a system overload. There is no guarantee that the central processor will not have to refer to memory during the transfer of information by the input-output processor. To allow both the central and input-output processors to operate nearly simultaneously, the concept of *asynchronous cycle stealing* has been developed. In a synchronous computer, each clock cycle group regularly results in the execution of an instruction by the central processor. In the asynchronous operation, occasional cycles may be ignored and the execution of the next computer instruction inhibited until some later time.

Cycle stealing by the input-output processor is one of the conditions under which instruction executions may be inhibited. Cycle stealing is implemented by assigning priority to the input-output processor that usually transfers information to some device in which the timing of each data word is critical but data transfers occur only infrequently. The plan works because it generally does not matter whether the central processor takes a few extra microseconds for its operation; the infrequent cycles stolen by the input-output processor are hardly noticed. Real-time operation of computers, however, may limit the applicability of asynchronous operation.

MULTIPLE ARITHMETIC AND LOGICAL UNITS

Many computer applications make great demands for ultrareliable systems. In others, the work load exceeds the capacity of the largest available single central processor. In each case a solution to its problem is offered by connecting two or more central processing units together into a *multiprocessor system*. Such a system would have its two central processing units connected through a bus arrangement to a single magnetic core unit. The magnetic core unit, of course, must be of the type with two portals through which information may pass (as shown in Fig. 5-13) so that both processors have equally uninhibited access to the memory.

Since each processor is capable of referring to memory at any time, a division of labor between them is possible. For example, one of the central processors might preprocess incoming information and store it in the core memory for later access and further processing by the other. Alternatively, one processor might be on a standby basis, idling until an overload of work or an actual component breakdown in the other required it to take over part or all of the work load. This example of a multiprocessing system is, however, an unlikely one, since multiple memory units would certainly be required in all such applications. But it does illustrate the basic idea of multiplying central processors to add to systems capability.

A single system with both multiple memories and multiple central processors represents the closest current approximation to the

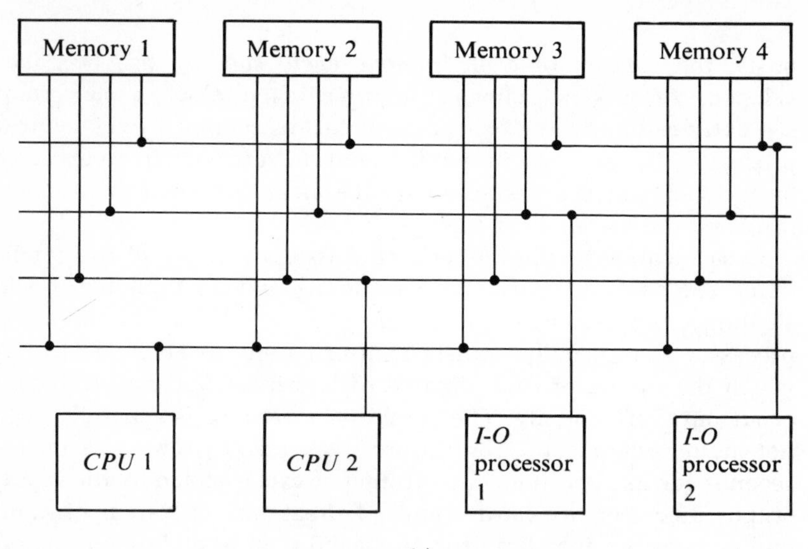
Memory 1
Memory 2
Memory 3
Memory 4
CPU 1
CPU 2
I-O processor 1
I-O processor 2

(*a*)

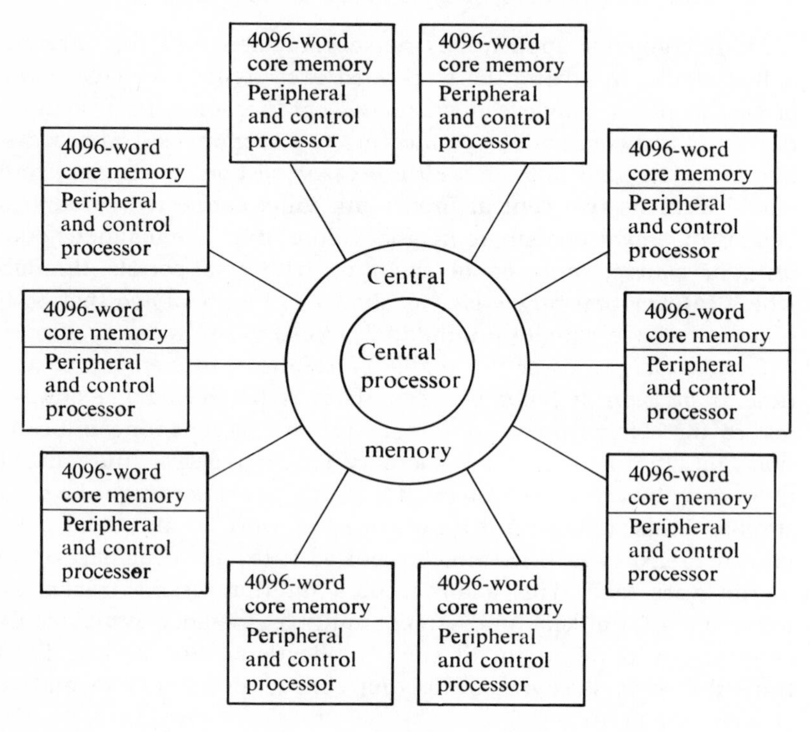
4096-word core memory
Peripheral and control processor
Central memory
Central processor

(*b*)

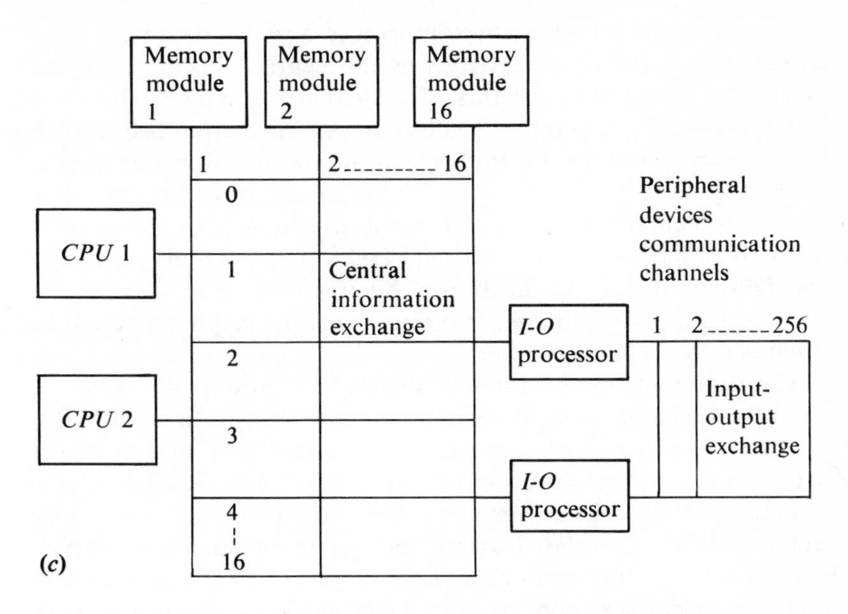

Fig. 5-14. (a) *A large computer system with multiple memory units and multiple processor units interconnected by a bus intercommunications system. The organization of the PDP-6 computer manufactured by the Digital Equipment Corporation is typical of such an organizational scheme. (Courtesy of Digital Equipment Corporation.)* (b) *A large computer system with a somewhat different pattern of organization. A large central processor has available to it a central memory that is shared with a large number of smaller memories and peripheral processors. This type of computer system organization is typified by the Control Data Corporation's 6600. (Courtesy of Control Data Corporation.)* (c) *A large computer system that is organized around an elaborate central information interchange capable of interconnecting input-output memories and processors as required by the various problems being run. This sort of arrangement is typified by the Burroughs Corporation's B-8500. (Courtesy of Burroughs Corporation.) All three of these computer systems organizations are to a degree topologically equivalent, but the different organizations emphasize to an increasing degree the information flow between units rather than the characteristics of the units themselves.*

Holland machine, which itself is probably not realizable with present technology. Figure 5-14*a* is a block diagram of a very large system with a bus arrangement linking a group of core memory units to a group of central and input-output processors. This type of computer organization is illustrative of one current design of a large system.

An important factor in multiprocessor and multimemory computers is that the characteristics of the central processor are no longer the prime determinants of system performance. The characteristics of the core memory alternatively have often become the most critical concern of the person responsible for selecting a specific system. Rather than choosing a central processor and then attaching memory units to it, the modern systems designer is more likely to be concerned with the addressing scheme and "relocation capabilities" of the core memory. This important fact is related to the development of on-line, real-time computer applications, to be discussed in the next chapter.

The computer organization as shown in Figure 5-14*b* utilizes a similar pattern of multiple memories, but arranged in a spiderlike manner. Topologically, this system is very similar to that in Figure 5-14*a*, but more emphasis is placed on the centralization of the switching device interconnecting the various components. This trend and the associated stress on the interconnection unit is carried one step further in Figure 5-14*c*. Here the various memories and processors are considered merely modules connected to a powerful information interchange system—another change of emphasis which is becoming increasingly prominent. In the very near future it may develop that neither the characteristics of the central processor nor those of the memory are of prime importance, but the availability of a wide variety of such units of varying power will shift the emphasis in computer system specification to the characteristics of the interchange. Again it should be noted, however, that all of these systems are logically and topologically similar, but vary in the emphasis on and in the physical location of the components of the bus or interchange circuitry.

MULTIPLE ACCUMULATORS

In modern systems, multiple accumulators have often satisfied the need for parallel operation. Many computer programs utilize a large number of instructions simply to load the accumulator with information to be processed in subsequent instructions; temporary storage is then used for intermediate results, which are sent back to the accumulator as needed. With multiple accumulators, much of this wasted time can be regained. An accumulator can be used to receive information from some storage unit and immediately to process that information without unloading another accumulator which may have been active until that time.

Another important timesaving feature of multiple accumulators is that they may be designed to operate at higher speeds than the rest of the circuitry directly associated with the core memory. A core memory requiring one microsecond to complete its cycle of operation would delay high-speed transistorized accumulators that might operate in a tenth of a microsecond (100 nanoseconds). If a small program loop is short enough to be stored entirely within the group of accumulators, it might be operated at very high speed with only occasional delaying references to the slower magnetic core memory circuitry.

Any gain in speed for a particular program cannot be stated a priori. The gain will depend on many programming and engineering factors specific to each machine and program. But it seems certain that for time-sharing computers, in which a number of programs are running nearly simultaneously, multiple accumulators can be critical factors for successful operation.

Telecommunication among remote computers

Several of the figures presented so far in this chapter have shown simple interconnecting lines between the various systems components. It may have been inferred that these lines represent wires laid between physically adjacent units, whereas they may have represented links to remote installations at distances restricted only by the ability of special communication equipment to handle high rates of information transmission.

There are two types of limitations on the distance between the central computer and its peripheral units. The first is one of data rate; the second lies in the number of required parallel lines. As we shall see, these two criteria are interchangeable.

Let us consider the problem of data rate. Communication from a central computer to a distant typewriter capable of printing data at a rate of twenty characters per second does not require very high-speed capacity of the interconnecting line. On the other hand, information communicated from one magnetic core memory unit to another may require that millions of bits be transmitted in each second.

To meet this variety of needs, a family of long-distance communication links has been developed which is often associated with commercial telephone and microwave service. A number of physical parameters determines the speed of transmission of any given link, the most important of which is the frequency characteristic of the various components in the system. An ordinary telephone system, for example, can transmit electrical signal frequencies ranging between 300 and 3000 cycles per second. As a general rule the bit-per-second rate of any communication link is twice that of the highest frequency it can pass. Thus a telephone line would be able to pass information at a maximum rate of about 6000 bits per second if all the components in the system also had that frequency capability. Actually, the rate over common telephone lines is usually limited to about 2000 bits per second.

For higher-speed communication, telephone service is inadequate. But, by simply substituting a coaxial cable for the ordinary telephone line, a much higher-speed transmission and receiving system may be employed, increasing the data rate to over a million bits per second.

The fastest communication channels available today are in the form of microwave links. These very-high-frequency radio communication systems do not use wires at all but project highly directional radio waves toward a distant receiver. The signals are detected at distant locations by appropriate receiving equipment. Microwave equipment is now available which is capable of transmitting several million bits of information per second.

This brings us to the second important consideration in discussing remote transmission links: the number of channels of information required to communicate between systems. Assume for a moment that we are dealing with a magnetic core memory capable of transmitting information at a rate of one million words per minute. Each word may consist of 36 bits of information. Usually this means that the 36 bits are available simultaneously on 36 different signal lines. But 36 channels of microwave communication, each capable of a million bits a second, would be extremely expensive for a single application.

In order to transmit the information more economically, engineers have developed *parallel-to-serial converters*. These devices trade time for space. The 36 parallel lines in our example would all be fed into a single channel in such a way that the first bit was transmitted in the first time unit, the second in the second time unit, and so on. In order to achieve the million-word-per-second transmission capability, the time allotted to the transmission of each bit could be no longer than 1/36 of a microsecond. Figure 5-15 depicts the parallel-to-serial operation. At the receiving end additional equipment is required to perform the inverse process of serial-to-parallel conversion.

The 36,000,000-bit-per-second rate described in this example is at or beyond the limit of current technology. Usually the transmission rate is artificially slowed down to a speed that is within the limits of the available equipment.

In the future, higher-speed data transmission may be possible through the use of optical signals, which can carry information at a faster rate because the component frequencies of light are much higher than even the microwave frequencies. The recent development of lasers holds great promise in this regard.

Another complication arises from the fact that it is often necessary to add other bits, conveying control information, along with the data bits. For example, Figure 5-15 shows an end-of-word bit

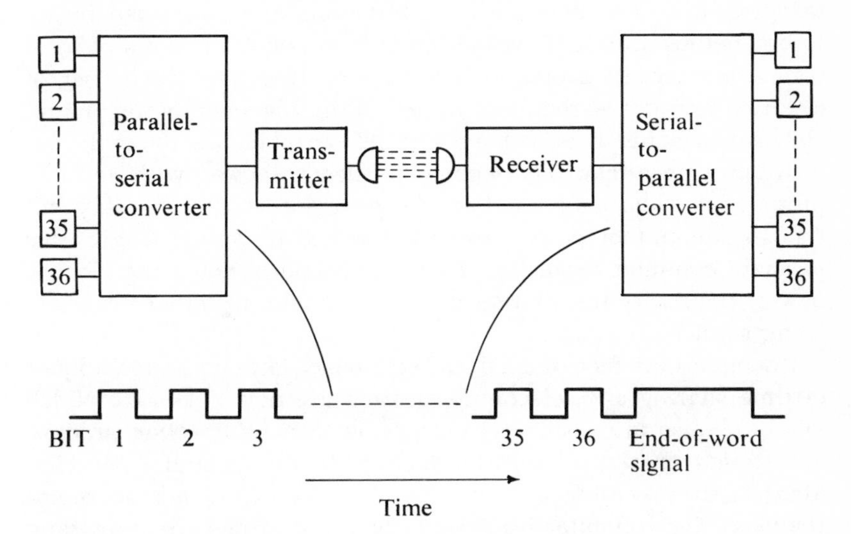

Fig. 5-15. *A block diagram of a communication system that transmits parallel information from a register to a distant point by converting it to a serial form and then transmitting it over a single information channel. The serial representation of the data is shown in the inset. At the receiving end the data is reconverted to parallel form and placed in an equivalent register.*

defining the limits of that particular word. This may be in the form of a space rather than an enlarged pulse duration; still, it represents an additional bit of information and as such places an additional burden on the communication system.

We have come to the end of this brief introduction to computer systems organization. With the idea of multiple computer components and telecommunication among remote components becoming widespread, another major development is almost immediately suggested. The next chapter will discuss the technological details of time-sharing and on-line computer operation, but the discussion of computer systems organization would be incomplete without mention of the concept of the *computer utility*.

At present most computers are used by single organizations,

and computing power is relatively centralized within these organizations. The organization purchases or rents an entire computer facility specifically tailored to its needs. It must deal with all the problems of maintaining a computer, such as hardware maintenance, supply, space, and acquisition. Yet the user is really concerned only with the capability of the computer to execute his programs. The housekeeping functions are considered by all to be onerous and aggravating burdens to which directors of local computing centers sacrifice their careers. It is as if each user of electric light were required to maintain his own power plant. How much better it is to have a small receptacle in the wall, out of which comes relatively dependable electric power, with no more profound logistic concern than the payment of one monthly bill for the amount of power utilized. Electric power users are able to share common resources. Thus when one is not using electric power, the entire installation does not sit idle, for other users are being serviced.

An important fact of modern technology is that the techniques of time sharing and telecommunication are now at a state which allows us also to consider seriously a *central information processing station* or *central information utility* for computer services. Many of the advantages of the shared utility would then accrue to the user. The computer itself could be a monstrous one, providing at different times to different users capabilities far beyond those available on local smaller machines. The problems of computer logistics could be handled by a central staff of specialists. In countless other ways the user would find his burden lightened by his ability to connect a specific input-output unit to a receptacle in the wall only for the hours he needs information services.

The relevance of the idea of the computer utility to this chapter on computer systems organizations and multiple computer components lies in the fact that such a utility would make it very difficult to distinguish the beginning of one computer from the end of another. Indeed, since many of the terminals of this giant utility might themselves be complex computers with independent memory or information-processing capability, the whole idea of speaking of individual computers might be inappropriate at that time. A single giant information-processing net might evolve with local terminals and central nodes of storage or processing capability much like the modern telephone system. Like the telephone system, the computer utility might make computing power available to the individual user in his home, school, or small office, thus providing an impetus to social change that has not yet been fully appreciated.

6: REAL-TIME COMPUTERS

Introduction

So far we have concentrated mainly on the hardware technology of digital computers. We have progressed from the technologies of individual logical units to the organization of the entire information-processing system itself. This chapter will be transitional between the hardware emphasis and a concentration on the use of these facilities. Such a chapter is particularly pertinent, for before we can begin to discuss specific behavioral science applications of information-processing systems, we must consider the major methodological innovations introduced into the discussion by the real-time, on-line use of computers. To do so requires that we define some of the terms in the rapidly developing vocabulary of real-time computers. Since certain terms are used in different ways by different authors, our definitions may not satisfy all readers. Nevertheless, it is possible to make some of these definitions at least internally consistent for the purposes of the discussion. After illustrating a number of the uses to which techniques can be applied, we will descend once again into the internal workings of a computer to see how the requirements of real-time computing are actually met. We will discuss these requirements in terms of both the necessary controlling programs and new equipment configurations.

Real-time computing has such an immediate and significant potential for behavioral sciences research that this chapter will end with a brief discussion of some of the current controversies concerning large time-shared systems versus small independent systems—an issue that is peculiarly important to workers in this field.

ON-LINE COMPUTER OPERATION

During *on-line* computer operation information is transmitted directly to the computer, without resorting to some intermediate storage medium such as a deck of punched cards or a punched paper tape. Implicit in this statement is the notion that the data or program entry device is directly connected by actual electrical links to the central processor of the computer. Thus, a programmer sitting at a typewriter console which is connected to the computer input-output mechanism is just as much on line as a measuring instrument feeding data directly into a computer. *On line*, therefore, describes a special mode of data communication between the user and the information-processing system. It is a term for a particular kind of equipment configuration.

REAL-TIME COMPUTER OPERATION

In contrast, the term *real time* is not a definition of equipment organization or interconnection. Rather, the real time of a computing system is determined by the temporal characteristics of the external environment with which the computer is interacting. The term originally grew out of the tradition of process control computers. In control applications, the computer gathered data from one or more sources in the external environment and then, on the basis of its analysis of these input data, sent output control signals back to some destination in the external environment. The acquisition, processing, and generation of control signals was said to be carried out in real time if the control signals returned to the external device quickly enough so that the external operation was not obstructed, hindered, or delayed by any time delay injected by the computer processing. It should certainly be obvious that what is one application's real time may be another's disastrous time delay. If the external system is a social or economic community, the real-time data need may be satisfied by an information transmission medium such as punched cards. In this application, even with time delays on the order of twenty-four hours, the computing would still be rapid enough to be considered real-time operation. On the other hand, in a physiological control situation, a delay of a few milliseconds may actually be detrimental to the analysis of the data being accumulated. In sum, the term *real time* is one defined by the external system rather than the computer, is variable from application to application, and has nothing to do, in its main sense, with the actual hardware interconnections between the computer and the external environment.

To elaborate this notion further, it would be useful to consider some other kinds of real-time computer usage. One of the most important of such interactions with a computer has been the real-time preparation of computer programs themselves. In this procedure, the computer programmer writes his program on an electric typewriter which is connected to a computer. Later we will discuss the procedure in greater detail, but for the moment let us consider the nature of the real-time domain it specifies. A programmer will usually be well satisfied if the response to his instructional entries is obtained in a second or two; he is likely to be content if he has to wait for a few seconds. But he becomes restive and disgruntled if the waiting period extends to tens of seconds. Thus real time in this type of interaction requires responses that occur in less than five seconds.

Another kind of real-time interaction in which computers are increasingly involved is the tabulation of statistics of neurophysiological recordings. One application (to be described more fully in a later chapter) is the interval histogram technique, in which the intervals between successive responses are measured and tabulated. It is fairly certain that there is very little useful information in the timing of neurophysiological events to a precision greater than a tenth of a millisecond. Hence, in order to gather all the information necessary for this type of measurement, the computer must be available to record the time of an occurrence of a nerve spike action potential within a tenth of a millisecond of its occurrence. This time requirement, therefore, defines a real-time domain different from that specified above for on-line programming.

Now that the nature of the term *real time* and its dependence on the external environment of the computer are clear, we should consider an important notion. We submit that *real time* is the *key concept* in the entire development of the technology of multiple-access, time-shared, on-line computer systems. That is to say, all the technology of multiple-access computers with massive memories and the related developments in computer programming systems are merely means of implementing real-time service and use. The need is for a highly interactive computer capability which does not inject any delays beyond the actual computing time required to execute a given problem. On-line computer operation is a means of gaining rapid access to the computer, and time sharing is a means of providing a large number of people with it economically. But the central idea, the creative force behind this modern technological development, and the main goal of the future are based on the need to serve some specific function in a particular real-time environment. The enormous emphasis on technology often obscures the fact, but the *raison d'être* of this development is the external one of application, not the internal one of systems design.

Multiple-user operation

Real-time, on-line operation might initially appear to be a costly luxury, but it is actually an eminently economical and sensible process. It might seem necessary that each user possess his own computer in order to take full advantage of real-time, on-line operation. In some cases on-line operation may actually be feasible with independent computer installations. But in other cases a need for a large computer capacity, and for the additional advantages that centralized facilities may offer, specifies that a large facility be shared by a number of users. The question then is how the facilities of the large system can be optimally shared among the group of users so that real-time needs are adequately satisfied.

In the usual computing center a central administrative agency is responsible for providing facilities and services to a large group of users. Let us consider how such a centralized system has operated in the past. Conventionally, it was shared by allowing users access to the machine at different times. Thus a single central computer was shared by sequentially allotting each user time blocks of several minutes or longer. The user inserted his program into the system in a more or less formalized manner and then allowed it to run to completion or until it exceeded his allotted time interval. Early in the history of computer systems it became clear that this was a most uneconomical way of utilizing the very expensive computer. Manual loading and unloading of a program was a time-consuming process.

The next step, therefore, was the development of automatic routines—i.e., other computer programs—which gathered a group of programs together into a *batch*. The batch might be gathered on one of the usual computer input media such as a magnetic tape and then read into the computer for rapid sequential execution. Each program was run until it was completed, until it encountered a programming difficulty or "bug," or until it exceeded the allotted time. Smaller peripheral computers might even prepare the batches of programs by reading punched cards and transcribing the results onto the magnetic tapes. These tapes might also contain the information necessary to allow the larger computer to link one program batch to the next. Thus a *queue* was formed, in which a program had to wait its turn, but the waiting period was more efficiently utilized because automatic procedures rapidly converted from one program to the next. The waiting time for a given program, however, still depended on the temporal requirements of all the other programs in the queue. Even the best-run computing centers would have a lag of several hours between the submission of a program and the return of results; the worst might require the programmer to wait as long as a day or two for his results.

Batch processing techniques gave rise to a programming approach essentially designed to handle large amounts of data at rates which were, to say the least, not real-time. But many, if not most, users now have begun to demand real-time computing capabilities far exceeding the best response times of the best conventional batch processing procedures. They require response times of a much different kind from that described above. To reduce response time, the computer must be shared in a far more subtle and intricate fashion than was allowed by running each program sequentially to completion. This is being achieved by means of a more microscopic form of time sharing.

In this microscopic form of time sharing, the time allotted to each user's program may be as small as a few hundredths of a second. Thus, even for computers that are able to execute a million or more instructions a second, most programs will not be run to completion. The criterion for the termination of a program, therefore, is usually that a given program has exceeded its time allotment, rather than that a programmed "halt" has been executed at the end of the routine. The change in termination criteria results in a wide variety of segmentation problems. There are hardware segments, time segments, and program segments. The rest of the chapter will be devoted to the problems of segmentation.

To summarize: in order to reduce the response time of computer facilities, a technology has been developing that will allow many different users to share a very large computer system. This technology is based primarily on a microscopic form of time sharing. It appears that this microscopic form of real-time time sharing will supplant, in large part, computational batch processing program techniques. On the other hand, for some small proportions of computer applications that are naturally suited to it, batch processing will be retained in the form of *background processing*, which is used to fill in empty time intervals between active real-time users. With this preliminary introduction to the notion of time sharing, we are in a position to add some definitions to our lexicon.

MULTIPLE-ACCESS COMPUTERS

The use of a single computer by a large number of users, in what appears to each of them to be independent operation, requires that there be an equally large number of terminal devices. At each one a user may enter data and receive processed results in the very same way the sole user of a computer might at the main control console.

The important point to be noted here is that complete control of an individual program is vested in a specific terminal. The central console operator has a certain amount of special control over the central computer not available to the individual user, but each user has great control over the details of his own program. Therefore, it is said that access to the computer is multiple—manual changes can be made at a variety of terminal positions rather than only at the central console.

With the development of digital communication links, the terminals need not be located near the computer. But location of terminals is a technical consideration secondary to the concept of multiple access to a central processor.

TIME-SHARED OPERATION

Time sharing (on the microscopic level with which we are presently concerned) is defined as the sequential allocation of the facilities of a single computer system to a number of users, so that all of them apparently receive complete real-time service. Today, the term implies that the amount of time allotted to each user is very short, perhaps only a few milliseconds.

Time sharing may be compared to a juggling act in which the juggler is so fast that he can keep many balls in the air simultaneously, though he is actually able to touch only one at a time. The difference between this procedure and the time sharing used in the batch processing computing center is but a quantitative one, yet it gives rise to a quasi-qualitative difference in total performance on the part of the programmer. Some authorities have suggested that a programmer's efficiency may be increased by an average of 1000 percent in terms of the length of time required to develop a debugged and useful program. In other instances attempts at certain programming tasks may now be contemplated which could not have been realistically considered within the framework of the older batch processing system.

MULTIPROGRAMMED OPERATION

Multiprogramming (as defined by many computer specialists) is the operation of a single computer to execute a number of different programs, such that none of the individual programs need be run to completion before another one is serviced. The term therefore not only includes the real-time time-sharing operation described above, but it also includes other types of computer applications which are not so finely subdivided in time.

MULTIPROCESSOR OPERATION

A closely related term, already alluded to, is *multiprocessor computer operation.* Multiprocessor operation refers to the use of more than one central processor in a given computer system, so that the two or more processors can share the work load of a single program. For example, input-output and bookkeeping operations may be relegated to one central processor and arithmetic processing to the other. Other forms of cooperative interaction between two central processors are also possible. Some applications have involved the preprocessing of data by one unit and a final processing by another. In each case processing capability is added in an effort to enhance the overall operating speed of program execution. Some systems have a standby central processor which can take over the functions of the primary processor in case of a breakdown; the standby central processor, however, is more appropriately considered a "spare tire" for the system rather than a true form of multiple processing.

Before discussing specific applications we must digress for a moment to a brief discussion of computer languages.

Assemblers and compilers

Although programming has been excluded as a topic of this book, it is now necessary to add a few definitions concerning programming languages. The discussion of on-line programming in the next section of this chapter is dependent on at least a modest understanding of the differences between various types of computer languages.

Computers speak with many tongues in the sense that they deal with information coded in different forms at different stages of their operation. A *computer language* is defined as any coding scheme that can be used to represent numbers or instructions. A modern digital computer operates at the most basic logical level in terms of binary coded symbols and logical operations implemented by binary coded electronic circuits. Because of its intimate relation to the hardware, this level of computer language is called the *machine language* of the computer. But programming in machine language would be difficult and time consuming. It would call for a complete knowledge of each of the computer instructions and of the binary coding scheme for addressing storage registers. Further, it would require that each storage register be labeled with its *absolute* (or real) address whenever it is used. To reduce the difficulties, other languages called assemblers or compilers have been developed. These *higher-order* or *meta* languages allow the programmer to write programs in his own language and are capable of translating his symbols to those required to operate the computer.

The first group of higher-level languages which help the programmer avoid some of the handicaps of machine language programming are called *assembly languages*. An assembly language permits the programmer to use simple mnemonics to call up machine language instructions. Ordinarily called *symbolic instructions* (although this term is also used for the more complex instructions of the compilers described below), these mnemonics are usually simple alphabetic symbols that are easier to remember than the binary code for each instruction. *Symbolic addresses,* mnemonic names given to a memory location, are also used. Thus, a program can be written in a form which is independent of actual hardware memory locations or instruction codes. The *assembler* itself is a program that converts a symbolic program consisting of these mnemonics into the specific machine language instructions required by the electronics. It therefore acts as a *translator,* converting the more easily written symbolic program into the more precise and usable machine language program. In general, each symbolic instruction of an assembly language is converted into a single machine language instruction.

The nature of a given assembly language for a special computer is determined by the nature of the individual machine. As we have said, each machine language instruction is likely to have a symbolic code associated with it. The assembler translates and inserts numbers wherever they are required, but its form is dictated almost totally by the machine language of the computer itself.

In order to meet the needs of special users and to provide languages that are common to many different computers, another type of computer language—the compiler—has evolved. Compilers are more elaborate translation programs. They accept instructions which are closely allied to the language of the user; they translate these symbolic instructions into sequences of machine language instructions that may be composed of a large number of instructions. Of the many compilers that have been written, perhaps the most famous is the Fortran language, whose name is an acronym for *for*mula *trans*lator. Fortran was developed primarily to provide an algebraic language for mathematical analysis.

Fortran and other user-oriented compilers are much more complex systems than the simple assemblers which simply translate mnemonic instructions and addresses into machine language. Fortran achieves its great successes and wide application in mathematical analysis because of the highly ordered nature of algebraic formulas. Other types of compilers, however, are required for other types of computer applications—for example, to meet the needs of users who are most interested in verbal materials and nonnumerical data processing. These compilers are particularly useful in such applications as information retrieval, nonnumerical pattern recognition, and the simulation of cognitive processes. It should be noted that while compilers provide a common language which may be used on several different computers, the compiler itself must be written in the machine language of each computer independently.

Another important but less rigorously defined term is *interpreter*. An interpreter is a language that accepts symbolic instructions, translates them into machine language, and then immediately executes these machine language instructions. The main difference between a compiler and an interpretive language lies in the fact that a compiler translates all of the instructions of a symbolic program prior to execution while an interpreter may perform some of the translation at the time of execution. Execution times for interpretive languages are therefore considerably slower than for precompiled programs.

It is now worthwhile to study real-time computer applications in detail. The exact nature of the real-time interaction between the user and the computing system, and the advantages of this mode of operation, can thus be made much clearer.

Real-time program preparation and checkout

Let us figuratively sit down with a computer programmer at an on-line typewriter terminal and watch him write a program in real time. This typewriter terminal is supposedly connected to a computer which, for the purposes of our example, is at some distant location. The programmer sees before him only what appears to be a standard electric typewriter. We will ignore until later all the electronic and programming technology represented by the small electrical connection on the wall of the cubicle enclosing the programmer and his typewriter. Through this connection signals pass to and from the computer. As far as the programmer is concerned, he has only a remarkably active and responsive typewriter; it accepts his typing and responds with a series of printed messages appropriate and timely to his needs.

Before entering his cubicle, however, the programmer must have been prepared in a number of ways. First, he must have been instructed about the nature of the dialogue that will pass between the typewriter and himself, and about the rules governing the initiation and continuance of the dialogue. We will illustrate some typical rules as we proceed in the presentation of this example. Second, he must be able to speak and be aware of the availability of the various programming languages he may use to develop his program. Such knowledge will allow him to select the most appropriate language for the particular programming application with which he is concerned. Third, he must come prepared with an explicit statement of the program he wishes to write. It may be in the form of a detailed flow chart or even a handwritten preliminary copy of the sequence of instructions he feels may do the job. With this preliminary information he is ready to develop his program. The following steps are required:

1. The program must be typed instruction by instruction in the appropriate *metalanguage*.
2. The program must be assembled or compiled by the assembly or compiling language, able to understand the terms used by the programmer.
3. The program must be test-run by the computer in *machine language*, running either to completion or until a programming error is encountered that halts the program or results in some other detectable error.
4. After the program is completely error free, it must be available for reuse as required.

It should be noted that this sequence of operations is nominally identical to that followed by the programmer in a batch processing operation. In the latter mode of operation, a program is written on programming sheets and transcribed to punched cards. The program is then compiled or assembled by passing it through the computer, in which the appropriate translation system has been stored. The results of the compilation are usually repunched on an additional set of cards, which are then reintroduced into the computer for testing, correcting, and subsequent recompilations. This is a time-consuming and tedious process. Each test may reveal only one error and yet require a day or more of waiting for the program to pass through the queue. But, as has been pointed out, there is a quasi-qualitative difference between batch processing and the procedure we are about to describe, due to the much more rapid response time of the real-time system. Because of long delays, conventional programming of the type just mentioned has heretofore been an unreinforcing, even negatively reinforcing, procedure. It drove some fine workers who badly needed computation capabilities away from computer usage. The batch processing procedures limited the range of possible applications of computers to problems in which data analysis was not required in short-latency real time, and in which huge masses of data could be accumulated for massed evaluation.

There is a vigorous dialogue now about the future of batch processing. Our opinion is that it will diminish in importance, finally being used only for the very special types of problems for which it is uniquely fitted. On the other hand, more and more problems requiring computers will alter their research and evaluative strategies in order to take advantage of the real-time capabilities of the newly developing technologies.

But let us now turn to the programmer, his hands outstretched toward the reactive typewriter, and consider his actions in some detail.[1]

PREPARATION OF THE PROGRAM

The preparation of a program, or sequence of computer instructions, on line with a time-shared computer is a highly dynamic and satisfying experience for the programmer. We will present a sample series of statements which might be typed by the programmer and the responses typed by the computer. The statements

[1] In order to illustrate the various techniques involved in on-line program generation and checkout, we will imagine a hypothetical system. But this section has been especially influenced by the programming system developed for the PDP-6 computer by the staff of the Digital Equipment Corporation, Maynard, Mass. We would like to acknowledge their cooperation in providing us with manuals describing the many aspects of their system.

from the computer will be identified, as they might be on a real system, by the prefix *C-*, while programmer-generated statements will be terminated with a colon (:) signaling the computer that a message is ready to be interpreted. Though we will analyze these statements individually, remember that, in actuality, they appear on the printed paper in a continuous list like that in Figure 6-1.

```
SIGN ON:
C-IDENT?
12345:
C-PROG?
I PROG:
C-12345-07
GET ED:
CORE 2:
I 10-10:
C-READY FOR PROGRAM PREPARATION
C-00010 X=10:
C-00020 A=5:
C-00030 B=3:
C-00040 CLA:
C-00050 LDA:
C-00060 SQA:
C-00070 ADD B:
C-00080 PNT AC:
C-00090 TST X=0:
C-00100 HLT:
C-00110 TRR 40:
C-00120 END:
```

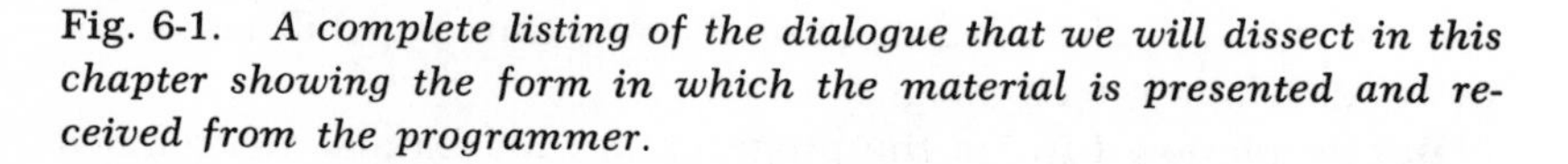

Fig. 6-1. *A complete listing of the dialogue that we will dissect in this chapter showing the form in which the material is presented and received from the programmer.*

The programmer must initially *sign on* to let the operating system[2] of the computer know that he is at a terminal and awaiting service. In our hypothetical system, this signal would be the first line of the dialogue between the computer and the programmer.

SIGN ON:

After a delay, depending mainly upon its current work load, the computer would type,

C-IDENT?

thus asking the user to identify himself for bookkeeping purposes. The programmer would respond with his name or a code number such as,

[2] The nature of the operating system will be described later in this chapter. For the moment, consider it the master controlling program of the entire family of software operating within the computer system.

12345:

This brings us to the first procedural problem. The computer need not acknowledge the acceptance of the code number. Nevertheless, there may be an extensive delay here or at any other point in the program while the computer executes some other operation for a user with a higher priority. How does the programmer know that the machine has actually accepted his entry and is ready for the next statement? In some systems the typewriter mechanism is activated either by advancing the platen one line or by unlocking the keyboard. Let us adopt the somewhat hopeful convention for this example that the completion of a response by either the computer or the programmer is associated with computer readiness to accept the next message.

The computer now types,

C-PROG?

This statement asks the programmer to identify by number the job on which he desires to work. If the program is already stored in the computer, he enters its code number. If the program is a new one and not based on any previous files, he types,

I PROG:

This shorthand code informs the computer that the program is a new one and that a new assignment number should be made for it. The computer, after attending to the various bookkeeping operations required, returns the newly assigned number to the user in the following way:

C-12345-07

In this case the programmer's number and additional serial number have been used as the code for this particular program. If the program had been an older one on which the programmer wanted to do further work, his response would have been to type the code number for that program. In either case, the computer now requires the programmer to define certain other aspects of his work.

First of all, he must select, from the family of translation programs in the computer memory, the program he wishes to work with. In the current example, he probably would require a special editing program to help prepare the new program. Such an editing program is not a simple clerical assistant but is intimately associated with one of the compilers available to the programmer. It would, in addition to carrying out certain organizational and bookkeeping functions, make preliminary checks on instruction format and perhaps, even at this early stage of program development, have certain diagnostic aids that could distinguish other procedural errors. It would also have facilities to help the author correct any errors which he noted in the preparatory phase. In order to make the editorial program available, the programmer would type some message like,

GET ED:

This statement would cause the operating system of the computer to bring the assembler editing program into its active memory.

In most time-sharing systems the programmer must also estimate the amount of magnetic core memory he thinks he will require for his program. Since the system is servicing many people at the same time, and since there is no a priori way for the operating system to judge the potential size of any program, the user must make this estimate. It is entered typically in the following way:

CORE 2:

Thus the programmer estimates that he will need two blocks of core memory for his program. The size of the block will vary from one time-sharing system to another. Later we will see how the block arrangement of core memory significantly influences the organization of several aspects of the real-time time-sharing computer. In our current example, the computer uses this estimate of anticipated core storage requirements to help allocate its total core memory resources. The computer may also require the programmer to specify where he would like his program stored after it is completed. For the purposes of our hypothetical machine, we will assume the ideal case—that the system can actively select whatever appropriate storage medium is available.

In his final preparatory statement the programmer types,

I-10-10:

This message instructs the computer to label every tenth instruction with the first label beginning at count 10. Thus, at some later time, the programmer can insert instructions of intermediate counts without renumbering the entire programming sequence. If each instruction were serially numbered, the addition of a single instruction would require the renumbering of all subsequent instructions. Since there is no reason all numbers must be used, the counting-by-ten procedure eliminates the bookkeeping of renumbering which would otherwise be required whenever any alteration was made.

When this introductory information has been entered into the machine, the computer responds with a positive indication that all is ready:

C-READY FOR PROGRAM PREPARATION

The computer then types out the first label:

C-00010

and pauses to let the programmer type in the first instruction.

The programmer responds in the language he has selected as being most appropriate to his problem. He is constrained by his knowledge of the compilers or assemblers available to him, and by his knowledge of the details of each. At this point he is also constrained by the selection of ED and the limits of its ability to handle only a single language. Let us assume that he has decided to write a program in a simple assembly language, and that subsequently he plans to call upon the assembler to translate this symbolic program into machine language instructions. Let us further assume that the assembly language has a single mnemonic code for each machine language instruction. Let us even further assume that the programmer wishes to write a program calculating the value of $A^2 + B$ for values of A and B increasing in steps of 1 from initial values of $A = 5$ and $B = 3$ for $x = 10$ iterations. The programmer now types the first instruction after the serial label previously typed by the computer.

C-00010 X = 10:

This instruction defines the initial value of x. The computer accepts this instruction and types the next instruction label. It too is followed by an instruction from the programmer. The dialogue continues until the programmer encounters some kind of diagnostic signal, such as a format error or an unknown instruction, from the assembler editor; or, if he is very clever, until he has finished typing the entire program. When the program is complete, he types a termination code such as,

END:

after the last instruction address typed by the computer.

The sequence of instructions and labels constituting this initial attempt at the program might look like the list of Figure 6-1. (This is a program written in the editorial mode for the system assembler. We will not define each instruction but discuss below the meaning of specific instructions as required.)

Let us now consider the program in more detail, particularly the instruction labeled 00090. This instruction is a test—a branch point that will cause the computer to skip an instruction if the specified condition is not met (i.e., if x is not equal to 0). But an error has been made in the generation of the program! Nowhere in the preceding instructions has the value of x been decremented; and since x would always be equal to 10, the program would thus run continuously without terminating. If the error were not detected at this stage of program development, it would certainly show up when the program was tested after assembly. Let us assume that our programmer spots the error at this time. Our hypothetical editor allows corrections to be made by means of two additional commands: one allowing the programmer to insert an instruction, the other allowing him to delete an instruction. These instructions might have the mnemonics ADD and DELETE. In this case the programmer would want to insert an instruction capable of decrementing the contents of x by 1 into the program sequence by assigning a label intermediate between the appropriate preceding and succeeding instructions.

```
ADD 00085 DEC X:
```

The programmer may also notice at this time (or after a test run at some later time) that his answers will all be the same. There is obviously another mistake. He has forgotten to increment the values of A and B each time he iterated the evaluation of the formula. This would be corrected by inserting the following instructions:

```
ADD 00086 INC A:
ADD 00087 INC B:
```

If the programmer is now satisfied that his program is ready for assembly, he might ask for a corrected print-out of the whole program. The following instruction would initiate a print-out of lines 10 to 110.

```
PNT 10,110:
```

The typewriter would list the desired sequence of corrected instructions with all identifying information properly placed, as shown in Figure 6-2.

The program is now ready to be translated into machine language instructions by the assembly program. Let us assume, however, that the programmer wishes to do this at a later time; he prefers to sign off from the computing system for the present. It is only necessary to indicate that he wishes to terminate his typing activity in some simple but stereotyped way. He might type,

```
SIGN OFF:
```

```
C-00010 X=10:
C-00020 A=5:
C-00030 B=3:
C-00040 CLA:
C-00050 LDA:
C-00060 SQA:
C-00070 ADD B:
C-00080 PNT AC:
C-00085 DEC X:
C-00086 INC A:
C-00087 INC B:
C-00090 TST X=0:
C-00100 HLT:
C-00110 TRR 40:
C-00120 END:
```

Fig. 6-2. A listing of the revised program.

We need not describe in detail all of the possible instructions which might be used in such an editorial program. The examples above illustrate the general nature of the interaction between the typewriter and the programmer. Each editorial system has a different family of capabilities, limited only by the efforts of the program system designers and by the capacities of the computer system on which it is being processed.

There is an important general concept that should be elaborated upon at this point. The computer commands used by the programmer can be utilized only because of the interpretive capabilities of the editorial program itself. As each command is typed, it is inspected, analyzed, and identified as one of a specific list. The programmer is free to type only those commands that the computer is preprogrammed to recognize and to which it can respond. Once the instruction has been recognized, a predetermined manipulation is called out from another portion of the computer memory and applied to that particular instruction. A very important general notion is illustrated here. It is the *principle of limited anticipation,* limiting the messages from a human being to a computer to those that have been previously anticipated. We have already discussed this point in Chapter 1. It is generally true, we saw there, that unconstrained verbal inputs to a computer will lead only to chaotic responses. All inputs must be limited to a list of items (or classes of items for more sophisticated interpretive routines) for which preparations have been made in advance. We shall see again in discussing several other areas of application how universal a constraint of computer usage this is at the present time.

ASSEMBLY OF THE PREPARED PROGRAM

When the programmer returns to the typewriter to assemble his program, he repeats the sign-on procedure.

```
SIGN ON:
C-IDENT
12345:
C-PROG?
12345-07:
CORE 2:
```

Thus the programmer has identified himself once again and has made available the desired program. He now calls up the assembly program:

```
GET ASEM:
```

It is appropriate to point out that throughout this entire interaction the operating system is performing a diagnostic check on the input commands from the programmer. Thus, if he should ask for a non-existent program or make some other error of sequence or protocol, the computer could respond with a comment such as,

```
C-NO SUCH PROGRAM
```

or

```
C-OUT OF SEQUENCE—SPECIFY CORE
REQUIREMENTS FIRST
```

When the computer has accepted the necessary information, it may begin the assembly automatically or in some systems wait for a START instruction from the programmer. Once the assembly is started, the computer usually will indicate, via the typewriter, that the assembly is complete or that an error is preventing further assembly of the program. An example of an error response might look like this:

```
C-UNDEF INSTR 00030
```

Most assemblers have certain on-line editing features that allow the programmer to correct such errors immediately before the assembly process continues. This editorial subroutine may also be capable of making the correction in the original symbolic program 12345-07.

Let us assume that the program has been successfully assembled. Though this does not mean that it will perform perfectly, at least a large number of the obvious typographical and procedural difficulties have been removed. The typewriter may then be commanded to list the machine language instructions or the revised symbolic program. It would also list the addresses of all constants, and perhaps additional diagnostic materials that did not halt the assembly.

Note that a new list of instructions has now been formed: the *object program* or machine language program produced by the assembler from the symbolic program. We will attribute sufficient power to our hypothetical operating system so that it will automatically assign the next highest number available to this particular program, store the program under that code, and indicate to the programmer that such assignment has been made. Let us assume that the new object program has been assigned file 12345-08.

RUNNING AND TESTING THE ASSEMBLED PROGRAM

At a still later session the programmer might wish to test his program by actually running the assembled machine language program on the computer system. Once again he would perform the initial sign-on procedure.

```
SIGN ON:
C-IDENT
12345:
C-PROG?
12345-08:
CORE 2:
```

Now, instead of the assembler, he calls for a special test program, or *debugging* program, that allows him to run the program under very precise control. Let us call this program TEST:

```
GET TEST:
```

The test program permits complete control of the operation of the program to be tested. A START instruction usually must be given to indicate where the program is to begin; a STOP instruction is likewise needed to stop the program at a location other than the end. Thus it is possible to run a small intermediate section of the program independently in order to check its function. Finally, a GO statement is often necessary to initiate program execution. This series of instructions would be entered into the computer as follows:

```
START 00040:
STOP 000110:
GO:
```

The computer then executes this portion of the program, indicating completion by typing out the address of the last instruction.

The programmer can then inspect various memory locations to see if various intermediate calculations are correct. TEST might also contain other diagnostic features allowing termination of the program and indicating whether a predetermined amount of time has been exceeded or whether some other programming error has been detected. In the event of an error, an important feature of TEST is the wide variety of repair techniques available. Since the program is being run under the tight control of the TEST routine, the programmer is able to halt the program at any point to examine or alter the contents of a given register. This intimate and immediate interaction has no real analog in the batch processing system short of turning the entire computer over to a single programmer. Even then, not all computers have the ability to stop on a given instruction.

Assume now that our sample program is not producing the correct results. Having detected an error in the middle portion, the programmer types in,

```
START 00040:
STOP 00080:
GO:
```

The program stops just before the execution of instruction 00080 and types,

```
C-00080
```

The programmer could then ask for a display of the contents of the accumulator:

```
DIS ACC:
```

to which the computer might respond,

```
C-ACC-20
```

If this number is incorrect, the TEST program would allow the programmer to insert or delete the necessary instructions to make the program operate properly. Finally, after successful testing and the making of all necessary corrections, the program would be used or filed away for future use.

We have presented an example of a program written by means of real-time, on-line program generation. So far, the example has been explained completely from the programmer's point of view, describing his overt interaction with the computer-controlled typewriter. In subsequent sections we will discuss the complex system of control programs and electronic hardware that makes the interaction possible. This sample interaction, it should be remembered, is only one of many that may be occurring simultaneously at widely scattered terminal devices, similarly connected to the computer and controlled by the same set of system programs.

It is also clear, hopefully, that the techniques described in this section are but one possible set and that other real-time, on-line programming systems may have different modes of operating. We have artificially emphasized some of the differences between some of the steps in the development of the program, which may be more or less fused in a real operating system.

On-line data collection, analysis, and control

In the on-line programming application described above, real-time requirements are defined by the characteristics of the human programmer. A number of different operating systems have been developed that allow this type of real-time interaction on experimental and more recently on commercially available computer systems. So far, however, there have been only isolated attempts to implement other kinds of time-shared interaction with more rapid real-time requirements. These other kinds of real-time applications are exemplified best by environments that generate data timed by other aspects of human physiology than the temporal properties of creative thought processes. Since we will discuss many such applications in later chapters, here we need only point out that these more rapid real-time applications exist and that the solution of the problems they generate requires a significantly different approach from that in the example of programming interaction presented above.

For instance, in the interactive programming process the delay between a message from the programmer and the response from the computer might be several seconds. In many physiological data collection and analysis applications, however, such a delay would be disastrous. Thus, problems of the latter class must be given very high priority. It is a moot point whether a mix of the two types of real-time programming is possible, or whether it is preferable to meet the needs of the physiological problems with small independent machines that compensate for their lower speeds and lesser capacities with a full-time commitment to a single problem.

Another major difference between these two types of real-time applications lies in the terminal equipment required. For instance, the computer-controlled typewriter is ideally suited to the needs of the programmer whereas analog-to-digital converters or other input devices that transform voltage signals to digital codes are more suitable for physiological applications.

Software requirements for real-time time-sharing systems[3]

In the preceding sections we observed the external interaction between programmer and computer. In order to understand more of the underlying processes with which systems operate, we must explore both the programming and the electronic technology of time-shared systems. This section will take up the developments in software important to successful operation of real-time time-shared computer systems.

We have earlier referred to the operating system in the general sense of a master executive program controlling the various operations of a time-shared computer. On a more detailed level the operating system must be considered a family of specific computer programs, each designed to handle a different aspect of the system operation. *Executive control system* and *monitoring system* are other terms frequently used to describe this family of routines. All three terms refer to programs that coordinate the activities of the users and synchronize user requirements with the timing specifications of the various hardware components of the system. Some functions performed by the operating system are common to all complex computing systems; others are specific to the special requirements of multiple-access time-shared systems.

All of these control and coordination functions may be placed in the following categories.

ACCEPTING

When, in the example above, our programmer indicated that he wanted to SIGN ON, the computer responded appropriately to his signal. Thus the first requirement of the operating system is that it be able to accept and merge the activities of a particular terminal into the time-sharing operation. Acceptance usually involves some initial dialogue to define the user's identification codes and determine his requirements for specific services and facilities. This section of the program also places the new program in the list of active programs currently being run by the operating system.

ALLOCATING

Once the program has been accepted, an allocation portion of the time-sharing system is required to assign the necessary components

[3] The term *software,* ill defined but often used, refers generally to the parts of a computer system that can be stored in the memory: both executive control and user's programs, lists of data, and any other bodies of information not constructed from—although they may reside in—electronic components.

of the system. For example, the signal from the programmer CORE 2: indicates to the allocation subroutines that two blocks of core memory must be assigned to this particular problem whenever it is being run. Similarly, this portion of the program must weigh a request from the user for magnetic tape facilities for storing large amounts of data against the availability of tape drives. It is evident that, as the number of users increases, the problem of allocation of computer resources becomes very complex. Effective and efficient allocation is, then, one of the most important requirements for a successful time-shared system.

The allocation of core memory has been greatly simplified by an idea evolved in the last few years: the concept of *relocatable programs.* Relocatable programs are those assembled or compiled so that they can be executed regardless of their location in the computer core memory. There are many advantages to such a system. First, a program assembled or compiled into a relocatable code can be placed in any core memory block that is available when the program arrives at the head of the queue of waiting programs and is moved into the central memory from some more peripheral storage. It need not wait for a specific block of core memory to become available. Second, well-designed relocatable programs need not even be run in adjacent blocks. Thus, if programs are already occupying major portions of the memory, another long program may still be brought into the core memory and stored in whatever nonadjacent blocks remain.

In a time-sharing system there is a constant flow of programs into and out of the core memory. This process has come to be called *swapping,* or more specifically *storage remapping,* for the contents of a given core memory block may be exchanged from moment to moment with information from some other storage medium. The allocator has the additional duty of recording the current contents of the core memory and perhaps even information concerning its future availability, since the operating system must have a record of the available storage at any given moment. The execution of a relocatable program is accomplished by storing the address of the first register in the block containing a given program or program segment in a special register called the *relocation register.* In order to address a register in this block, the contents of the relocation register and the partial address specified in a given instruction must be combined to specify an *effective machine language address* within the actual block in which the program is physically stored. The contents of the relocation register and the relocatable address of the specific instruction are added together electronically at the time of instruction execution so that no additional delay is introduced in the system operation.

In order to take full advantage of the relocatability feature, programs are best written in segments no larger than the core memory block size. Intelligent program segmentation on the part of the programmer therefore plays an important role in time-shared systems. The programmer can segment his program by preparing it in relatively independent chunks, each of them equal to or less than the size of an individual core memory block. Some systems are capable of automatically segmenting the programs as they are written so that they can be easily relocated in a future pass through the computer system, but the burden of reducing the number of jumps between storage blocks still rests on the programmer.

Another function of the allocation routines is that of *memory protection*. Because the operating system and the various user programs are circulating through the computer memory in so intricate a manner, there is a constant danger that one program will affect the operation of another. Most disastrous, of course, would be the effect of an intrusion from a user program into the area in which the operating system is stored; such an intrusion would immediately destroy the operation of the entire time-sharing system. Less serious, but also very inconvenient, would be an intrusion by the program of one user into the core memory area of another. The concept of memory protection has evolved to prevent these situations from occurring. In most time-sharing systems, memory protection is implemented by means of *memory protection registers*. These registers are loaded with the address of the limits of the core memory area for a given program. Before an instruction is executed, the contents of the address register and of the memory protection registers are compared. This electronic procedure can occur simultaneously with other operations so that no delays are introduced into the execution of the instruction. If the contents of the address register are within the limits defined by the contents of the memory protection registers, the execution of that particular instruction is allowed. If not, the instruction is not executed, and the control of the programs is branched to some remedial area of the operating system that indicates the error to the user or the system operator.

Another kind of protection for the operating system is provided by distinguishing between two different kinds of instructions: privileged instructions and user instructions. Certain instructions must not be made available to users. For example, most computers have within their machine language repertoires the ability to HALT the total computer operation. This instruction must never be executed at the command of the user, since an unintentional error by an inexperienced programmer could cause the entire system to cease functioning. Such an instruction is therefore said to be *privileged,* in the sense that it may be executed only when the operating system is in control of the computer operation but not when a user program is being executed. Privileged instructions can generally be executed only when the computer is operating in the *executive mode;* they cannot be executed when the computer is operating in the *user mode.* In the executive mode, instructions of the operating system are being executed. In the user mode instructions of a user program are being executed. As one might expect, change of mode occurs very frequently but most importantly when one user program is being exchanged for the next.

SCHEDULING

With the resources of the computer allocated and the list of active programs up to date, the operating system can attend to scheduling the activities involved in running the various programs. A time-sharing system, as we have stressed before, provides apparently simultaneous service to a large number of users. This means that the amount of time scheduled for any one program must be relatively short so that the illusion of simultaneity is achieved. On the other hand, it must not be so short that scheduling activities of the operating system become too large a percentage of the total available computer time. To use an exaggerated example, such an effect could occur if the time-sharing operating system transferred to a different program every user instruction and required several instructions to accomplish the transfer.

A fairly common compromise has been to use a time interval of about 1/100 or 1/60 second so that several thousand instructions of a given program can be executed within one interval.

This sort of scheduling requires that the computer operating system be alerted when a time interval has been completed. This is done by a periodic clock signal which actually interrupts the execution of the current program. It then diverts the operating system to the subroutine that stores the information about the status of the various programs in the queue. The clock interrupt signals received periodically by the computer, therefore, act to define the basic *time quantum* of the entire time-sharing operation. The electronic design of the individual system governs the mechanism of the actual interruption of the computer, but in general the effect is to enable the scheduling part of the time-sharing system to produce a change after a fixed period of commitment to a program.

Many other conditions can also interrupt or trap the computer and shift program control to any one of a number of special locations. Interrupts may occur when the computer senses a signal from an input-output device such as a remote typewriter or magnetic tape unit. An invalid address or instruction or the violation of a memory-protected region may also interrupt the computer and transfer control to some appropriate storage location. In light of this constant stream of interruptions, in addition to those introduced by the basic time quantum, the problem of scheduling becomes extremely complex.

To add to the complexity, it is not always true that the next program in the queue is the most appropriate one to service. For example, a program that was interrupted to wait for some input-output service might reinterrupt a current program or "jump" its position in the queue. The fact that some programs require more immediate service than others raises the question of priorities. The lack of resolution of two competing priorities can be the cause of many users' dissatisfaction. This is, indeed, one of the most difficult problems of the modern time-sharing computer technology.

Some interrupts, for instance, are of such high priority that they must be allowed to interrupt an ongoing program in the middle rather than at the end of a time quantum. Data arriving from a magnetic storage device (with its mechanically moving medium) have high priority because they are available only within a very short period of time. Similarly, some physiological and other real-time control experiments require high priorities to guarantee sufficient precision in measurements of their time of occurrence. A flexible design of the scheduling portion of the operating system is, perhaps, the most important single programming requirement for modern time-sharing systems.

INPUT-OUTPUT CONTROL

Because the timing of input-output devices is so crucial in the scheduling of the time-sharing operation, the input-output operations are usually controlled by the operating system itself rather than by the user programs. In the simplest system, the programmer need only indicate that a file or record is to be transferred to a given input-output device. Within its family of programs, the operating system would contain special subroutines for transferring this information between the central core memory and some peripheral storage medium. Input-output control programs must be designed to place data in the proper format for a given input-output device. In addition to relieving the programmer of all except the most idiosyncratic problems of data transfer and format, vesting control in the operating system prevents him from interfering with optimum timing of these input-output functions.

LINKING

The operating system also must insure a smooth flow of instruction execution by *linking* together programs that have been written independently of each other. The act of linking involves not only loading the relocatable programs into available regions of the core memory but also resetting the various registers and counters needed by the new program. These may include index registers, the memory protection and relocation registers, and some of the accumulators. Their contents at the moment of interruption must also be stored, thus guaranteeing that when the interrupted program again comes to the head of the queue it can begin at the exact same state at which it was interrupted.

INFORMATION TRANSMISSION BETWEEN STORAGE UNITS

On some machines that are not time-shared, many useful computer operations are simply information transmissions between two different storage media and involve little or no manipulation of the data themselves. For example, information on punched cards might be required to be printed on a high-speed line printer by means of a card reader and printer. In some systems, such a transmission process can be accomplished by manually disconnecting the card reading and printing equipment from the central processor when it is not needed. In the highly dynamic environment of a time-sharing system, manual intervention would be an obstacle to a smooth, uninhibited flow of information. Special routines are therefore called for that are capable of transmitting information between any possible combination of input-output or storage media while the computer is executing other programs. Often this transfer can be accomplished with very little interference with the ongoing central processor programs within any brief intervals that might be available. Peripheral equipment with critical timing requirements can also inhibit instruction execution in the central processor whenever it must transfer a word of data, but this contingency arises infrequently enough so that little delay is introduced into the ongoing program. The combination of such input-output manipulation with capabilities of the input-output processor described in the previous chapter can result in highly efficient data transmission within the time-sharing system almost simultaneously with program execution.

Previously, this type of transmission work was carried out on the peripheral listers, sorters, card-to-tape converters, and many other special-purpose machines. Adding to the trend, a vast reduction in needs for card punch and verifier equipment introduced by the use of on-line typewriters has occurred. In sum, it seems that the roomfuls of accounting machines and key punches now surrounding most digital computers will gradually disappear.

LIBRARY SEARCH AND USAGE

Another advantage of a large time-shared system is that it allows a group of users to pool their resources to develop a common library of routines. In order to call up a particular mathematical function, a user could simply type in some standard code instead of re-creating the entire routine. The operating system would search out the location of the routine, tell the programmer the correct format for his data, and even insert the routine in the proper place in the new program. Among the most important of the items in this library, of course, are the compilers, assemblers, and other high-level languages, but to the list must be added all those useful statistical, mathematical, and other special-purpose tools commonly employed by programmers.

In summary, a time-shared computer is controlled by the *operating system,* a family of programs that organizes the flow of user programs and gives each user access to a wide variety of auxiliary aids. The operating system is capable of calling up any of the available languages from a library stored on some peripheral storage medium. Although operating systems of different time-shared computers may have substantially different designs, our general description accounts for most of the important common characteristics of these powerful control programs.

Hardware requirements for time-sharing systems

Our emphasis in the previous section on programming (software) systems may have obscured the fact that these systems must be run on a complex piece of machinery. Therefore, the electronic (hardware) issues of time sharing are equally important to consider in equivalent detail. In general, the new time-sharing ideas were developed on older systems whose specifications can be considered only the minimum requirements for time-sharing operation. But time sharing on these machines was not efficient, owing to a lack of some of the special features described below. In addition to the memory protection and relocation registers already noted, other necessary electronic requirements have emerged for satisfactory time sharing. Some of them are special devices; others, as will be seen in the following sections, represent organizational changes of the entire computing system.

THE HIERARCHICAL ORGANIZATION OF MEMORY

Chapter 5 introduced the family of computer memories in terms of access times and capacities. It is now becoming clear that such a group of memories of different access speeds and sizes is an important requirement for successful time-shared operation. All time-shared systems need a large basic storage capacity. The library of utility routines and programming languages available to various users amounts to a vast number of machine language instructions. To this number must be added the extensive files of programs written by the users and the storage necessary for the perpetuation of data.

But all storage requirements are not alike. Some archival files of programs are needed only infrequently, so it does not matter whether there is a substantial delay when such an old program is first referenced. Another class of storage is required for programs that are inactive for a day or a week but may be called upon suddenly for additional use. Most demanding are active programs that have completed the time quantum allotted for their execution and have been temporarily displacd from high-speed core memory to allow the next program in the queue to be processed. These programs must be available in a few milliseconds for reentry into the core memory. However, the active programs are relatively few compared to a computer system's total historical record of programs. There is, therefore, also in this case a compensation between the storage capacity and the access time requirements.

The solution to this diverse set of problems lies in the comparatively good match between these needs and the capabilities of the various kinds of magnetic moving-medium storage devices. For instance, archival records can be kept on removable magnetic tapes or disk cartridges and placed on the appropriate mechanical drive equipment whenever they are needed. Disk files without removable packs but of a fairly large permanent storage capacity provide an appropriate means of storing the next echelon of programs, those that are recent but not in the current queue. Furthermore, the programs being processed or awaiting service can be stored temporarily on magnetic drums, storage media with rapid access speeds but only moderate capacity.

Clearly, the input-output and information transmission routines of the operating system must be able to transfer information from one level of the memory hierarchy to another as the status of a given program changes. Perhaps someday there will be storage devices with both high-speed access and very large capacity; for the present, the hierarchical organization of magnetic memories provides the best means of meeting the diverse needs generated by programs of varying status.

At the top of the hierarchy, of course, is the magnetic core memory, where the programs actually being executed at the moment are stored. Much larger magnetic core memories are rapidly becoming available, and it is safe to say that such very high-speed storage devices or their technological successors will ultimately take over some functions of other levels of the memory as their capacity comes close to that of certain drum and even disk storage devices.

MODULARITY

Modularity is another hardware feature that has become increasingly important owing to the development of time sharing. A computer system is modular if its subunits can be interchanged or added to existing systems without any special reworking of the electronics other than a simple plug-connecting operation. The best historic example of a modular system component is the magnetic tape drive. All magnetic tape drives of a given type are functionally identical and interchangeable. An interchange may be an actual physical change or a simple change in the address of a particular tape drive so that it serves another function in the computer system. The concept of modularity also extends to the central processor and memory modules, as described in the previous chapter. Furthermore, the concept of modularity may apply to software as well as hardware. Software should be organized in a modular form so that modules or sections of programs can be easily detached or added, especially in a time-sharing system written for a family of similar machines.

INTERFACE HOMOGENEITY

A concept closely related to modularity is *interface homogeneity*. As we have said, ideally the time-sharing operating system can take any batch of data and write it on any memory or output device. A standard interface between the peripheral equipment and the computer can simplify this operation and make it much easier to connect modules of peripheral equipment to the computer. In the present context, the interface is a hardware unit—the organization of electrical connections between the two devices. If it is so standard that any input-output device may be connected to it, then the input-output devices are said to be homogeneous. Often such homogeneity allows the computer language to have a single standardized input-output instruction for the execution of any data transfer to any peripheral device. In each case the only difference would be a varied address specifying the particular device to which the information is directed.

Homogeneity of this sort is limited, however, by the simple fact that the physical mechanisms out of which the various memory units are constructed are not naturally homogeneous. For example, the basic word size of a magnetic tape memory unit may be six, seven, eight, or nine bits of information, whereas the word size of a magnetic drum may be thirty-six bits. Thus, to achieve interface homogeneity it is often necessary to pay a price in increasingly complex equipment required to control the memory device. A 36-bit word emitted by a computer must be separated into six 6-bit words for magnetic tape, a process needing additional electronic equipment. However, for time-sharing systems this penalty seems well worth the cost. Otherwise, much valuable central processor capacity would be wasted on a task that could be handled more economically by a specially designed controller.

ASYNCHRONICITY

It is also desirable to have a computer system that is not restricted by the temporal qualities of either the basic clock cycle of the central processor or the various input-output devices. This independence is particularly desirable in the time-shared system, in which access times of the various memory units differ greatly. *Asynchronicity* is the term for such independence from a regular sequential execution of a program sequence. An asynchronous machine need not follow a steady rhythm of instruction executions; it may occasionally skip an instruction or two in order to provide time for another important purpose, when the central processor is signaled that either its services or those of the memory are required. Perhaps the most common reason for skipping instructions is that a previously addressed input-output or memory device suddenly makes information available for transfer to the memory. The computer must immediately take advantage of the availability of the information. It is thus designed to inhibit a memory reference by the central processor while the input or output transfer takes place. By measuring the pulse of the instruction executions in an asynchronous system, one would discover that it is not perfectly periodic. This is the strictest meaning of asynchronicity.

The process of *overlapping*, discussed in an earlier chapter, is also a deviation from a strict serial execution of instructions. In one form of overlapping, the central processor is released by the core memory after a certain portion of the memory reference cycle. The central processor is therefore free to continue to process data without waiting for the information in the memory buffer register to be rewritten into the cores erased by the reading cycle. In another form of overlapping, the address portion of the next instruction may be acquired while the preceding instruction is being executed. This "looking ahead" process, invented by S. W. Dunwell of the IBM Corporation, contributed importantly to the achievement of high speeds in the STRETCH computer. The latter, although it used only conventional transistor components, achieved computing speeds only now being achieved by super-high-speed systems using integrated circuitry.

THE HIERARCHICAL ORGANIZATION OF INTERRUPT CIRCUITRY

The general nature of an interrupt signal has already been mentioned. Now let us consider specifically the interruptions initiated by a peripheral device when it is ready to transmit or accept information. When such a state exists, an electrical signal is applied to the central processor of the computer. The signal diverts the computer program to some specified location in the core memory where a special instruction is stored; the execution of this instruction is therefore contingent upon the presence of the interrupt signal.

On small machines this location might contain the initial instruction of an interrupt testing routine. Such a routine exhaustively tests each of the possible input-output devices in order to determine which one actually caused the interruption. This simple procedure improves upon the older one of continuously testing each possible device in a *round robin* fashion, in which every device is tested periodically independently of the presence or absence of an interrupt signal. A crude form of priorities is established by the interrupt testing routine, since the higher-priority devices may be placed first in the queue of queries initiated by this program. When certain high-priority devices are being serviced, an auxiliary capability is also necessary to disable the interrupt mechanism. Thus, a device of a lower priority will not interfere with the action of a higher-priority device.

The addition of a *special interrupt address register* to the circuitry is the next step in improving an interrupt system. Upon an interrupt, the program immediately refers to this register, the contents of which identify the interrupting device. The program is thereby directed to the appropriate service routine without the delay of searching all possible devices for the interrupting one. It is relatively easy to provide an electronic circuit that will allow only the highest-priority address to be in the interrupt register at any particular time.

A separate memory location automatically reserved for interrupt signals from a given individual or group of individual devices represents the next highest development in interrupt systems. Each given type of interrupt traps the program to a different programmed routine stored at a particular location. In some systems this multiple-location concept is associated with hardware capable of automatically storing the status of all the critical registers that contain information about the interrupted program. Thus, in a hierarchy of sequential interrupts, program *A* may be interrupted by *B*, *B* by *C*, and *C* by *D*. As soon as *D* is finished, control returns to *C*, and the process continues until the original program is serviced. However, the success of such a process is intimately related to the priorities assigned to certain types of programs. If *A* or *B* has high priority, then *C* and *D* may simply have to wait even though they initiated an interrupt earlier.

PAGING

Closely related to program relocatability is paging. *Pages* are analogous to the addressable pages in a book and refer to the blocks of core memory in which computer programs may be relocated. A page of core memory is treated as a unit by the operating system. Pages are, therefore, the irreducible unit of computer memory into which programs may be relocated. From one point of view a computer memory is an assembly of pages. The storage of a simple program may require several pages, but no page may be shared by two programs. If it were shared, the advantages of the memory protection would be lost, since this feature is usually designed only to prevent interference from other pages of memory.

Paging is ordinarily implemented electronically by considering the more significant, or high-order, bits in the address of each of the core memory words separately from the low-order bits. The high-order bits are common to each page and define a particular page, whereas the low-order bits define specific locations on a page. When the two sets of information are combined, they define a specific location in core memory. For example, in a thirty-two-page computer core memory, the five most significant bits of the address indicate the page specifically referred to; the low-order bits define a given word on that page. The number of low-order bits also specifies the number of words on a given page, but not the number of bits in each word.

Independent real-time computers versus time-shared real-time systems

In this chapter we have emphasized time sharing as a means of providing real-time service. However, time sharing is not the main subject of the chapter or of this book. The book is primarily concerned with the real-time use of computers to solve problems for behavioral scientists. Our view is that, in deciding between a time-shared and an independent system, the ultimate criterion must be the ability to synchronize the time domain of the total computer system with the specific application. It must be remembered that sometimes a small independent computer is actually more efficient than a large time-shared system because time sharing involves so many compromises in reaction time and other capabilities. Some compromises allow users to take advantage of otherwise unobtainable computer services; others, however, often drastically reduce the effectiveness of a computer. We can make no absolute judgment about the criteria for this decision. The idiosyncrasies and personal preferences of scientists, though aggravating to administrative order, still must play an important role in the decision-making processes. Though we cannot pretend to resolve the dilemma, we can list some of the respective advantages of time sharing and independent computer operation.

In such an assessment, certain issues are taken as already resolved concerning any given application. The first is that the real-time environment itself is indeed the most suitable approach for the application. The second is a nontechnical issue. Ideally, the best possible service would be to provide each user with as large a machine as he requires to pursue the solution of his problem. The second resolved issue, then, is that the priorities of the problem do not justify an economic commitment of such magnitude.

An easy resolution can be made between programming tasks in which the real-time domain is specified only by the real-time programming process and problems requiring higher-speed responses than a small fraction of a second. The former are currently most effectively accomplished on large time-sharing systems, the latter on small independent computers. However, technological developments in time sharing suggest the possibility that the latter applications can also be profitably carried out by a time-shared system in the near future.

Currently, it is more difficult to resolve the issue for problems in the middle ground of time requirements. The particular specifications and response times of the particular time-sharing system must be compared with the needs of the problem on an individual basis.

As one analyzes the advantages and disadvantages of time-shared and independent computer operation, it is clear that different conclusions will be drawn by different types of observers. For instance, for the analytical programmer, time-sharing a large system, with its constant availability of many languages, is ideal. An important factor in a program's efficiency is the specific compiling language in which it is written. Different languages are suited to different problems. Thus, the wider the variety of compiling languages available to a programmer, the more likely it is that he can optimize a given program. For the on-line experimenter, the small machine with its instantaneous although less powerful response is ideal. For the administrator concerned with cost accounting, large machines promise desirable economies. These apparent economies, however, often result in an inadequate consideration of the technical difficulties of time-sharing computers for the on-line experimenter.

Nevertheless, since there is a large group of users, the overall utilization of the computer is more evenly spaced. Though occasionally the system may be over- or underloaded, the work load is generally stable. To an administrator, this is an important advantage. Another major advantage of shared computer operation is that centralization of services (i.e., maintenance and administration) also seems more effective and economical.

Time-shared systems tend to be larger than independent real-time systems.[4] Thus with a bigger capacity, a wider variety of storage media may be available, and very special access time requirements may be met. Furthermore, it is usually cheaper to execute an instruction on a big machine than on a small one because of the high speed and large repertoire of machine language instructions. Some single additional instructions of a larger machine can perform operations comparable to a complicated subroutine of many instructions carried out on a smaller machine.

The advantages of a time-sharing system are most attractive, then, to two groups of people: the administrative cost accountants

[4] This is not universally the case; consider some of the computer systems used for single purposes in the space programs.

who are trying to economize, and the users who demand large, though occasional, computer capability. However, the advantages of economy and occasional power have their drawbacks; when a large computer is shared, the necessary compromises limit its overall capability. Some computer power is lost because of the operating system and the related programs. Priorities and the ever-present queue often cause delays. With manifold service responsibilities, it is difficult to make changes in the hardware of the system. How, for example, could the computer be turned off in order to make an electronic change, without interfering with the work of many other users?

Obviously, some of the most intangible disadvantages of time sharing lie in the nature of the democratic collaboration, in which system specifications are constantly subject to compromise between competing, though equally legitimate, needs.

The major advantage of the independent computer seems at present to lie in its speed of response. Although small computers are only a third (on the average) as fast as large ones, their complete dedication to a single problem can often overcome this apparent disadvantage. Some observers feel also that the disadvantage in speed will become less and less in the future and that eventually memory capacity will more specifically define the limits of independent computer operation.

Another difficulty in decision making is the constantly changing specifications of the different kinds of systems involved. Ten years ago it would have been hard to believe that the most powerful computers then available could be purchased as cheaply as they are today.

Finally, we should reemphasize that the choice between an independent computer and a shared system depends on the basic nature of the application and the real-time domain specified by it. The desired environment must be compared with characteristics of both large time-shared and independent computer installations. Thus, the decision must be made separately for each application. Though the ultimate resolution of the question is never absolute, a reasonable estimate of an optimum strategy can be made as long as the vested interests of the users are not allowed to prejudice this technical decision.

Perhaps the worst thing we could do would be to "resolve" the issue at the present time. To do so would imply that there is a correct answer and one "best" way to do real-time computer research. This would be a fallacious argument as weak as those single "strategies" put forth by some as the "only" way to pursue scientific research in general.

Should one use computers at all?

Although this book is dedicated to the use of real-time computers, we must also consider whether or not a computer should be used at all for a given application. Even though there was a degree of ambiguity in the issue of time-shared versus independent computers, some standards for decision making were proposed. The specifications of response times and storage capacities were clear-cut considerations. On the other hand, the intangible factors involved in the decision to utilize or reject the on-line concept in any form are even more formidable.

Extreme positions are often taken, both of which are oversimplified and difficult to justify. For example, the most skeptical viewpoint sounds like this: "If you can possibly do without, don't get involved with a computer." Skeptics often overlook the peculiarly advantageous psychological effects introduced into experiments by the mechanical experimenter. We will discuss these effects in a later chapter. The overly enthusiastic viewpoint—that a computer should be used wherever possible—is just as hard to justify. One possible objection to the latter point of view is that the operation of even the smallest independent computer involves a staff of at least a technician and a programmer as well as the user himself. Added to the administrative problems of space, equipment, and supplies, this represents a substantial administrative effort that may not be worthwhile.

Fortunately, there are alternative mechanized approaches for applications not requiring complete computerization. One alternative approach is to use the logical and functional blocks described previously to construct simple special-purpose logical control units. Another is to record data on some intermediate storage medium for later off-line computer or hand analysis.

To implement the first alternative, many commercial lines of general-purpose logical units are available with which to construct custom-designed control units appropriate for particular psychological or biological experiments. These systems of logical units have the advantage of being less expensive for simple applications than a whole computer but suffer from the disadvantage of being relatively inflexible. Each time a change in experimental procedure is desired, major reconstruction of the entire system may be necessary. On the other hand, some of these systems have interconnections that are easily and quickly changed. The main danger in such an approach is that the user may initially underestimate the difficulties and complexities of an application. The device he actually constructed, though far less powerful and general-purpose, might really be more expensive and less dependable than a commercially available computer.

The other approach is to purchase only the necessary storage device so that information can be recorded as it is produced. This approach might later involve a computer, since data recorded in machine-readable form is ideally suited to subsequent processing by a computer. However, off-line application of computers is appropriate only if the collected responses are not intended to influence subsequent stimulus patterns in the same experimental trials. Otherwise the delays introduced into the experiment would be incapacitating and would require the full-time use of an on-line computer.

Punched paper tape has frequently been used for this type of data recording, but punched cards are also feasible. A particularly useful suggestion has been made by McConnell, Polidora, Friedman, and Meyer (1958), and further developed by Uttal (1962*c*) and Haber, Hershenson, and Schroeder (1962). It involves the use of a card punch as both a data-logging unit and a controller for stimulus presentation. A deck of cards can be punched with stimulus pattern sequences and fed through the duplication station of a standard card punch. The duplication station—the second of two stations on a conventional card punch—is capable of reading information from cards passing through. The information on a given region of the card is usually duplicated only on the next card. However, electrical connections can be made to the outputs of the duplication station and used to set up a stimulus pattern through appropriate transducers. The subjects respond by means of a set of keys, the output of which is directly connected to the inputs to the punch magnets of the punch station (the first of the two stations, able only to punch information on cards). Thus, a card at the punch station would have the stimulus information duplicated on it from the previous card passing the duplication station and the response information also punched on that same card. Since other information such as a subject identification code could be punched on the card too, a set of cards would comprise a complete protocol of an experiment.

Another more complicated, though conceptually similar, procedure is the use of magnetic tape recording to log data. Analog magnetic tape recording is a familiar procedure for many forms of audio and other continuous signals. Not so familiar, however, are digital recording techniques using magnetic tape media. Analog-to-digital converters may be used to convert analog signals of different kinds into the appropriate digital codes for magnetic tape recording. Digital tape recorders rapidly move the magnetic tape past the reading and writing heads. As a result, this method has been limited primarily to information being generated so fast that the tapes may be written with packing densities sufficient for computer entry.

One method of synchronizing data acquired at a slow rate with the speed of a conventional magnetic tape is to place the data in a temporary storage device until a sufficient block of information has been accumulated. The complete block of data is then transferred at high speed to a block of tape storage. Unfortunately, this is often a very expensive expedient. However, a device recently made available, an *incremental tape recorder,* may serve a wide range of data collection needs.

The problem described above—the lack of synchronization between the real-time availability of data and the high writing rates of conventional magnetic tape—arises from the fact that, while data can be written in 5/100 or 1/1000 of an inch on a conventional tape drive, it takes about ¾ of an inch to start or stop the mechanical motion of the tape recorder, owing to the mechanical inertia of the tape and the usual drive mechanism. This ¾ inch gap is used in conventional tape units to bring the tape up to a speed at which the writing heads are effective. Thus, in order to write a word of low-speed data on the conventional magnetic tape, the tape must be started and stopped for every word. Otherwise an entire roll of tape would be run out in a few minutes. Nevertheless, the starting and stopping result in a loss of most of the magnetic storage capacity of the tape.

Incremental tape recorders overcome this obstacle. They depend on a new concept of mechanical drive and the related writing circuitry. The components have been modified so that each word of data can be written in the small space desired for normal packing densities. Thus, the tape is advanced only the small fraction of an inch allotted to the storage of a single word. This brief motion is achieved by attaching an *impulsive stepping motor* to the drive capstan of the tape unit. Stepping motors are motors that convert electrical energy to rotary mechanical displacements; when the electrical current is applied, they merely rotate through a small arc and then halt, rather than rotating continuously. This angular rotation is very precise and repeatable. Repeatedly impulsing the stepping motor causes it to move in a stepwise fashion. Therefore, data so recorded can be packed at the normal packing densities appropriate for reading into a computer, even though they might have been collected with great asynchronicity between successive samples. The critical advantage of an incremental magnetic tape recorder is that, while the intervals between sequential steps may be very large, the packing of the data on the tape will be as regular and as small as required by the digital computer into which the tape will ultimately be read.

As ever, unfortunately this advantage is gained only at some cost—in this case twofold. First, because of the mechanical construction of stepping motors, they may collect data only for rates up to approximately 500–1000 steps per second, The awkward range between this data speed and that of the slowest of the high-speed data recorders is left uncovered by an appropriate magnetic tape recording device. Second, information concerning the time the events occur is lost. Data recorded asynchronously by means of an incremental recording system leave no trace of when they arrived. It is possible to solve the problem by adding a mechanism to record arrival time. However, this timer adds complexity and reduces the amount of space available for data and the rate at which it can be accepted.

We have been considering alternative ways to take advantage of the calculating capabilities of digital computers without actually going on line in real time with an entire computer. In the end, the specifications of a problem and the capacities of the family of available devices determine whether or not these alternative methods will satisfy the needs of the problem.

We now have come to the end of our discussion of the technology of computers and their component parts. Part II will be concerned more with the uses to which this technology has been applied.

II: REAL-TIME APPLICATIONS IN EXPERIMENTAL PSYCHOLOGY

7: INTRODUCTION TO REAL-TIME COMPUTER APPLICATIONS

The nature of the interaction

Computers and men now interact and will soon interact in manners so diverse that it is impossible to list exhaustively the "varieties of computer experience." We can, however, point out some of the areas in which important, successful, or promising uses have been made of the capabilities of computers to interact directly with human beings.

Perhaps one of the most useful notions is presented by J. C. R. Licklider (1960) in what has become one of the classic documents of the computer age. His paper joins the contributions of Turing (1950), Babbage (in Morrison and Morrison, 1961), and von Neumann and his colleagues (1947) as a basic source of the philosophy of computer usage. Entitled "Man-Computer Symbiosis," it discusses the ideal relationship between man and machine as one in which the strongest virtues of each are used to expand and supplement the capabilities of the other. In a biological sense, Licklider points out, this is exactly the definition of a *symbiotic* relationship, because it exists between two organisms that are useful to each other and live in community. He sees a new form of this relationship developing especially strongly between the scientists and the computers they use in their work. He emphasizes the fact that both man and machine have certain specific capabilities exceeding those of the other. Thus, there is presumed to be some most suitable combination, or rather separation, of tasks that will most enhance the execution of a specific job. Unlike conventional computer programming, in which the sequence of operations is spelled out for the whole problem in advance, it appears that this relationship between the scientist and the computer will be in the form of a highly interactive process. With the appropriate input-output equipment, the computer should be as usable as a blackboard or as scrap paper is for "thinking with the hands," but in a profoundly more effective manner providing manipulative, library, and tutorial services. The routine aspects of information retrieval from data storehouses, crucial to the scientific process, seem particularly amenable to such automation.

Licklider's point of view, while not specifically solving any of the manifold technical issues still inhibiting the actual realization of so powerful a symbiotic relationship, does emphasize a different approach to computer usage from that which was current until the early 1960s. In a sense he has defined a pattern of computer use that will provide scientists with highly efficient technicians and has specified an approach in which much greater emphasis will be placed on the wide use of real-time and nonnumerical techniques in direct interaction with humans.

To introduce the range of activities included within the symbiotic approach, we may profitably cite a report by Clapp and Kain (1963), who used a medium-sized computer as an aid in symbolic mathematics. Algebraic equations could be entered into the computer, where they were stored as well as displayed on the face of a cathode ray tube. The mathematician used a typewriter to enter equations into the system. A system of controls working either from the keyboard or from a light pen (see Chapter 9) allowed him to manipulate the structure of the equation. A number of different operations on the equations are possible. For example, after an equation has been entered into the computer and displayed on the oscilloscope, correction factors may be inserted or substituted in the equation, in addition to the usual arithmetic manipulation. Factoring of terms is also within the spectrum of possibilities described in Clapp and Kain's program.

An enormously significant part of their technique is the ability to display graphically the algebraic functions described by the state of an equation at any given time. The intuitive feeling which a mathematician might obtain from seeing such a display can be expected to be a very powerful aid in accelerating the development of formal relations, or, for that matter, in the training of student mathematicians.

The important basic notion illustrated in the Clapp and Kain technique is the sharing of the work load between the man and the computer. Since the computer removes much of the tedium associated with routine manipulations, the man is free to become more involved in the more intellectual and creative aspects of the problem. The computer can thus act as an amplifier of human intellectual resources by freeing men from the trivial and allowing them to concentrate on the significant.

The "man-machine symbiosis" concept thus defines an especially significant stage in human development. It is important to stress the fact that the amplification of human intellect is a reality now, just as is the amplification of the mechanical forces generated by men's muscles. Within the framework of this general notion, then, we can consider a partial listing of the different types of man-computer interactions currently being developed.

THE ROLE OF COMPUTERS IN AUTOMATING THE RESEARCH LABORATORY

It is becoming increasingly evident that computers can supplement conventional research techniques in many ways. A major purpose of this book is to point out that the interaction between men and machines is most obvious and may be most immediately useful in laboratories concerned with human and/or animal behavior.

Behavioral science experiments traditionally present controlled stimulus situations to subjects, who then emit responses by means of either verbal, other motor, or electrophysiological reactions. The real-time computer, it seems certain, will be able at least to supplant the human experimenter in the routine parts of the laboratory operation. More important, however, are the more complex computer techniques that significantly further laboratory research methodology and may allow deeper insight into human behavior. We shall discuss some of these more advanced techniques allowing the experimenter to do things not at all possible without the aid of a computer in Chapter 9.

A related issue of considerable importance is that, since computers can give constant and immediate feedback of experimental results, the experimenter can make intelligent decisions about such matters as the selection of stimuli or when to terminate the experiment. In experiments involving surgery on animals or humans, this feedback is especially vital. The monitoring of an experiment to see that data are, in fact, being collected is also a major computer function, particularly if the experiment is concerned with the retrieval of small signals hidden in massive amounts of noise.

THE ROLE OF COMPUTERS AS SUBSTITUTES FOR MAN'S HIGHER INTELLECTUAL PROCESSES

Another area of computer application has been in the simulation or modeling of thought processes. This area has been called by many names. Among the most appropriate and positive are *artificial intelligence* and *simulation of cognitive processes*. In general, two main approaches coexist here. They differ with respect to the motivation rather than the procedure or the details of the computer programs themselves. The first is that of the engineer or systems scientist faced with the practical problem of providing a certain pseudointellectual capability in an electronic system in which, for reasons of either hostile environment or inadequate processing speed, a man is incapable of serving. The other approach is that of the psychologist specifically interested in a theoretical explanation of the nature of human thought processes. He looks upon his problem from the same viewpoint as the mathematical physicist; both seek a model of the specific natural system of interest. The differing traditions of the systems engineer and the psychologist are, as we have said, very close to each other with respect to the actual operations that each is performing. This common thread is explained by the forces that make the systems specialist use the human as his best model on which to develop a system and those that force the psychologist to work within the intellectual constraints of modern-day technology.

A variety of research programs may be included within the category of computer simulation. Most obvious are the pattern recognizers and machines that adapt to their past experiences—the so-called learning machines—as well as the programs that solve problems. Also to be included in this group of activities are those explorations in which less formal or well-structured human intellectual processes are simulated. We are referring, in the latter instance, to such things as the diagnosis of disease by computers and the simulation of the tutorial process by teaching machines.

It is well to emphasize the nonmathematical nature of many computer models of human psychological processes. They are, in a sense, not mathematical models because they are more often concerned with the flow of information, such as that found in a highly branched and iterative computer program. They may involve the flow of information through a system of choice points until one of a set of end points is achieved. The final desired result, rather than being a number or a formal statement of relations, may be arrival at a certain state of the program. The term *information processing* has therefore come to be used frequently to describe this approach and some of its programs.

An excellent example of the information processing approach is the programming of game-playing behavior. It is certain now that a computer could hold the world championship in checkers if it were allowed into competition. To allow it to compete, of course, is as farfetched a notion as that of allowing a catapult to enter a high jump contest. But game programs do play an important role, for they represent the systematic study of very well-structured situations. The solutions to game problems can generalize to other complex forms of human behavior because the programs represent a model of problem-solving behavior, whether or not their authors intended them to do so.

Teaching machines and medical diagnosis represent a different approach to modeling in the area of cognitive simulation. The concept of a computer teaching machine originated from a context of linear programmed learning, which in turn developed from an earlier technology of psychological research that was limited to linear techniques by the then available instrumentation.

Perhaps better than any other single example, the real-time application of digital computers to tutoring illustrates the complex interactions between men and their available tools, both mechanical and ideational. Most present-day computer teaching machine specialists are converging on techniques of conversational interaction in which statements prepared by a teacher and stored in the computer are used to carry on a simulated tête-à-tête with the student. We shall discuss conversational techniques and some newer ideas in detail in Chapter 10, but for the moment it is to be noted that these ideas appear to be very promising and to represent an effective example of man-machine interaction.

Medical diagnosis is not so much a man-machine interaction as it is a symptom-machine interaction. In many ways medical diagnosis programs tend to be much like pattern recognizers. The reason for the similarity is clear: diagnosis of a disease essentially involves the tagging of a collection or pattern of symptoms, a syndrome, with the most probable classification.

Current techniques of both computerized medical diagnosis and teaching machines tend to be rather static. The major breakthrough in each of these areas will, of course, be the development of dynamic procedures in which the adaptive "learning machine" methods of the artificial intelligence field are applied. With adaptive techniques, the diagnostic procedure could constantly improve itself as more and more data were experienced by the program, and a computer teaching machine could improve its own criteria for branching toward rules more sensitive to the needs of the students.

USING COMPUTERS TO CONTROL LARGE COMPLEX SYSTEMS IN REAL TIME

The development of modern management and command systems created a new need for real-time computer applications. Such facilities were required because the interactions of large groups of units can quickly become so complex that no individual or group of individuals can absorb all relevant data. Computer systems were first used to meet the problems of these complex patterns of interaction as record keepers. Thus, the first decade of computer applications saw the largest area of interests in the business world, where the job was simply to keep track of accounts and to disburse payrolls. This activity was carried out in a non-real-time fashion. The computer needs were generated by an abundance of order, warehouse, and accounting information, none of which had any particular need for immediate servicing.

On the other hand, systems like air traffic control, military command and control, and even automobile traffic control demand almost immediate responses to data situations in which the relevant data have been collected only a few instants before. In these situations there has to be a real-time system to avoid the catastrophe that may ensue when the results of analyses become available long after the dynamic condition generating them has ceased to exist.

At the present time there are very few examples of completely automatic systems. In situations as complex as those mentioned above, the general tendency has been toward a semiautomatic computer configuration. By semiautomatic we mean that a man or even a large group of men are involved in the data paths to do those tasks performed better by men than machines, such as making decisions from data that are not well organized or that are in a form completely unanticipated by the system designer.

On the other hand, in certain classes of real-time computer systems men play such a minimal part that they are relatively nonexistent. These applications usually involve highly structured and quantitative problems in which the decisions to be made are dependent upon simple measurable criteria. An example is process control in the oil and chemical industries. The use of a real-time computer system for this application depends solely upon adequate sensors for measuring various chemical parameters. A similar area is that of inventory control. However, a realistic appraisal of inventory control systems may indicate that it is cheaper actually to overstock low-use items and allow spoilage than to control them completely.

THE PROCESSING OF NATURAL LANGUAGES BY COMPUTERS

One of the currently exciting areas of interaction between men and computers is the processing of man's natural languages by computers. Although considerable progress has been made, fundamental blocks to the solution of many really sophisticated problems still exist. It is almost axiomatic in the field that with only a modest effort some success is forthcoming; but often a tremendous economic and intellectual effort must be expended to carry the data processing to the next stage of efficiency or usefulness. The reason for this effect of diminishing returns with increased effort lies partially in the conceptual organization of current-day computer systems. In truth, computers are incapable of truly processing verbal inputs at all. Computers are designed to be arithmetic and logical machines, and the operations they can be coded to perform are, in general, most suitable for symbol systems in which the interrelationships are highly structured. A computer can make nothing of connotation or denotation but must retreat, when faced with verbal materials, to artificial techniques for handling such complex interrelationships. Verbal material is usually stored in a computer in the form of binary coded characters, but few operations can be performed upon words in this form. We rarely, for example, are interested in adding *apples* and *create* numerically, although we might be interested in retrieving information about the *creation* of *apple*-picking machinery. To do so means using one or another of the programming systems specifically designed for simulating relations of meaning by relations of propinquity.

Dictionary look-up procedures and list-processing languages are two of the syntheses that have been developed to meet these needs. Dictionary look-up procedures include storage, comparison, and selection on the basis of a "compare for equality" technique. List-processing languages substitute propinquity in lists of terms for similarities in meaning and therefore are freed from the simpler constraints of spelling and syntax that encumber the dictionary procedures. These approaches, unfortunately, still more closely approximate the exhaustive solutions to gaming problems, which are considered very primitive, than the deductive techniques used in the evaluation of a mathematical expression.

The point is that the manipulation of natural languages is a new application of computers to which contemporary machines and concepts are ill suited. There are no semantic computers at present, nor any leads as to how one can be built. The human being is an existence proof that such devices are possible; indeed, the most likely lead toward the development of a semantic computer may be in the studies simulating human thought processes. Perhaps the ultimate solution to the problems of handling natural languages will come not from those now most concerned with natural languages but rather from those who are actively involved in the study of how the human organism associates meaning with symbols.

On the nature of man and computer[1]

To appreciate fully the interaction between men and computers in real time, it is necessary to understand separately the nature of the man and the nature of the computer. Certainly we know little of the nature of man, but it is not so clear that, in fact, we are in a similar position with respect to computers. Engineers and logicians design ultracomplex systems called computers to do particular information-processing tasks, but when the mechanical system is completed, its nature is not modeled on any other conceptual structure. Often computer systems, upon completion, are found to exhibit unexpected qualities that, though understandable in retrospect, were not predicted in the initial engineering design. Furthermore, the development of a general-purpose system that can exist in an almost infinite number of states, depending upon the present program status, suggests that not only the hardware configuration but, perhaps more important, the varieties of system states attainable through programming must be understood. Of course, such an analysis is generally not possible. Therefore, both

[1] The reader's attention is specifically drawn to the discussion by W. Edwards in R. M. Gagné (Ed.), *Psychological Principles in System Development* (1962). Professor Edwards' insightful, though brief, discussion of the division of labor between men and computers for the systems designer has had an important influence on the thoughts discussed in this section of this chapter. Particularly note his section entitled "Men Vs. Computers."

computers and men remain relatively poorly understood components in the man-machine system. At the present stage of system development and usage in real time, however, certain touchstones for the separation of tasks between the man and the machine can be suggested.

If any single notion summarizes the difference between the attributes of people and computers, it is perhaps the definability of the task itself rather than the absolute nature of either man or machine. If a task can be defined in detail, and if every criterion used in making all the necessary decisions is known, then a predetermined program on a suitable computer would seem to be the appropriate way to proceed. However, if there is a great deal of ambiguity in the problem, and if, indeed, it is not at all clear what the decision rules will be, then a man, whose adaptive qualities are great, who in a sense automatically reprograms his behavior to meet the unexpected, would be the appropriate choice to accomplish that part of the total system task.

In real-time computer applications, the man-machine system is called upon to perform a variety of interrelated tasks, classified in the following way:

1. Detection (input)
2. Classification (processing)
3. Storage (storage)
4. Decision making (processing)
5. Controlling (output)

This paradigm is very close to the model so often presented as part of information-processing discussions and, indeed, describes the functions of both the computer and the man. The problem faced by the real-time systems designer is the separation and assignment of various parts of this work load to the appropriate entity. Let us consider the relative attributes of both man and computer in performing these general tasks.

DETECTION

Detection or input of information into the real-time system is the primary stage of system operation. We may start this discussion by considering the attributes of the sense organs available to both the man and the machine.

The detection capabilities of man. It is a remarkable fact that the absolute records for sensitivity of sensory processes still belong to the organic world. This statement must be qualified by the fact that these records obtain only under certain specific conditions.

The performance of the human eye, for example, exceeds that of the best electrooptical photodetector only under conditions of a specific optimum wavelength, a specific retinal location, and an extended period of dark adaptation. Similarly, the ear has an optimum frequency at which it is most sensitive. However, mechanical sensors and new transducers are being developed in which the range of operation is enormously wide for a single device, and families of similar instruments are capable of detecting minute amounts of energy over the entire range of the electromagnetic spectrum.

Thus, the continued utilization of man's senses in computer systems is based more often upon the ability of the higher portions of the nervous system to deal with very complex patterns of information than upon the absolute sensitivity of the organ. Where is the mechanical device capable of looking at an aerial photograph, for example, and detecting a portion of the map that is slightly shaded, of a specific shape, and located physically in a certain relation to other similarly ambiguous objects? Psychologists have known for many years that the human perceptual system is able to fill in missiing parts of figures. This single capability, realizable only in the most limited cases in machine recognizers, alone would continue to demand human intervention in complex systems.

Another important issue in the area of signal detection is that of the *limits of sustained vigilance*. Human beings suffer from serious limitations in a detection task when asked to observe a pattern for an extended period of time. The passage of time leads to vaguely defined states, called *boredom* or *fatigue*, that reduce the human's signal detection capability. Work in the field of vigilance has indicated that, curiously enough, the two factors of boredom and fatigue may be generated by opposite task situations. A situation having a high probability of signals leads to a heavy work load and fatigue but sustains the attention of the observer. On the other hand, situations in which there is a low probability of a signal lead to boredom and a low degree of attention but do not necessarily exhaust the observer's physical resources. Decrease in vigilance may actually accumulate over sessions (see Adams and Humes, 1963).

The human sensory system is also limited in other ways, one of the most significant concerning the information input load. Miller (1956) suggested that the number of information bits a person can take in is limited to perhaps three (about seven items) in a psychological instant. Other input-output rates that appear to exceed this rate, he adds, may be artificial and dependent upon a high level of redundancy in the languages human beings use.

Human sense organs do have certain other attributes that in some situations can be of considerable significance. For instance, the transport of the material to be sensed is often an expensive operation requiring electromechanical devices of considerable complexity. The human eye and hand, as Edwards (1962) has particularly emphasized, are capable, available, and inexpensive. Such issues, though seemingly of secondary importance, might be a factor of serious consideration in the early development of mixed man-machine systems.

The sense channels of computers. During the last few years the variety of input devices available for computers has steadily increased. We have gone far beyond the punched paper tape reader and punch (although they, of course, are still around). Transducers are now available with dynamic ranges that span the entire electromagnetic spectrum, and many transducers have been successfully employed as data inputs for computers. Any signal that can be transduced to some form of electrical signal can be entered into computers. For example, analog-to-digital conversion devices, which operate at megacycle speeds, are now commercially available, and some computer input speeds are ten times greater than that. The information rate in this situation is, of course, so much higher than the human capability that there is usually no question about whether the man or the machine should be used to enter such information into a computer system.

CLASSIFICATION OF STIMULUS PATTERNS

Human classification. The classification of stimuli by human beings can be viewed from several different perspectives. People are highly capable if the task is to discriminate between two different stimuli that are presented simultaneously and vary along a small number of dimensions. On the other hand, people have a relatively poor absolute pitch or absolute color capability. The usual human absolute identification capacity is about eight or ten different colors; although the ear is more sensitive, few individuals are able absolutely to classify the tones of a piano keyboard. Yet people skillfully handle patterns that are transposed from some standard registration[2] and size, and with proper training they can even identify patterns hidden in considerable amounts of noise. As to geometrical form recognition, people can ignore certain features, such as intersections of contours, that would completely confuse a computer. On the other hand, rotation, translation,

[2] *Registration* is a technical term referring to the alignment and positioning of a geometrical pattern.

and size changes have been severe obstacles to computer pattern recognition techniques, and most attempts to computerize character recognition, for example, have usually included preliminary efforts at registration and rotation adjustments.

Classification by computers. It is curious that modern computers appear to deal well with two completely opposite types of classification tasks but not too well with the intermediate types of classifications. At one extreme, computers can easily be programmed to classify well-structured input material into a very specific scheme on the basis of well-defined decision rules. Thus, the classification of noise-free geometrical characters into classes based upon number of sides is handled in a straightforward fashion. Similarly, computers do well when well-quantified information is presented without any predetermined classification scheme except a general procedure for setting up classes on the basis of adjustable parameters. The middle ground, in which input material of some complexity and considerable noise must be fitted to a highly determined classification schema, is not generally handled well by the computer. This middle area is exemplified by the problem of classifying printed characters or speech sounds, in which limited classification sets exist but items vary a great deal in form from the standard.

STORAGE OF INFORMATION

Besides speed and accuracy, the most fundamental difference between computers and men lies in the difference in the organization of their memories.

The memory of man. Little is known about the physical whereabouts or physiological mechanisms of human memory. It seems clear, on the basis of years of experiments, that learning—the dynamic process associated with memory—takes place only in the upper portions of the central nervous system and that cortical ablations generally create massive deficits in the acquisition of behavior patterns in experimental animals. The confounding of these experiments is great, however, and it is often difficult to distinguish whether an animal ceases to learn a visual task because he can no longer perceive the visual information or because some of the mechanisms of association and retention are destroyed. Even these statements of difficulty are fraught with unknowns, for it is not at all certain that there really are two separate mechanisms for perception and for learning. For hundreds of years, the conceptual framework of those who have been considering psychological problems has constrained the variability of the concepts that can be considered. It may well be that the terms *learning, perception,* and *problem solving* have little relation to the physiological mechanisms and that the search for specific locations or mechanisms to mediate these processes is a poorly formulated quest.

Current research suggests that there are several different types of memory. Short-term memory is defined as the temporary storage of new experiences. It corresponds, in a sense, to the buffer storage of computer input-output devices. The existence of a separate short-term memory is indicated by the fact that the ability to recall information is substantial during the first minute or so after presentation but then rapidly deteriorates. On the other hand, certain physiological evidence (mostly from the surgery of Penfield and Roberts, 1959) indicates a long-term memory capacity for complex patterns on the part of human beings. During open brain surgery, it was found that stimulation of the temporal lobe led to the release of complex and seemingly total recall of things that happened many years before. This experience was reported by the patients to be vivid, coherent, and very real, unlike the buzzing and flashing sensations generated by stimulation of the primary sensory areas.

It is, therefore, possible that among the 10^{10} central nervous system neurons with their multiple interconnections a great deal of information is being stored—indeed, vastly larger amounts than are possible in the largest current computer memory device. The most important advantages of human memory, though, do not depend upon its capacity, which is practically very limited since our retrieval of detail is so poor. Nor does it depend upon human access speed, which is extremely modest under the best of conditions. Rather, the advantages of human memory depend upon its ability to access information that is addressed or tagged in weakly defined ways. A simple example is both difficult to give and unnecessary, for the stream of consciousness and the tenuous thread of associations that lead from one idea or concept to the next are well experienced by all of us. The ability to be reminded of something by a pattern or to access a particular piece of information by means of another, relatively unrelated pattern is the great strength of the human memory system.

The memory of computers. Computer memories operate in better understood fashions than the human memory. We have, in previous chapters, discussed the technical details of their operation. Practically, they have usable capacities far exceeding those of man, and access times can vary down to trivially short periods of time. In general, for all computer memories there is a compromise made between access time and capacity. For instance, magnetic cores are relatively expensive and bulky but very fast. Information can be accessed from cores in submicrosecond intervals once an address is defined. On the other hand, magnetic tapes, which have literally unlimited capacities, often require access times on the order of minutes if reels of tapes must be physically changed. Unlike the human, magnetic memory systems have no such thing as short-term memory storage, unless one chooses to erase specifically a storage area after a certain length of time. Computer memories can retain information for indefinite periods of time and can be loaded and unloaded at speeds far above human perceptual and reaction times.

The strengths and limitations of computer memories complement those of the human memory. Computers do not, as a rule, tolerate any sort of ambiguity in the addressing scheme. One piece of information cannot address another because of certain general similarities in form, but rather specific addressing interrelationships must be used. The so-called associative memories now being discussed generally depend upon the matching of specific parts of the stored information with a computer memory address. Thus, very slight mistakes in format can destroy a computer's ability to access information coded in this manner. Nevertheless, as we have said, their speed and capacity for accessing detail are vastly superior to those of human memories.

DECISION MAKING

Once information has been entered into a system, the main task is to select the most appropriate response from the repertoire of alternatives. This holds true for the dynamic real-time computer as well as for the sensorimotor system of man. A comparison between man and machine again is based upon how well structured the input is and how well the rules for selection have been defined. Edwards (1963) has specifically suggested a mixture of man and computer in the form of a *probabilistic information processing system,* in which men make estimates of the probabilities of certain events and the electronic system computes overall probabilities based on these human estimates. A human being makes the final decision based upon his subjective estimate of the situation, taking into consideration the output of the computer and other current and historical information that he has available but that has not been inserted into the computer program. Such a mixture of human and electronic services has already saved us from disaster at least once. An unanticipated atmospheric electrical situation caused the moon to appear as a fleet of approaching bombers on one of our early warning radar systems, but the computer was overridden by the humans who were responsible for the final decisions.

In some situations, of course, the speed with which computers make decisions is the most important criterion for their selection. Human beings are not able to keep up with many chemical or nuclear processes, and although their senses may transmit the appropriate information, control action dependent upon human reaction time of a large fraction of a second or so may be too late. Similarly, the probability of an error in a human keyboard operation is so much higher than the probability of an error by the computer that this factor in itself might suggest the solution of the problem of assigning a specific task.

CONTROL

The final function performed by man-machine systems is control. In some simple situations it is not at all clear which is the better of the two—the man or the machine—to handle control functions. The solution to such a task-assignment problem often comes from some unexpected factor that determines whether the computer or the man shall do the job. One of the most surprising factors, as Edwards (1962) has pointed out, is that men are relatively resistant to damage compared to computers. Small amounts of damage in almost any part of a computer can completely incapacitate the entire system, while a man with damaged parts manages to go on fairly well for extended periods of time. Computers are also limited by the fact that not all control functions can be anticipated; thus man's unique ability to adapt or reprogram himself to the unexpected is an important attribute not shared with the computer. A man can be essentially reprogrammed by the flash of an emergency light or a simple verbal statement, whereas a computer may require a significant amount of instruction manipulation to adapt to its new environment.

Summary

In general, a computer is the logical choice for a task that requires high speed, high accuracy, repetitive functions, rapid search, or a large memory, and, most important, when the task can be defined in detail without ambiguous statements. A man is the logical choice for a task that is quite variable or ambiguous, or requires the manipulation of complicated concepts. Men are better suited to recognition tasks involving stimulus patterns in noisy surroundings but with few repetitive operations, while a machine is best able to handle structured materials that may require nearly exhaustive searches for appropriate classification.

It is important to remember that because of the nature of the interaction between the human and the computer, certain constraints are placed on the behavior of the computer, as well as on the person. Most obvious are those difficulties originating from difference in the languages used by the two symbiotes. The *machine* language of computers is most unsuitable for the human operator, and just as computer hardware has developed in the last decade, there has been a similar evolution in the development of translators or higher-order languages.

The language problem has been greatly alleviated by assemblers and special program compilers, but for the most part people dealing with computers are still constrained by the stylized language the computer can handle. Information must be presented according to certain rules prescribed by the computer's inability to handle generalized verbal inputs. Computers also are limited and must work in prescribed ways so that people can use their output. Among the most obvious constraints on a computer is the one generated by the great discrepancy between the real time of computers and the real time of people. No person is able to keep up with computer output displayed at the computer speeds. Buffer memories and hard copies for subsequent leisurely reading are required to properly match the human information rate with that of the computer. Computer controls and displays must be designed so that people can meaningfully and optimally use the computer capabilities. The field of engineering design to enhance the human use of machines is called *human engineering,* an enterprise heavily dependent upon knowledge of the properties of human sensory and motor processes. Research in tracking of targets and research in the field of human display stereotypes have been significant portions of the human engineer's work over the last decade.

It is not with human engineering that the remainder of this book will be concerned. Rather, we will discuss three dynamic situations, the real-time analysis of electrophysiological signals, the automated behavioral science laboratory, and computer teaching machines, from a different point of view, being more concerned with the dynamics of the interaction than with the design of the machine's displays and controls. This discussion will try to emphasize some of the major points of the interaction as they hold generally, rather than the specific design of one or another device. It will also take up the processes that are being automated in sufficient detail to determine how they specify the requirements of the total system.

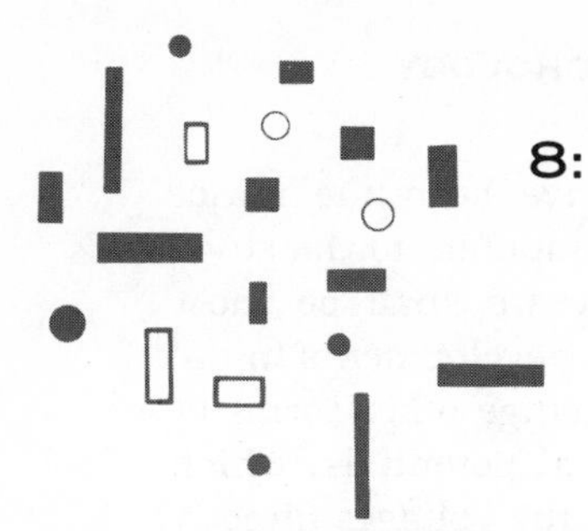

8: REAL-TIME DATA ANALYSIS OF BIOELECTRIC SYSTEMS

Many of the tissue systems of the living organism generate minute electrical voltages as signs of their basic biochemical activity. Although the voltage levels of these signs is very small, their information content may be quite large. Thus, ever since the development of the first amplifiers capable of detecting bioelectric potentials, investigators have been overwhelmed by the complexity and abundance of the recordings. The problems they encountered were manifold. Compound action potentials representing the sum of the electrical actions of individual units had to be analyzed into their constituent parts. Subtle patterns of the action potentials of single cells had to be not only interpreted but also described in dimensions of time and space that were beyond the analytical techniques of the day. Furthermore, many bioelectric signals had to be described in a reduced form that numerically conveyed the visible, but unquantified, properties.

Today computers have taken on a major role in solving these and related problems encountered in the electrophysiological laboratory. Although electrical signs are associated with many tissues, the analyses of the activities of the nervous systems and the electrical potentials directly generated by the heart have been the major targets of the recent surge of application of computers to the study of bioelectric potentials, and it is with these we shall be most concerned. However, there have also been new developments in the creation of *transducers,* special devices that change other forms of energy (thermal, mechanical, etc.) to electrical potentials, which may then be treated in much the same way as the voltages directly generated by biological tissues. Thus, many of the techniques to be described here can be applied to any time-varying signal with the appropriate frequency characteristics.

The general paradigm for the electrophysiological experiment in which digital data analysis is involved is shown in Figure 8-1. The

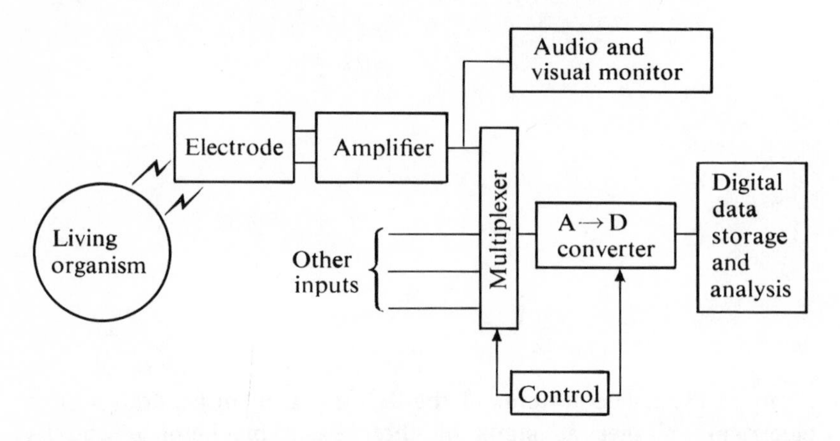

Fig. 8-1. *A block diagram of a typical bioelectric experiment showing the various components required for digital computer analysis.*

process usually involves an appropriate transducer that can pick up or create an electrical voltage signifying some sort of biological activity. The spectrum of available transducers and electrodes is enormously varied but not particularly germane to the topic of this book. We will be more concerned with the temporal pattern or other informational properties of the signal than with the physics of its generation. For our purposes it is sufficient merely to state that in some appropriate fashion electrical signals are detected and amplified so that their temporal and amplitude dimensions are within the range required by the display, logging, and analytical devices we shall describe.

Often a single analytical system is connected to a large number of biological potential sources. A switching device called a *multiplexer* can alternatively switch any source into the input channel of the system. A multiplexer can be controlled or sequenced in various ways, depending upon the driving control circuitry and the real-time requirements specified by the signals themselves.

The insertion of analog electrophysiological signals into a digital data-processing device depends, however, more directly upon the adequacy of the analog-to-digital converter, a device capable of converting the continuous voltage fluctuations from the final analog amplifier to the discrete digital codes required by the data system. A broad technology has developed for implementing this conversion. But the most important consideration in selecting the appropriate instrument is the dynamic properties of the signals themselves. It is now appropriate, therefore, to discuss the general characteristics of the more common bioelectric signals and how these characteristics influence the development of specific and appropriate analytical and hardware techniques.

Characteristics of electrophysiological signals

Bioelectric signals can be classified on the basis of their temporal characteristics. In general, the electric potentials reflecting the activity of organic tissues contain no very-high-frequency components. Certain muscle action potentials (electromyograms) display rise times that suggest component frequencies of several thousand cycles per second, but there appears to be an insignificant amount of distortion of these waveforms when an amplifier capable of passing signals only up to 2000–3000 cps. is used. The spike action potentials recorded from single neural cells display similar temporal characteristics. On a somewhat longer time scale are found the potentials produced by other portions of the nerve cell than the axon. These slower potentials, however, do not exhibit the very-long-duration and low-frequency characteristics that are recorded from groups of cells such as the ganglia of the brain. The latter potentials may exhibit fundamental periods greater than a second. In addition to frequency characteristics, it is possible to distinguish between events that are short-term transients and repetitive and cyclic waveforms that continuously fluctuate around some mean value. Since the specific mathematical tools we are concerned with are more directly determined by these properties let us discuss these signals within the latter frame of reference.

CONTINUOUSLY FLUCTUATING LOW-FREQUENCY SIGNALS

Many bioelectric signals can be recorded from the surface of the body even when there is no explicit stimulation. These potentials are usually rhythmic and as a rule are composed of low-frequency components. For example, if electrodes are placed on the surface of the head of a vertebrate, rhythmic activity of a complex spectral structure can be detected. The signals, *electroencephalograms,* are thought to be associated with the neural phenomena of the brain, and although no definitive theory of their origin has been completely accepted, they have often proved useful for medical diagnosis. Electroencephalograms, or EEG's, are characterized by frequency components concentrated in several frequency bands. The most energetic component is known as the alpha rhythm, with frequencies varying between 7 and 13 cps. Other frequencies that appear in large amounts include the beta potentials, with component frequencies above 15 cps., and delta waves, with very-low-frequency components between 2 and 6 cps. In addition to these cyclic components, the electroencephalogram exhibits some recurrent nonsinusoidal potentials, more properly described in terms of the features of their specific waveforms. One nonsinusoidal waveform is the anomalous wave and spike found in petit mal epileptics. The brain also exhibits even slower potentials; they seem to be very, very slow drifts in the overall direct-current potential of the brain. Measurement of the latter class of signals depends upon highly calibrated and well-balanced DC amplifiers.

Other more or less continuous bioelectric potentials that have been studied include the pressure waves associated with gastric motility. These mechanical pressure fluctuations can be converted into electrical fluctuations by appropriate pressure transducers. Speech signals are another class of signals we would place in this category. Breathing is an example of a "spontaneous" biological rhythm with relatively low-frequency components. Gross muscular responses can also be converted to electrical signals and in certain conditions can exhibit cyclic temporal characteristics like the EEG, although usually of a lower frequency. Thus, eye and manual tracking tasks are often analyzed by techniques similar to those used for the EEG. Very-long-lasting biological rhythms such as diurnal fluctuations in metabolic states or even population dynamics lasting over many years are examples of continuous cyclic fluctuations analyzable by similar techniques.

TRANSIENT BIOELECTRIC POTENTIALS

The mathematical techniques that have been developed to handle cyclic responses are usually described in terms of the frequency components of the repetitive signal. On the other hand, more or less transient electrophysiological signals, even though they sometimes nearly periodically repeat themselves, are usually dealt with in other fashions. For example, nerve impulses and evoked central nervous potentials, as well as the impulsive electrocardiogram, are more often analyzed in terms of their time of occurrence and their amplitude, shape, and interval characteristics than in terms of their component frequencies.

There are two distinguishable classes of transient signals. First are those complex transients that last for more than a few tens of milliseconds. An example is the compound potentials evoked from the brain, which have been found to be long-lasting events recordable over wide areas of the brain. These signals may last for 200 or 300 ms. or longer and are complex in that several subcomponents can be further distinguished.

The second class of transient signals consists of the simple all-or-none responses of individual axons. These potentials are of simple shape; they rise to a voltage maximum and then return to their initial resting states in a graceful course, reflecting ionic effects lasting for only a millisecond or two. Although the shape itself is of interest, often the investigation of a single neuronal impulse deals more simply with the fact that a response has occurred at a given time and perhaps that it is of a particular amplitude.

The electrocardiogram is another example of a relatively brief transient bioelectric potential. In this case the shape of the signal is, however, of more concern since it is frequently associated with certain anomalous cardiac conditions.

It has been well established that the amplitudes of nerve impulses generated by individual axons are independent of the stimulus amplitude but rather depend only on the metabolic state of the local region of the axon itself. The nerve either responds at the highest possible amplitude or does not respond at all. This is the famous *all-or-none law.* Nerve action potentials generated from compound nerves composed of a family of axons, however, vary in their amplitude as a function of stimulus intensity, as well as a function of other temporal and metabolic factors. This phenomenon is a reflection of the changing number of individual neurons participating in the compound response. Signals that vary in size are said to be *graded* and are found not only in the complex action of groups of neurons but also in the nonaxonal generator, synaptic, and cell body processes of single neurons. It is generally agreed now that the all-or-none spike action potential is but one of a number of action potentials with which neurons react when stimulated. (See Bullock, 1959.)

This brief discussion of bioelectric potentials has but introduced the wondrous variety of bioelectric activities of the living organism. The dimensions of these signals are, of course, significant criteria in determining the specific analytical techniques to be applied to a particular problem. The rest of the chapter will discuss the techniques in greater detail.

The analog-to-digital converter

Now that we have described the temporal characteristics of neural signals, we can return to the specifications of the devices necessary to convert the signals into digitally coded forms. Basic to all the applications of digital computers to the analysis of bioelectric potentials is some method to convert the analog signals picked up from the organism to the discrete digital codes used by the computer. Several different kinds of analog-to-digital converters have been developed, all of them based on a comparison between the signal and some voltage reference level.

In some of the earlier converters, a comparison was made between the input signal and a steadily increasing voltage with a constant slope. During the time the comparison voltage was rising, a counter counted out equally spaced pulses generated by an appropriately timed clock. When the comparator eventually detected equality between the input signal and the ramp voltage, the counter was turned off. Thus, if the increasing comparison voltage were linear, the counter would have a digital number in it representing the analog signal amplitude. The difficulty with the system was that the time required for the comparison could be relatively long. In fact, to have equally spaced sample points, each interconversion interval had to be as long as that required for the conversion of the largest possible amplitude. This meant that the rate at which signals could be coded was very low and, for signals that appreciably changed in amplitude during that interval, a sizable error could be introduced into the calculation. In other words, the coding used in this scheme of *A-D* conversion is uneconomical because every increment in the amplitude scale required another count to be accumulated in the counter from the clock. This was, indeed, classification by exhaustive inquiry, a most uneconomical process that in fact is not a coded representation at all.

The most satisfactory analog-to-digital conversion technique developed to date is the method of *successive approximations*. The type of converter using this method utilizes a much more economical code because, rather than counting each amplitude step, it essentially plays the parlor game of "twenty questions," classifying the signals into smaller and smaller groups with each successive "question." Thus only a few "questions" or successive approximations are required to identify a given amplitude. Successive approximation converters also use comparators. The diagram of a typical four-bit converter is shown in Figure 8-2. A greater precision would be obtained by adding more bit positions on each of the constituent registers.

The action of the successive approximation analog-to-digital converter depends, surprisingly enough, upon the action of a sub-

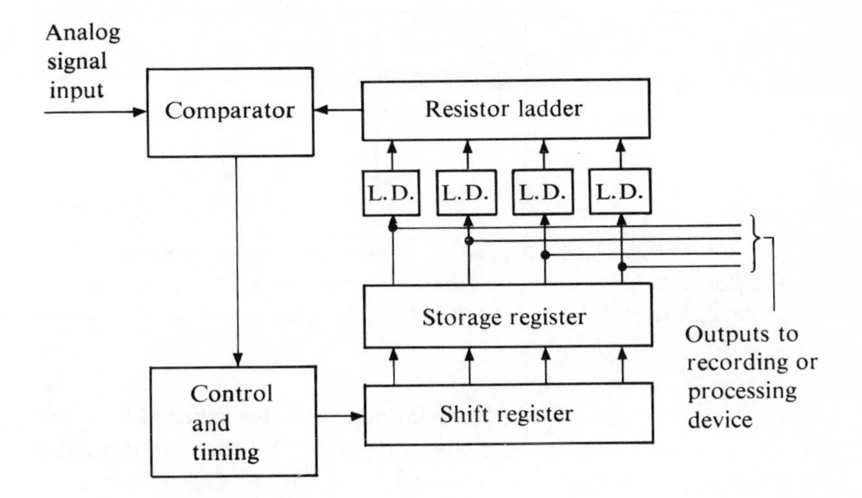

Fig. 8-2. *A block diagram of a sequential approximation analog-to-digital converter.*

device that is in fact a digital-to-analog converter. This device is usually implemented by means of a network of resistors such as those shown in Figure 8-3. The resistor ladder operates so that the output point X will have a voltage on it equal to ½ of the voltage on input 1 plus ¼ of the voltage applied to input 2, plus ⅛ of the voltage applied to input 3, and so on. Thus if the voltage applied to each of the various inputs is either of two well-referenced and highly stabilized voltages, one of which represents a 0 and the other a 1, the output will be an analog voltage closely approximating the voltage represented by the digitally coded signals on the input lines. One of these voltages is usually ground or 0 volts; the other is equal to the full-scale voltage representable by this digital-to-analog converter. In passing, it should be noted that digital-to-analog converters are useful in their own right, allowing the digital computer to drive devices requiring continuous voltage fluctuations for their operation.

In the specific device—the successive approximation analog-to-digital converter—we are describing here, however, the digital-to-analog converter provides the means for comparing a digital code and an analog input signal, by means of the feedback loop established through the comparator. Consider the device diagrammed in Figure 8-2. The analog signal input is fed into one side of the comparator,

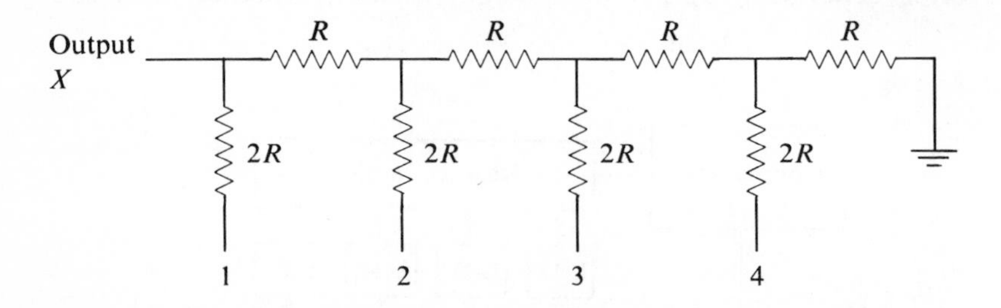

Fig. 8-3. *A ladder network used as a digital-to-analog converter. The output of* x *will be equal to one-half the voltage at* 1, *one-fourth the voltage at* 2, *one-eighth the voltage at* 3 *plus one-sixteenth the voltage at* 4.

and the output from the resistor ladder into the other. The comparator is essentially asking the question "Is the input signal greater than the output from the resistor ladder?" The device operates by having the first flip-flop (FF) in the FF register set to the 1 state, thus activating that input to the ladder. The voltage output of the ladder is then compared with the input signal; if the input signal is larger, the flip-flop is rejected, i.e., reset to the 0 state. The shift register then shifts one step, and the next flip-flop is turned on. It also may be rejected or left on. Thus by a process of successive approximations, testing the state of each flip-flop in the register, a final digital approximation to the input signal is established in the FF register. This register, in addition to driving the special stabilizing circuits that standardize the inputs to the resistor network, is also a buffer for the coded amplitude information to be transferred to the computer when the device has made a complete conversion.

Each of the sequential approximations themselves may take place in a couple of microseconds in the fastest modern circuitry. The length of time necessary to make a complete conversion, therefore, depends not only upon how long it takes to convert each bit but also upon the number of bits (the precision of the converter) desired in the system. A ten-bit converter that can make one decision every two microseconds requires at least twenty microseconds for a complete conversion. To this basic amount of time must usually be added time for control functions and for stabilizing the input signal. Ten bits represents a precision of 1 part in 1024 since that many discriminable units of voltage are so defined. Using equivalent speed circuitry in a ramp type of A-D converter would require over two milliseconds to accomplish the same precision of conversion.

The time taken for a single conversion specifies the sampling frequency capacity of a given analog-to-digital converter. Further, a signal that varies appreciably during the conversion time will be inaccurately encoded. To help overcome the latter limitation, auxiliary input circuits to the analog-to-digital converters have been designed. One of the most important of these is called a *sample and hold circuit*. Sample and hold circuits sample the magnitude of an applied voltage in a very short period of time and hold it throughout the remaining period of the conversion. This is accomplished by means of a capacitor, which is cut off from an input signal as soon as the converter is ready to perform its operation. The circuit is designed so that the capacitor is not allowed to discharge through any other current pathway during the cutoff time. Thus, the signal on the input of the analog-to-digital converter remains at the level at which it was at the beginning of the conversion process when the capacitor was electrically disconnected from the input.

Another auxiliary input circuit for analog-to-digital converters is required by the fact that a single converter may be called upon to convert signals arriving on a number of separate lines from separate sources. Thus it is important to be able to select one of these lines to be converted at any given time. The process of selecting and connecting one of a large number of lines is called *multiplexing* and can be accomplished either by relay contacts or by transistorized switches. An advantage of the relays is that they have very low input impedances when the switch is closed and very large impedances when the switch is opened, with little interaction between various components. Unfortunately, though, they take a rather long time to switch to alternative signals. A good relay multiplexer made from reed relays, a new type of relay contact, may switch in a millisecond or two. But even this speed of operation is far longer than the switching time available in solid-state multiplexers, which are capable of changing inputs in a microsecond or two.

Solid-state devices do have certain limitations. The actual implementation of a solid-state multiplexer switch is somewhat complicated. It takes a great deal of sophisticated electronics design to maintain the linearity and fidelity of the signal being passed to the analog-to-digital converter. Similarly, there is a tendency for solid-state switches to cut off incompletely when open and to have an appreciable signal loss when closed. Adjacent switches may also show some interaction unless a considerable amount of engineering skill is applied to their design.

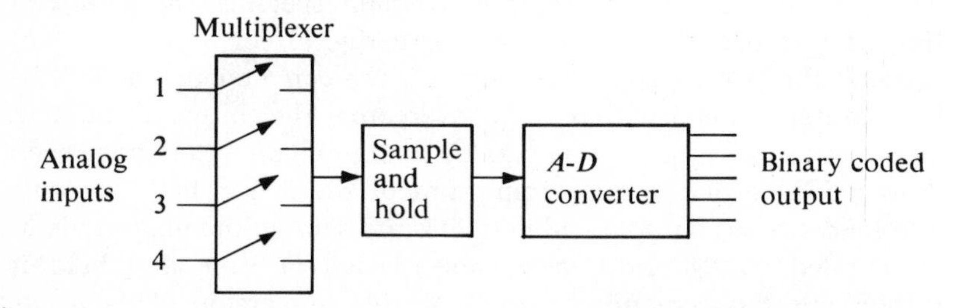

Fig. 8-4. *An analog-to-digital conversion system with some additional special features. A sample and hold circuit is used to guarantee correct digitization of a rapidly changing signal. A multiplexer has been added to allow one A-D converter to service a large number of analog inputs.*

Figure 8-4 is a diagram of a multiplexer implemented with electromechanical switches. A solid-state multiplexer is organized identically except that the electromechanical switches are replaced by solid-state switches. The proper placement of a sample and hold circuit is also indicated in this figure.

This discussion of the analog-to-digital converter helps us to understand in detail the means of introducing digital data into computers when the data originally are in the form of continuous analog signals. Let us now examine the recently developed techniques to analyze these data once they are available in the appropriate form inside the computer memory.

Analytical techniques for the study of continuous bioelectric potentials

During the last two decades scientists and engineers from many different disciplines have cooperated in developing devices that could exploit available mathematical techniques for solving problems involving bioelectric signals. This section of the chapter will survey these techniques and attempt to explain them in a way comprehensible to the nonmathematically oriented user. A number of important publications recently put out explain their mathematical and physiological implications in greater detail. Five recent volumes are specifically called to the reader's attention: Brazier, 1961; Communications Biophysics Group and Siebert, 1959; Tolles (Ed.), 1964; Lee, 1960; and Stacy and Waxman, 1965.

Now let us consider some of the details of the mathematical and *quasi*-mathematical techniques that have been applied to the analysis of bioelectric potentials.

FREQUENCY ANALYSIS

A basic concept of signal analysis is that complex waveforms can be represented by the superimposition of a set of simpler functions. A minimum set of functions able to serve as the fundamentals of this superimposition is said to be an *orthogonal set*. One of the most useful and most commonly used sets of orthogonal functions is the family of sine and cosine functions—sin nt and cos nt. According to the originator of this analytical technique, Fourier, any function $f(t)$, which is defined as a periodic function, can be analyzed into a specific set of sinusoidal component frequencies. Another way of saying the same thing is that any function $f(t)$ can be approximated to any arbitrarily small degree of error by the summation of a series of sinusoids. The mathematical expression for this relation is as follows:

$$f(t) = \sum_{n=0}^{\infty} (a_n \cos nt + b_n \sin nt) \tag{8-1}$$

For bioelectric functions, the variable t is specifically equal to time. The sine functions are, therefore, functions of time, although in general this need not be so. Equation 8-1 can be expanded in the following form:

$$\begin{aligned} f(t) = a_0 + a_1 \cos t + a_2 \cos 2t + \ldots + a_n \cos nt \\ + b_1 \sin t + b_2 \sin 2t + \ldots + b_n \sin nt \end{aligned} \tag{8-2}$$

The coefficients a_n and b_n are thus seen to be weighting functions that determine how much of each of the various sinusoidal components is added to the mixture to form the final waveform. Because it represents the base level around which the resulting function is oscillating, a_0 is particularly significant.

A number of conditions must be fulfilled by functions that are to be analyzed by means of the Fourier analysis or to be synthesized by the superimposition of an equivalent set of sinusoids. Most obviously, the function must be periodic. But often nonperiodic functions can be analyzed by the simple artifact of regarding the signal as only one period of a hypothetical waveform that is mathematically defined for other periods preceding and following the single real interval. Other conditions to be fulfilled by the function include the limitation that the number of maxima and minima, as well as points of discontinuity, must all be finite. These mathematical restrictions are all adequately satisfied by the continuous bioelectric potentials with which we shall deal.

The generation of the coefficients a_n and b_n actually determines the nature of the specific series that will fit a given function. For functions meeting the conditions described above, the coefficients are defined by the following two expressions:

$$a_n = \frac{1}{\pi} \int_{-\pi}^{\pi} f(t) \cos nt \, dt \qquad (8\text{-}3)$$

$$b_n = \frac{1}{\pi} \int_{-\pi}^{\pi} f(t) \sin nt \, dt \qquad (8\text{-}4)$$

As an illustration of the analysis of a given waveform by the Fourier series technique, consider the function for a straight line with a slope of 45° in time: $f(t) = t$. This function is defined for only one period, which we will arbitrarily place within the limits $-\pi$ and π. Nevertheless, for the purposes of the analysis, we artificially define it as a periodic function repeating itself every 2π time units. Substituting it in equations 8-3 and 8-4 we see that

$$a_n = \frac{1}{\pi} \int_{-\pi}^{\pi} t \cos nt \, dt = 0 \qquad (8\text{-}5)$$

$$b_n = \frac{1}{\pi} \int_{-\pi}^{\pi} t \sin nt \, dt = \frac{-2}{n} \cos n\pi$$

$$= \frac{2}{n} \quad \text{for odd } n \text{ and } = \frac{-2}{n} \quad \text{for even } n \qquad (8\text{-}6)$$

These two expressions tell us that all of the coefficients for the cosine functions are equal to 0, and that, since the coefficients of the sine functions are non-0, the Fourier series for this function is a sum of sine functions. In addition, since a_0 is equal to 0, the function is seen to be oscillating above a base level value of 0—a fact not too surprising since $f(t) = 0$ at $t = 0$. The Fourier series (equation 8-2) for this function can therefore be expressed as

$$f(t) = 2 \sin t - \frac{\sin 2t}{2} + \frac{2 \sin 3t}{3} - \frac{2 \sin 4t}{4} + \ldots + \frac{2 \sin nt}{n} \qquad (8\text{-}7)$$

For most practical purposes only a few of the terms in this infinite series are used either in reconstructing or in representing the original function. Figure 8-5 is a diagram of the addition of the first few terms of the Fourier series for the function $f(t) = t$, showing an increasingly good fit as more and more terms are added together. It should be remembered, however, that the triangular wave is only one-half of one period of a mathematical function that is

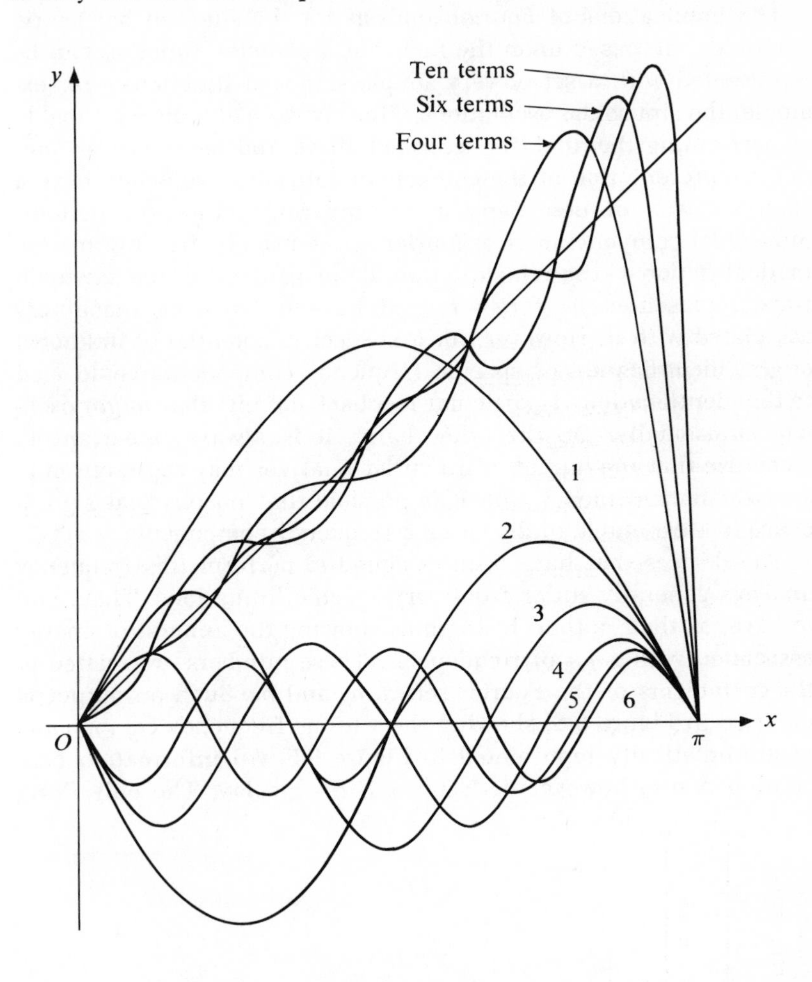

Fig. 8-5. *The synthesis of a triangular wave by the superimposition of several sinusoidal waveforms. Those sinusoids that are initially negative-going are the subtractive terms in Eq. 8-7. (From Ivan S. Sokolnikoff and G. S. Sokolnikoff,* Higher Mathematics for Engineers and Physicists, *New York, McGraw-Hill, 1941, p. 69, and used by permission of McGraw-Hill Book Company.)*

mathematically defined as extending continuously in both directions in time.

This descriptive discussion of frequency analysis is intended to emphasize the uses of the technique. The reader interested in a more rigorous mathematical discussion is directed to any of the standard treatments of analysis (see, for example, Sokolnikoff and Sokolnikoff, 1941).

The implications of Fourier analysis for the study of bioelectric potentials are based upon the fact that a complex function can be represented with a set of very simple standard functions—for example, the sinusoidal oscillations. Thus, if we had a device capable of performing the analysis described above and having as an output a representation of the component sinusoids, we would have a standard way of describing and comparing complex functions. Sinusoidal components of a Fourier series usually are only mathematical fictions—the relaxation oscillator generating the sawtooth wave represented by $f(t) = t$ need have no rotating machinery associated with it. However, for a bioelectric potential of unknown origin, identification of specific frequency components could lead to the identification of particular feedback circuits that might oscillate sinusoidally. On the other hand, it is always important to recognize that the output of a Fourier analyzer may represent only a mathematical model, and it is possible that no physical significance is attributable to the specific frequency components.

The devices that have been designed to perform this frequency analysis generally suffer from very specific limitations. They tend to have, as their output, histograms showing the amount of energy associated with a set of frequencies. These numbers are related to the coefficients of the Fourier series, a_n and b_n. Such an output is pictured in Figure 8-6, showing the various frequency components diagrammatically represented in Figure 8-5. All information concerning *phase*, however, is lost from this display. The only thing

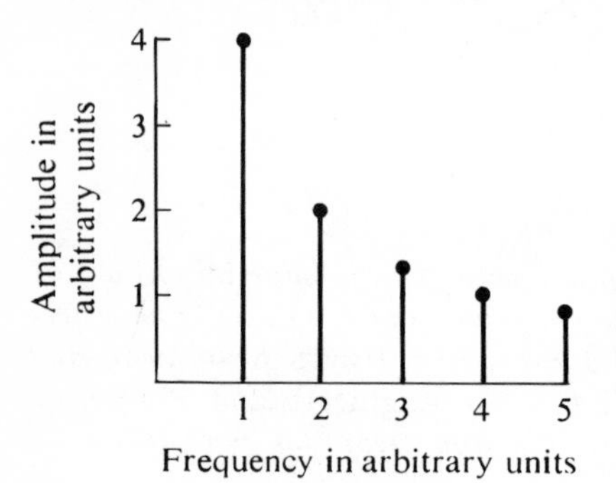

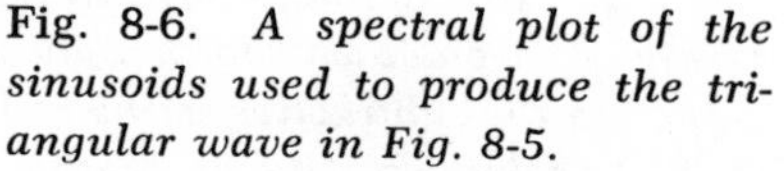
Fig. 8-6. *A spectral plot of the sinusoids used to produce the triangular wave in Fig. 8-5.*

left is a representation of the energy distribution in the various component frequencies. Frequency analytical devices that actually perform this type of analysis have been used for many years. Perhaps the first one was that designed by Grass and Gibbs (1938). Over the years others have been developed with more refined technical capacities. Figure 8-7 is a typical output plot made by a frequency analyzer superimposed on the usual EEG recording (Hughes, 1961). These records are of the frequency components of the electroencephalographic waves from the human brain.

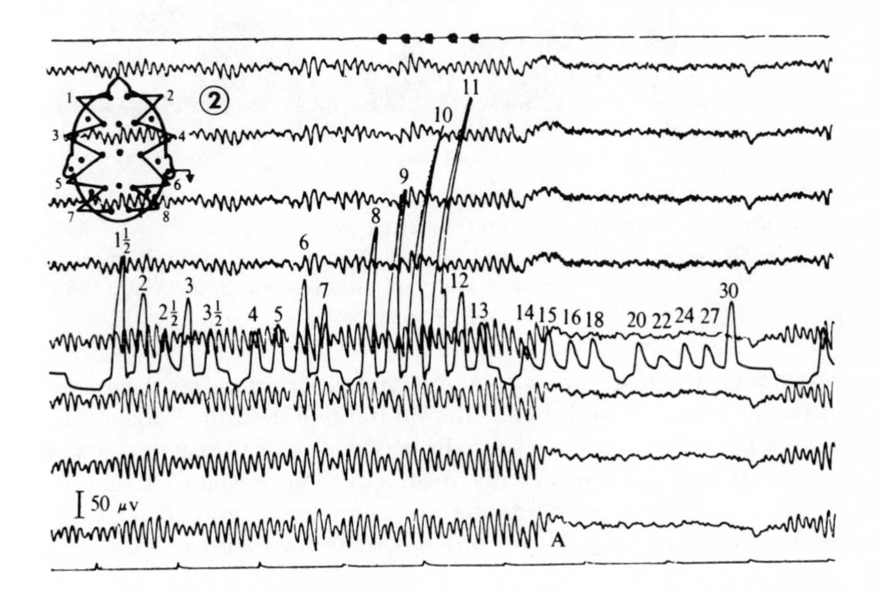

Fig. 8-7. *A frequency analysis of an electroencephalographic trace. The spectral plot (frequency analysis) is drawn on top of the more usual representation of the EEG. The alpha rhythm (10-12 cps. component) is suppressed in this set of records at A by the subject's having opened his eyes. Note that the frequency analysis does not show this sudden change. (From Robert R. Hughes,* An Introduction to Clinical Electroencephalography, *Bristol, England, John Wright and Sons, 1961, p. 11, and used by permission of author and publisher.)*

More recently, digital computers have been applied to the spectrum analysis of electroencephalographic signals. Other problems to which the frequency analytical techniques have been applied include the display of speech sound waveforms. These displays show the amplitude of various frequency components during the time of utterance. Such a "sonogram" is illustrated in Figure 8-8. Time is varying along the horizontal dimension, frequency along the vertical. The density of the trace indicates the amount of energy at any given frequency at any given time.

Because of the numerous limitations of the frequency analytical

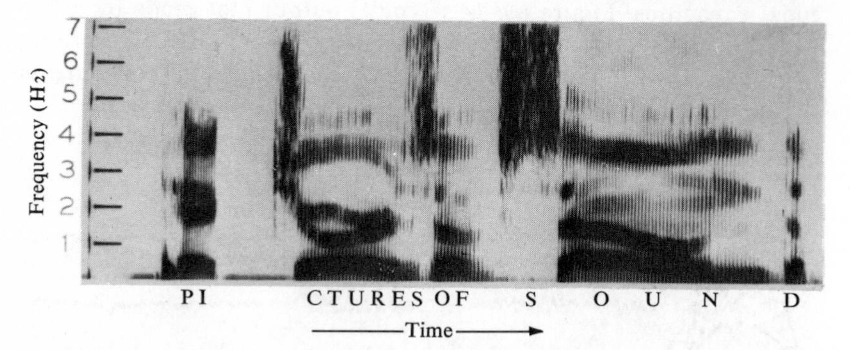

Fig. 8-8. *A sonogram, or frequency-time plot, of a speech signal. This particular sonogram shows the frequency pattern for the words PICTURES OF SOUND. (From A. J. Presti, "High Speed Sound Spectrograph,"* Journal of the Acoustic Society of America, 40, *September, 1966, p. 632, and used by permission of the author.)*

techniques, interest in this type of signal description has decreased in recent years. In addition to the limitations described above, the analyzers are very insensitive to the occurrence of transient signs of particular significance. For instance, spikes or waves that may be significant in a given syndrome are completely ignored by these devices since they require repetitive activity for their analysis.

CORRELATIONAL TECHNIQUES

We have seen how the frequency analysis technique decomposes a complex waveform into a set of simpler waveforms. This technique provides a simple metric of the nature of one waveform in terms of a standard classification system—the frequency spectrum. Other complex waveforms can be similarly analyzed and then compared with the first waveform by means of the standard. In a sense, we have reduced the information content of the signal but at the same time have made it more amenable to interpretation by the human observer. Another mathematical technique that allows us to compare two signals directly is formulated by the following expression:

$$C_c(\tau) = \frac{1}{T}\int_0^T f(t)\, g(t-\tau)\, dt \qquad (8\text{-}8)$$

$C_c(\tau)$ is defined as the *temporal cross correlation* between the two functions $f(t)$ and $g(t)$, and τ is a displacement of one function with respect to the other in time—a lag or lead in time. T is the duration of the signal. It should be noted that $C_c(\tau)$ has a single value for each value of τ. $C_c(\tau)$ is, therefore, not a number but itself is a function of τ.

What does the function $C_c(\tau)$ mean, and what are its potential applications in the study of bioelectric potentials? We shall first consider the meaning of the function. Perhaps the best way to illustrate the practical significance of the cross correlation is to consider the two functions $g(t)$ and $f(t)$ at a single time delay τ. A separate scatter plot can be made between the values of $g(t)$ and the values of $f(t)$ for each time delay τ. Figure 8-9*a* is an example of a scatter plot for two sinusoidal oscillations, $f(t) = \sin t$ and $g(t) = \sin t$, which are in phase—i.e., $\tau = 0$. In this case, each value of the y coordinate of one sinusoid is equal to the corresponding coordinate of the other sinusoid. The scatter plot then becomes a straight line with an upward slope, as illustrated. In one sense such a scatter plot represents a maximum correspondence between the two signals. They can be said, therefore, to be perfectly correlated. By one correlation formula, Pearson's ρ, this would mean a correlation of 1. However, in the generalized correlation equation 8-8, the specific number for perfect correlation is a function of the scaling of the various constants and is consequently unnormalized. Nevertheless, the two sinusoids are maximally related. If we now insert a time delay or phase shift between the two signals, $f(t)$ is no longer equal to $g(t)$, and the perfect relationship between them tends to diminish. Figure 8-9*b* is a plot for a delay of 1/4 wavelength (a phase shift of 90°). The scatter plot now is in the shape of a circle, a plot that is associated with a relatively low degree of correlation and, when formalized with the above expression, gives a medium value of $C_c(\tau)$. Figure 8-9*c* is a scatter plot of the signal for a 180° phase shift that results in a straight line with a downward slope. This represents a perfect inverse correlation and reflects a more negative value of the correlation coefficient described above.

A plot of the entire correlation function $C_c(\tau)$ for all possible phase shifts also results in a sinusoidal waveform, since it reflects the periodic properties of the signal (see Fig. 8-9*d*). In the case of perfect sinusoids, the application of the correlation expression would be trivial, since it only reproduces the sinusoids and indicates the phase angle between them.

Cross correlation is extremely useful, however, for inspecting

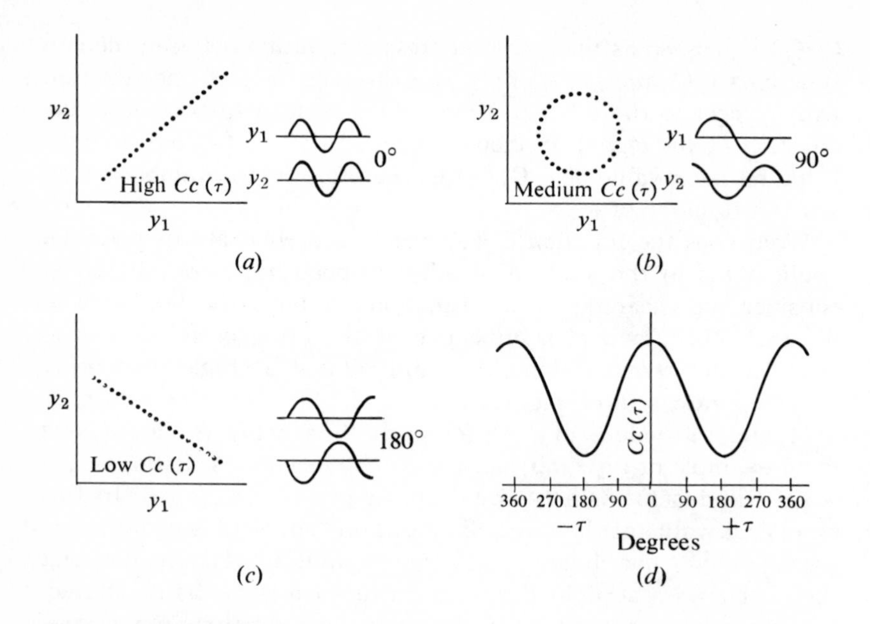

Fig. 8-9. *Scatter plots of $y_1=f(t)$ and $y_2=g(t)$ at various times. Each of the three figures represents a single delay τ in the total correlation function.* (a) *The scatter plot for in phase signals in which high values of y_1 are matched with high values of y_2. This corresponds to a perfect match and a high correlation.* (b) *The scatter plot for two signals 90° out of phase in which high values of y_1 are matched sometimes with low values of y_2 and sometimes with high values of y_2. This corresponds to a very low degree of correlation.* (c) *The scatter plot for two signals 180° out of phase. In this case high values of y_1 are associated with low values of y_2 and the signals are therefore inversely correlated to a high degree.* (d) *A plot of $C_c(\tau)$ as a function of τ for two in phase sinusoids, showing the replication of the original sinusoidal waveform. If they were not in phase, the central peak would be shifted by an amount equal to the phase angle between the two sinusoids.*

two periodic signals whose waveforms are relatively irregular over the total duration of the record. Under these conditions the periodic nature of the signal, if any, tends to emerge and to be displayed in the correlogram. The cross correlogram can, therefore, be considered a long-term averaging process that tends to emphasize the periodic properties over the aperiodicities. Thus, two sets of data having very-long-term trends or sequences common to both signals can be reduced to the form of the correlogram. From this point of view, the cross correlation function can be seen to be closely similar to the frequency analysis technique described previously. By actually reducing the amount of information present, both help to make the important data more amenable to interpretation. It should be noted that one of the signals could be a standard sine wave, or even a train of pulses.

There is a special case of the cross correlation—equation 8-9—that is particularly useful because it allows the same kind of processing to be applied to a single signal, without reference to any other signal. This special case occurs when $g(t)$ is equal to $f(t)$. Equation 8-8 is then altered as follows. $C_a(\tau)$ is defined as the *auto-*

$$C_a(\tau) = \frac{1}{T}\int_0^T f(t)\, f(t-\tau)\, dt \qquad (8\text{-}9)$$

correlation function, and it describes the periodic properties of a signal when it is compared to itself. In this case also, any periodic properties of the signal will tend to be enhanced in the autocorrelogram, just as they were in the cross correlogram. The important notion is that this enhancement occurs because of the properties of the signal itself rather than because of similarities it may have to another signal. The sequence of steps required for the computation of $C_a(\tau)$ should be spelled out in detail, to help the reader develop a more complete understanding of the processes represented by this equation.

1. First, the entire signal must be shifted in time. It must be either delayed or advanced a particular amount of time equal to the unit τ selected.
2. After being shifted to the selected τ, the value of each point on the original function is multiplied by the equivalent value on the shifted curve.
3. All of these products are summed (or integrated, if the function is continuous and the process is being carried out electronically).
4. The sum or integral is divided by the scaling factor T—the duration of the signal—to give C_a.

This number C_a is now one point on the autocorrelation function for a given time delay τ. The process is repeated for all possible values of τ, each time adding a new point on the function $C_a(\tau)$. $C_a(\tau)$, it should be remembered, is really a function of τ, the time delay between the two signals, and not of the original time base of the signal.

An autocorrelation function can extract the repetitive or periodic components that are invisible to even a highly trained observer. A perfectly aperiodic or random function will, on the other hand, have a very typical autocorrelogram. The autocorrelation function of a random process will have its greatest value for $\tau = 0$, and it will decrease continuously as τ increases in either direction. Figure 8-10 is the autocorrelogram of a random process showing this effect. The autocorrelation function of a signal with periodic properties will, however, have cyclic components visibly displayed as they are reinforced at certain values of τ. A mixture of both random

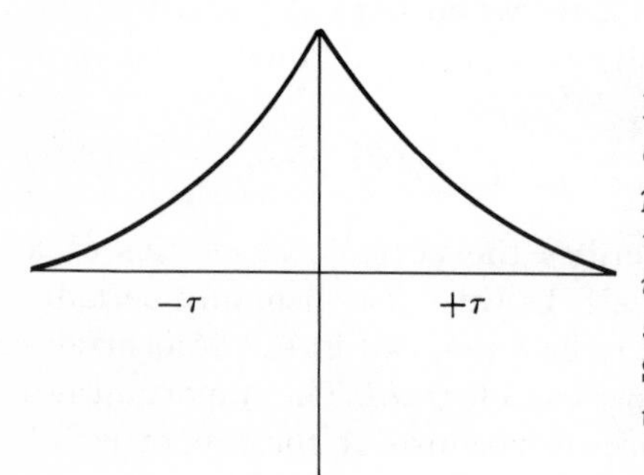

Fig. 8-10. *The autocorrelogram of a random signal. Since there is no periodic component, the highest value of $C_c(\tau)$ occurs at $\tau=0$. As τ increases, the correlation progressively decreases. (From Y. W. Lee,* Statistical Theory of Communication, *New York, Wiley, 1960, p. 53.)*

and cyclic signals will also have the cyclic components displayed throughout the entire correlogram, but in the middle region, where τ is small, the influence of the random signal will have the effect of raising $C_a(\tau)$.

There is an intimate relationship between the frequency analytical techniques and the correlation techniques, arising from the common mathematical base upon which each is founded. Lee's (1960) rigorous and detailed discussion of this relationship may be of specific interest to the more mathematically oriented reader.

Now we shall consider some of the applications of the correlative techniques for the study of bioelectric potentials. Although the mathematical basis of the correlational techniques is well developed, there is still no agreement about what the slow rhythmic potentials recorded from physiological sources really represent. Particularly in studies of the electroencephalograph there is no definitive statement of the relation of these externally recorded potentials to the activity of individual neurons. Some have surmised that the EEG is a summation of the slow graded activity of synaptic processes having similar slow and graded dynamic properties. Other authorities have suggested that if one samples properly, the integral of the spike action potentials from axons will approach distributions like those of the slower potentials recorded with gross electrodes. All of the electroencephalographic literature must be evaluated in terms of this current controversy.

As an example of an effective use of the autocorrelation function, we will now consider Brazier's work (1963). Brazier used the autocorrelation technique in an attempt to determine the origin of oscillatory potentials recorded from the cat's brain. The use of this technique is especially appropriate since the waveforms picked from the cat's brain do not display the obvious rhythmicity recorded with equivalent electrodes on the human brain. Thus, the autocorrelation technique was necessary even to extract the subtle periodicities that did appear when the records were analyzed. Figure 8-11, a figure from Brazier's work, is a set of autocorrelograms

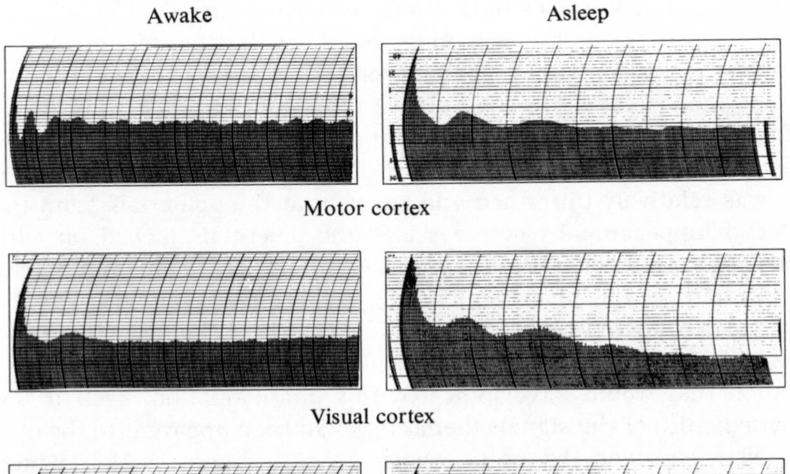

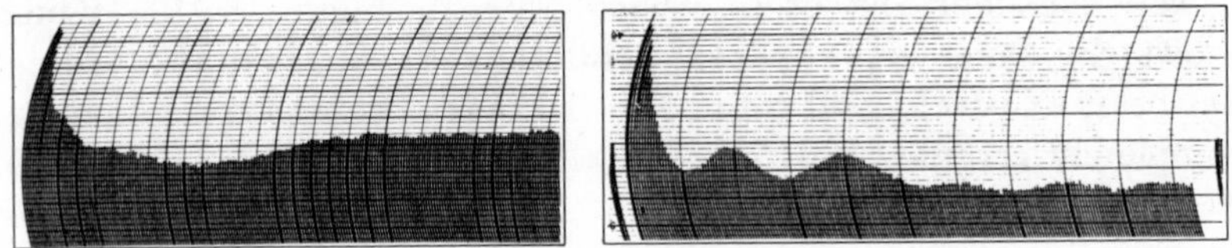

Fig. 8-11. *Brazier's use of the autocorrelation function to show the differences in the patterns of activity of three different areas of the brain between the awake and asleep state. (From Mary A. B. Brazier, "The Problem of Periodicity in the Electroencephalogram: Studies in the Cat,"* EEG and Clin. Neurophysiol., 15, *1963, p. 293.)*

from three different portions of the cat's brain comparing the enhancement of long wavelength activity for a sleeping animal with that for an awake animal. The results of this study were important for our understanding of brain mechanisms. Brazier suggested that in the awake animal inhibitory systems obscure the activity of the generators responsible for rhythmic potentials. Similar effects could be produced by artificially deactivating the animal with light doses of barbiturate.

Brazier's work was carried out on a special-purpose computer (Barlow and Brown, 1955), which used analog techniques to compute the autocorrelation function. There is no reason, however, that the analysis could not have been accomplished on a general-purpose digital computer.

An example of a cross correlation accomplished on a general-purpose digital computer is the work of Adey, Dunlop, and Hendrix (1960). Among other problems, they considered the phase relationship of the slow waves in the brain of a cat—specifically, the relationships between the potentials generated by the dorsum of the hippocampus and the entorhinal cortex. A set of their cross correlograms is shown in Figure 8-12. These two records were taken from the same cat, but at different times in the training program. The first cross correlation (Fig. 8-12*a*) is from the animal when it was relatively untrained and shows that the potentials from the dorsal hippocampal electrodes lead the potentials picked up with the entorhinal electrodes by about 35 milliseconds. This not only is indicated by the placement of the central peak but also can be calculated on the basis of the displacement of the other peaks of high correlation. There is no possibility of making a visual interpretation that would have indicated this phase relation, even if the periodicities of the signals themselves had been apparent to the eye.

Now consider the cross correlogram in Figure 8-12*b*, which shows the same experimental conditions except that the animal has been relatively well trained in the task. The phase relation has completely reversed itself, and the potentials from the entorhinal electrodes now lead those from the dorsal hippocampal electrodes. In the opinion of the authors of this paper, these correlograms may demonstrate a learning mechanism that operates on a phase comparison basis. The important fact for our present discussion is that the cross correlation method discovered a possible bioelectric sign of neural plasticity, a discovery that would not otherwise have been possible. Without such an analytical method, the subtle relationships within the electrical waveforms would have been completely obscured. No new data have been extracted from the signals; in fact, information in its formal sense has been lost. However, the important relationships have been enhanced enormously.

FEATURE RECOGNITION

Frequency analysis and correlation are both analytical methods that depend upon the fact that the time-varying signal has certain repetitive properties capable of being enhanced by appropriate mathematical manipulation. There are many other classes of signals, however, that do not vary simply along a single dimension and are not nearly repetitive enough to allow the investigator to abstract *their* critical properties with these methods. Alternative

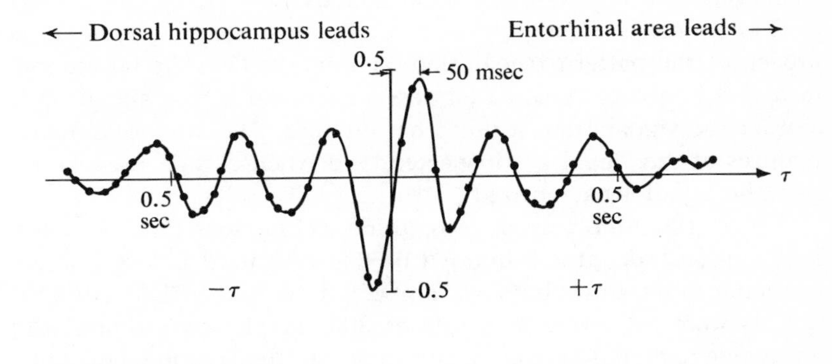

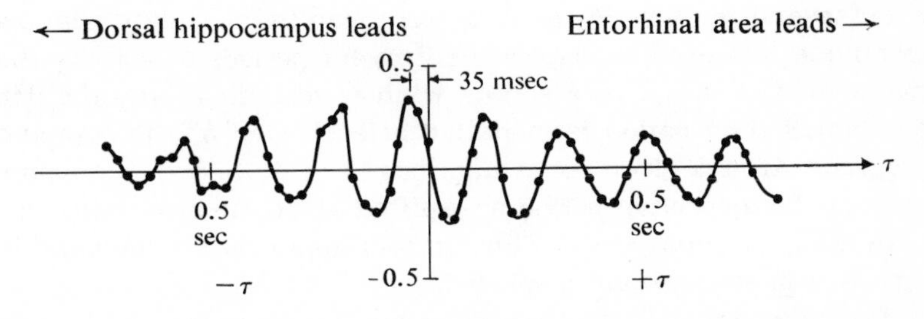

Fig. 8-12. *Data from the laboratory of W. R. Adey, showing the use of the cross correlogram to illustrate the change in phase angle between two signals from different areas of the brain as a function of number of training trials in a learning experiment. (From W. R. Adey, C. W. Dunlop, and C. E. Hendrix, "Hippocampal Slow Waves: Distribution and Phase Relationship in the Course of Approach Learning,"* A. M. A. Archives of Neurology, 3, *1960, p. 106, Figs.* 9a & 10a.)

techniques have been developed to classify signals having sufficient stability of form and an adequate signal-to-noise ratio to allow an inspection of their critical features. Such classification schemes are usually collectively called pattern recognizers.

Though we have lumped pattern recognition techniques together for the purposes of this discussion, they are not necessarily related to one another by formal mathematical procedures. In the past, many heuristic or other informal methods have been applied by the individual experimenter in order to implement a specific classification scheme. One of the earliest was a simple metering procedure invented by Bickford (1959) to recognize the spike-and-wave component of the EEG during the petit mal epileptic seizure. The Bickford device simply turned on a pen-and-ink recorder when this particular type of pattern occurred. The device acted as a monitor for a particular type of signal that, once recognized, could then be compared with any associated motor activity.

This simple, noncomputerized device illustrates the typical approach of the pattern recognition techniques. There is no attempt to derive analytically some expression specific to the signal or to extract the signal from a noisy background. The simple temporal features of the signal are inspected, and when certain criteria are met, the signal is categorized.

A more elaborate pattern recognition technique is that of Farley, Frishkopf, Clark, and Gilmore (1962), who used a large digital computer to recognize bursts of alpha activity in the EEG. The EEG signals were converted at a rate of 300 samples per second with an analog-to-digital converter and read into the computer memory. After several minutes of the data were read in, a "sliding window" technique was used to inspect the data for periods of activity that met specific criteria. In a sliding window technique only the data of a small time period is inspected at each step of the computer program. After a given set of data has been processed, the boundaries of the inspection period are shifted by an amount that is less than the inspection period. Thus an overlapping set of temporal intervals was sequentially inspected.

The pattern that Farley *et al.* were attempting to identify was the spindle-shaped burst of alpha (10 cps.) activity shown in Figure 8-13. The specifications of the occurrence of an alpha burst required that a certain minimum number of peaks and troughs of a

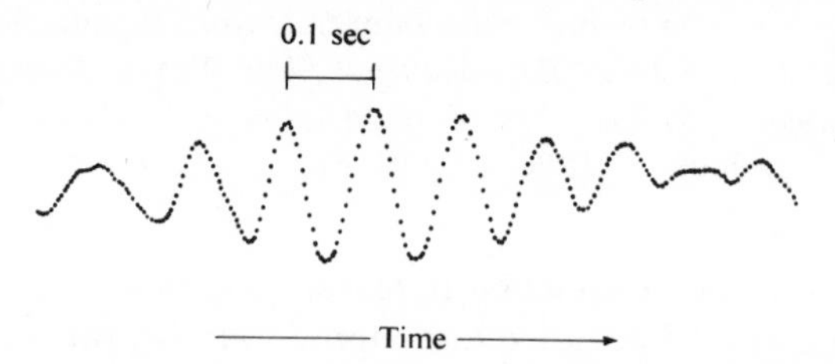

Fig. 8-13. *An electroencephalogram showing an alpha burst. This is the record after processing by a computer and represents the input to a feature identification system developed by Farley, Frishkopf, Clark,and Gilmore. (From B. G. Farley, L. S. Frishkopf, W. A. Clark, and J. T. Gilmore, Jr., "Computer Techniques for the Study of Patterns in the Electroencephalogram,"* IRE Transactions on Biomedical Electronics, *January, 1962, p. 6, Fig.* 1a.)

minimum amplitude and separated by specific time intervals be recorded. Because the peaks and troughs were fairly broad, there was some indeterminacy about their exact location in time. Therefore, the experimenters suggested the use of the *mid amplitude value*—the instant of time at which the amplitude of the signal was halfway between a peak and a trough. This time point was more sharply defined than the time of the peak or trough, since the rate of change of voltage at the mid value was very large compared to the rates at either a peak or a trough.

An alpha burst was thus defined in terms of a sufficiently long string of mid amplitude values separated by appropriate intervals. For each test an *amplitude criterion* was established. The amplitude criterion was the minimum peak-to-trough voltage that would be considered as a real "wave." Increasing the amplitude criterion decreased the amount of the total activity identifiable as burst activity. The number of bursts identified, however, varied less simply as a function of the amplitude criterion. For very low amplitude criteria, the number of bursts identified was moderately low, since the low criteria allowed extremely long strings of the EEG to be accepted as alpha bursts. For medium levels of the amplitude criterion, a rather large number of alpha bursts was accepted, since the discontinuities between bursts were detected, yet the criterion was still low enough to allow many bursts to trigger the detection program. When the amplitude criterion was quite high, however, only a few bursts had components of sufficient amplitude to activate the signal. The result was that the number of bursts detected was quite low. Considering all of these interactions, it is clear that a plot of the number of bursts as a function of the size of the amplitude criterion will display an inverted U shape.

This technique was applied to the EEG's recorded from a number of people under various conditions. The results indicated that it was able to discriminate not only between various psychological states of the subjects but also between individual subjects. Alpha bursting behavior, therefore, seems to be a function of the individual, as well as of his psychological or metabolic state. Plots of the percentage of total activity as a function of the amplitude criteria were particularly useful in describing individual differences in a quantified fashion.

Analytical techniques for long-duration transients

The analysis of transient potentials requires different techniques from those used for continuously oscillating signals. The reasons for this fact are related not only to the temporal patterns of the signals themselves but also to their physiological origins. Often the critical features of a response are hidden in the biological and electronic noise of the preparation; under these circumstances the signals must literally be extracted from the background noise. Once extracted, transients can be further processed by applying shape recognition and other discrimination and classification techniques. This section will discuss a variety of techniques for processing transient bioelectric potentials and some specific problems of their interpretation.

STATISTICAL AVERAGING

Averaging of evoked brain potentials. The mass brain potential evoked by impulsive peripheral stimulation has recently proved to be a useful measure in a variety of behavioral and neurological problems. However, investigations of the evoked potential are beset with a classic signal-to-noise problem. The signal is typically so small, particularly when it is being recorded through the intact skull and scalp of the animal, that it is hidden in the ongoing noise. The noise consists of the ordinary nonevoked EEG, the electromyograms from widely separated parts of the body, and electronic effects introduced by the amplifiers used in the system. One might find, for example, that many of the important components of the evoked potential from the human somatosensory system are only fifteen microvolts in amplitude, whereas the amplitude of the usual electroencephalographic activity is on the order of a half-millivolt. The problem, then, is to extract the evoked potentials from the other signals. Such a procedure is possible. It depends upon the fact that evoked potentials are synchronized with the impulsive stimulus that generated them. In contrast, the noise is, by definition, activity not related to the stimulus. Therefore, at any given delay following the stimulus, the amplitude of the ongoing activity or noise tends to be randomly distributed. When averaged, the randomly fluctuating signal will tend to converge on the value zero. On the other hand, when one averages a signal that is synchronized or time-locked to the stimulus, the average value at each delay following the stimulus will converge toward some nonzero value. A mixture of the two types of signal, synchronized and random, will tend, then, to reproduce the waveform of the time-locked signal, even though it may be many times smaller than the larger unsynchronized activity.

During World War II repetitive sweep techniques were used to enhance radar displays. The conceptual problem is exactly the same as described above for bioelectric potentials, except that the stimulus is the original burst of transmitted radio waves and the response is a much smaller radio wave reflected from the target. The various types of receivers capable of receiving the tiny reflected signals all had rather poor signal-to-noise characteristics. In addition, meteorological conditions contributed to the irrelevant noise. The method used to extract the significant signals was to send a signal to the target area repeatedly and to superimpose one response after another on the same display. Thus very small changes could often be seen with the naked eye.

In 1947, G. B. Dawson suggested that similar superimposition techniques could be used to detect small evoked potentials from the human brain. (He also pointed out that the technique, like the radar solution, was functionally identical to the idea used by Galton in 1883 to enhance the similarities among a collection of facial portraits.) Dawson's contribution to the sciences of brain and behavioral physiology has been most promising. His techniques created an almost unprecedented opportunity to do electrophysiological studies of the intact human. Although Dawson's first photographic superimposition techniques are primitive in comparison to the sophisticated real-time computer techniques used today, the general nature of the concept is identical. Dawson (1954) also developed what was perhaps the earliest electrical device actually to perform a pseudo-averaging function, a commutator-driven bank of capacitors, each of which charged to a level corresponding to a weighted algebraic sum of the signals at a given time after the stimulus. Figure 8-14*a* is a sample record from Dawson's original photographic superimposition technique, and Figure 8-14*b* is a sample record from the electromechanical device he subsequently invented. For comparison, Figure 8-14*c* is a plot of an averaged brain potential generated by one of today's general-purpose digital computers.

Averaging may be formally defined by an equation of the following form:

$$E_t = \frac{1}{N}\sum_{n=1}^{N} (E_t^n) \qquad (8\text{-}10)$$

In this equation E_t is the average value of the signal at a given time, t, following the stimulus, N is the number of sequential responses averaged, and E_t^n is the voltage at time t for the nth record. The equation represents but one point on the averaged curve for a particular time t after the stimulus. The variable t must be varied systematically to plot out the entire time function. In practice, the

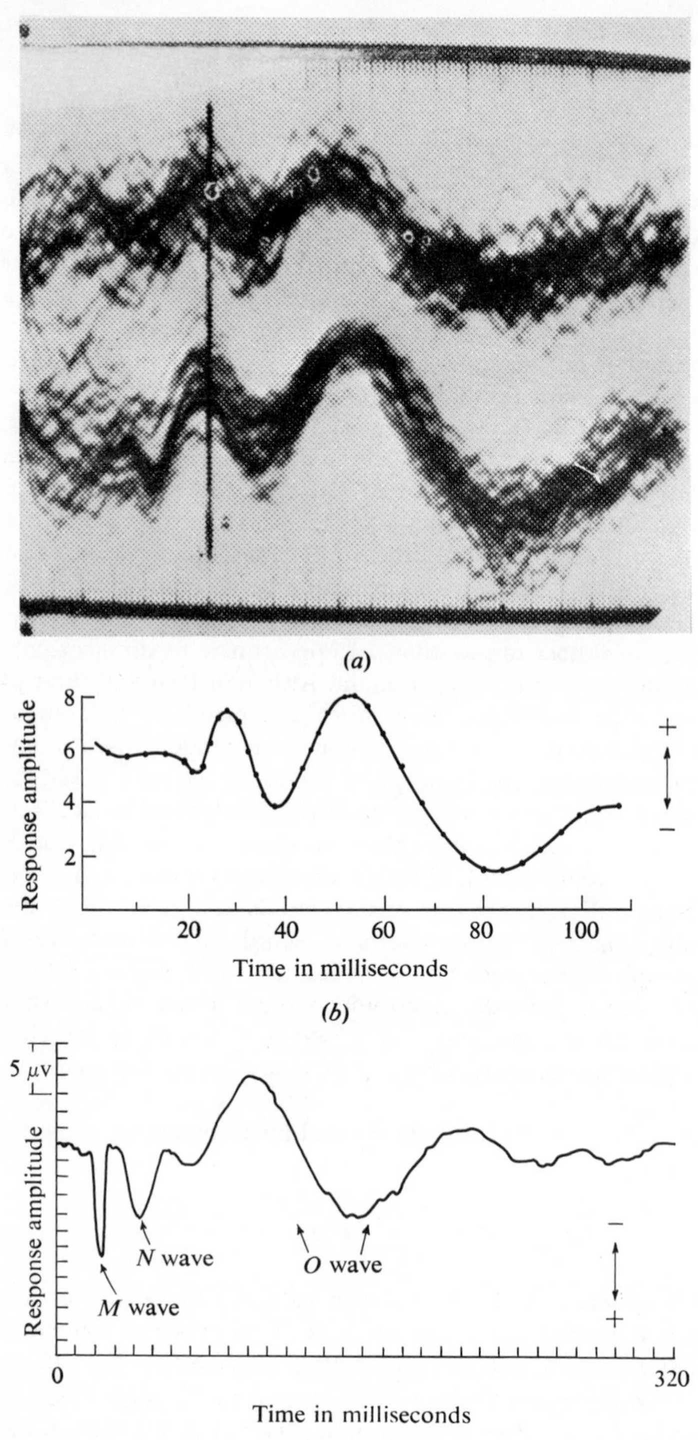

(a)
8
6
4
2
Response amplitude
20
40
60
80
100
Time in milliseconds
+
−
(b)
5 μV
Response amplitude
N wave
O wave
M wave
−
+
0
320
Time in milliseconds
(c)

preparation of an average response involves the presentation of a repetitive number (N) of stimuli. For digital computer averaging, each evoked potential is then digitized by means of an analog-to-digital converter, at a rate sufficient to provide an adequate density of sample points. A large number of averages, equivalent to the family of t's, is then computed using equation 8-10, and the values of this family of averages are plotted or displayed on some appropriate output device to represent the average time course of the response.

In the most sophisticated digital computer averagers, a true division by N is made with each successive stimulus presentation. Performing a division, however, is a complicated logical operation that may be avoided by a simple expedient. Thus, most commercial special-purpose averagers do not actually average but are serial accumulators, the operations of which we will now consider. Each time a stimulus is presented, an analog-to-digital converter samples the data, as described above. These coded values may be summed according to equation 8-10, but the division by N is never accomplished. Instead, the cumulative value in the register corresponding to a given $\sum_{n=1}^{N} E_t^n$; i.e.; corresponding to a given t, increases throughout the entire experiment. In this manner, the values accumulated in each of the registers gradually increase in magnitude up to the maximum capacity of the storage registers. Since there is just as much likelihood that an unsynchronized signal will be above the mean value as there is that it will be below after any given number of stimuli, once again the tendency is for

Fig. 8-14. *The development of the averaged evoked potential technique has been considerable since it was first suggested by Dawson.* (a) *An evoked potential produced by repetitive tracing on a cathode ray tube. This is a 75 ms. long sample from two electrodes on either side of the central fissure of the brain. (From G. D. Dawson, "Cerebral Responses to Nerve Stimulation in Man,"* British Medical Bulletin, 6, *1950, p. 329, Fig. 2.)* (b) *A 100 ms. plot of an evoked brain potential produced on the electromechanical mechanism developed by Dawson. (From G. D. Dawson, "A Summation Technique for the Detection of Small Evoked Potentials,"* Electroencephalography and Clinical Neurophysiology, 6, *1954, p. 67.)* (c) *An averaged evoked potential produced by a general purpose digital computer for a longer period of time following the stimulus (320 ms.). (From W. R. Uttal and Louella Cook, "Systematics of the Evoked Somatosensory Cortical Potential: A Psychophysical-Electrophysiological Comparison,"* Annals of the New York Academy of Sciences, 112 *(Art. 1), 1964, p. 65.)*

the contents of each register to tend toward some mean value. However, in this case there will be produced an increasingly non-zero mean value as the number of stimulus presentations increases. The division by N, therefore, simply acts as a scaling factor to normalize the amplitude of the signal for any N. It is here that the price is paid for eliminating the arithmetic circuitry necessary to accomplish the division. Since the scale of the oscilloscope display is usually set to display the final reading properly, it is not possible to see the unaveraged results of a single sweep during the early stages of the averaging process. Furthermore, only after a number of stimuli have been presented do the characteristics of the signal begin to become visible to the observer.

We have previously pointed out that the major criterion for successful averaging is that the signal be time-locked to some reference. Usually the reference is specifically the stimulus. Averaging thus can be considered a special case of cross correlation in which a correlation is made between a repetitive transient signal, the response, and a periodic pulse, the stimulus. Often, however, there is no externally controlled stimulus that can be used as the reference for averaging the responses. Schmitt (1964) has suggested several techniques for artificially producing reference points. One of the most obvious—the signal itself—is usable for signals in which the signal-to-noise ratio is not too unfavorable. A signal-to-noise ratio is satisfactory for this purpose if any single portion of the response can be precisely located in time even if other parts are hidden in the noise. The central peak of the electrocardiogram —the *R* wave—for example, is relatively large compared to the noise in which it is embedded and can be used to trigger the averaging device. The averaging in this case is not performed on the same signal that triggers the device but on a recording of the signal that has been delayed sufficiently long to allow its complete course to be analyzed. This technique, though, does depend upon a relatively noise-free signal, and thus the utility of the averaging procedure may be seriously reduced.

Schmitt has also suggested that the electrocardiogram could be used as an artificial reference point for other signals generated within the same organism. Hence an internally generated response can be used as a reference for averaging other activity. This may prove to be a formidable method for identifying causal relationships between interacting physiological systems. For example, it may prove very useful for elaborating the relationship between cardiac cycles and the electroencephalogram.

Averaging techniques have gained much popularity since they

were first introduced to the study of microsignals. In a collection of papers recently published by the New York Academy of Science (Katzman, 1964) several studies described evoked potentials recorded from the brains of normal and abnormal subjects who were stimulated by acoustic, visual, and/or somatic stimuli. We should discuss certain technical cautions about the use of the averaging technique expressed by some of the authors. For instance, Bickford, Jacobson, and Cody (1964) demonstrated the possibility that some of the potentials recorded from the human scalp when acoustic stimuli are used may not be cerebral electropotentials. By intentionally flexing or relaxing the muscles of the subject's neck during the acquisition of averaged evoked potentials, Bickford showed that under certain conditions of flexure the potentials were enlarged, while under other conditions they were diminished. This result originally suggested that there might be some contamination of the evoked brain potential by muscle activity that is equally well synchronized with the stimulus.

In a more recent paper, however, Domino, Matsuoka, Waltz, and Cooper (1964), who worked with human subjects undergoing open brain surgery, showed that the evoked potentials recorded from the surface of the brain were identical in shape to those recorded from the outside of the skull, although the former were much larger in amplitude. The result is to be expected because of the attenuating characteristics of the skull. Domino and Corssen (1964) also worked with patients who were given succinylcholine to produce a muscle paralysis. Since the induced paralysis had no attenuating effects on visual evoked potentials, these workers feel that there is in fact no contamination of the evoked potential as a result of muscle activity. Thus, their results seriously challenge the assertion of Bickford and his colleagues that the evoked brain potential is not completely neurogenic. However, they do not *explain* why the effects were obtained.

Brazier (1964) also expresses cautions about the application of the averaging technique. One of the most obvious limitations is based upon the fact that the technique requires a large number of signals to be collected sequentially. This means that, since the signal may be varying widely during the sequence without the knowledge of the experimenter, using the technique may seriously distort the data on a statistical basis.

Such artifacts in the evoked potential include the distortions generated by the variability of the response amplitudes themselves. But, as Brazier also points out, evoked potentials with much variability in latency, for example, would tend to average out to zero and not appear at all, even though the individual records might contain signals of considerable amplitude. Furthermore, a large variance in the signal amplitude might be obscured because of the averaging process. This difficulty can be controlled by means of variance measurements, but few of the special-purpose accumulating type of averagers are capable of performing this operation, so a general-purpose digital computer is required.

Other uses of the averaging process. Averaging merely extracts the part of the response time-locked to an impulsive stimulus from the background noise. In many types of experiments, particularly in the early stages of research, this analysis is sufficient since explorations being carried out are attempts to define the nature of the response and the variations in it that are dependent on stimulus variations. There are studies, moreover, in which changes in the response are not simple changes of magnitude but less obvious variations of the overall form of the response. For example, a very interesting problem is the attempt to demonstrate electrophysiological signs of conditioning. Evoked potential experiments have been performed in which significant pattern changes occur during both conditioning and extinction. The remaining difficulty is that, even though identifiable, these changes are essentially unquantified and thus are not susceptible to systematic comparison without additional processing.

Consider two averaged evoked potentials differing considerably in shape but of generally the same amplitude. How "dissimilar" are the two results, or, for that matter, how much do the sequential records taken during a conditioning sequence vary as a function of the training experience? It is this question, the one of quantity, to which we now turn.

A number of investigators have proposed the use of correlational techniques to compare records against a standard, perhaps one that has even been collected at the beginning of a given experiment. Other standards from typical cases might also be used. Ruchkin, Villegas, and John (1964) have suggested specifically that the simple product moment correlation (the Pearson ρ) may be used to generate a correlation matrix comparing each record with all others. If there is reason to suspect some fluctuation in latency, correlations of the form defined by the general correlation equation (equation 8-8) could be made for various values of delay (τ). A latency fluctuation would then show up as a peak at a certain time in the correlation plot, varying with τ.

Ruchkin and his colleagues also point out that these correlation matrices can be classified into groups of similar wave shape. In particular, the standard statistical factor analysis techniques are applicable in this situation to group correlated signals into clusters.

All correlation techniques have the advantage of being relatively insensitive to amplitude changes and of being dependent upon similarities in shape. Thus, signals from electrodes that are generally alike in their waveforms can often be described as being similar, even though there may be wide differences in signal strength as reflected by the recorded amplitude.

Another interesting technique for emphasizing spatial patterns has been developed by Rémond (1964). Although most evoked potential techniques are plots of voltage as a function of time, he has developed an ingenious device for mapping the evoked potentials collected from a line of electrodes mounted on the human scalp. His method can be used to show the time course of the pattern of potentials occurring along this line. In his plots the vertical dimension is the distance along which the row of electrodes is arranged, while the horizontal dimension is time after stimulus presentation. *Isoelectric lines* connect regions of equal electrical potential, i.e., of equal voltage with regard to a common reference point. Rémond's display technique is shown in Figure 8-15 for a one-second-long averaging period.

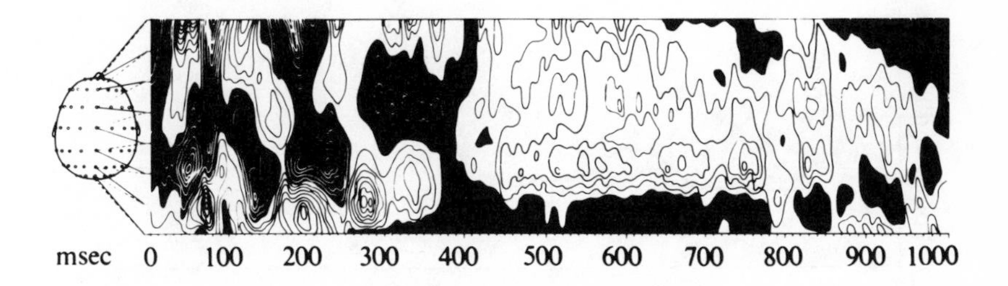

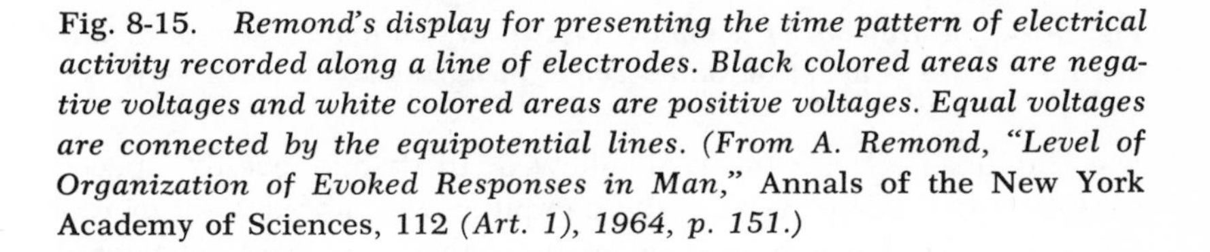

Fig. 8-15. *Remond's display for presenting the time pattern of electrical activity recorded along a line of electrodes. Black colored areas are negative voltages and white colored areas are positive voltages. Equal voltages are connected by the equipotential lines. (From A. Remond, "Level of Organization of Evoked Responses in Man,"* Annals of the New York Academy of Sciences, 112 *(Art. 1), 1964, p. 151.)*

PATTERN CLASSIFICATION OF LONG-DURATION TRANSIENTS

Unlike the evoked brain potential, the *electrocardiogram* (EKG) usually has such a good signal-to-noise ratio that it is completely visible in a single recording. It lasts long enough for the details of the shape of the signal to be used as important diagnostic cues. Therefore, the electrocardiographer is likely to be interested in more than the simple occurrence of the EKG signal. He may also be concerned with the dynamics of rise time and relative size among many other possible parameters. The origins of EKG's are more thoroughly understood than are those of evoked potentials. Because of their larger relative size and easy detection, EKG's have been common diagnostic tools for many years. In fact, specific variations in the shape of this transient potential have been associated with specific cardiac anomalies. For these reasons, the application of pattern recognition techniques to EKG's has progressed farther than their application to sensory evoked potentials.

An excellent example of a digital computer pattern recognition approach to EKG's is illustrated by the work of Okajima, Stark, Whipple, and Yasui (1963). Electrocardiographic data were fed through an analog-to-digital converter into a general-purpose digital computer. Okajima and his colleagues were particularly interested in the largest and most obvious component of the EKG, the central QRS complex illustrated in Figure 8-16. The component

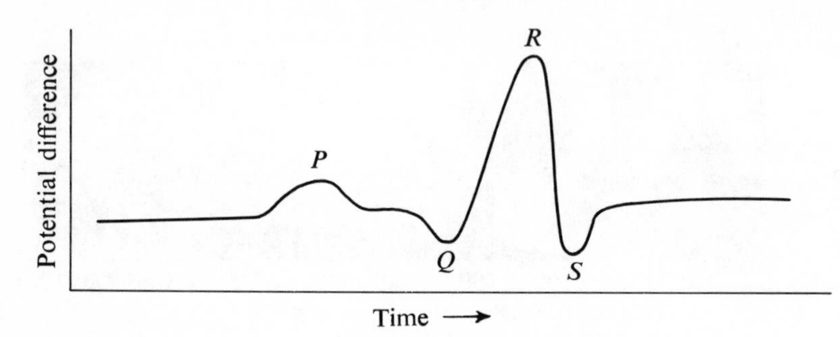

Fig. 8-16. *A drawing of a typical electrocardiographic waveform. The central R wave is about 50 milliseconds in duration.*

was digitized at a rate that allowed thirty-one evenly spaced samples to be taken. Within the computer was stored a set of real clinical EKG's that had been selected because they were considered typical responses associated with diagnosed pathological conditions. The problem was to classify the incoming signals by means of the set of prestored signals. Each prestored EKG record was in the same form as the sampled signal, with thirty-one evenly spaced points tracing out its time course. As the new EKG entered the system, it was compared with all of the prestored signals by means of a normalized cross correlation. Finally, the computer had been programmed to select the highest correlation as the critical sign of association. In this way an interim diagnosis of the clinical condition could be made by the computer.

So far this technique is fairly straightforward, adding little to conventional classification techniques beyond automatic metricization. The investigators, however, went on to devise an ingenious way to improve the set of comparison records prestored in the computer. Their program allowed the incoming signals so to modify the comparison records that they improve with the experience of classifying these signals. After the highest correlation had been established, the new signal was averaged into the specific existing comparison record with which it correlated best. Thus, if this signal were the tenth to correlate maximally with this record, its coefficients would alter the existing coefficients by one-tenth of the difference between them. So, as the classification process gained more and more experience, a given comparison record would tend to represent more closely the statistically typical features of either a particular cardiac difficulty or a normal subject. Such a computer diagnostician, therefore, gradually learns to make better and better classifications in a fully automated way.

It was made clear by the authors that no a priori decision must be made by the human diagnostician concerning the nature of the prestored set of records. These records might just as well have been a set of flat lines before the classification procedure. If no single correlation exceeds a given criterion, a new comparison record can automatically be set up. There is, therefore, a gradual development of a set of records based completely on the experience of the computer. Furthermore, because of the adaptive nature of the computer, almost any set of records could be used as the prestored comparison. If they are badly out of line with the distinguishing features of the electrocardiograms, they will tend to converge on a new set that is more appropriate. The ultimate utility of such a development is obvious. It is no longer necessary to depend upon a predetermined classification system, but the computer program can generate classes of association just as in a factor analysis. These classes may prove later to be associated with specific cardiac pathologies not identified in the past as specific syndromes.

Okajima and his colleagues performed experiments with the classification technique in which the number of classes of EKG's developed was shown to be a very sensitive function of the criterion used for associating a new record with one of the prestored records. Yet the order in which a given set of EKG signals was fed into the computer had little effect on the final set of comparison records.

This technique is an excellent example of an important general concept underlying all computer classification, analysis, and problem-solving activities: *adaptive reaction* by the computer program to its experiences. The study of Okajima and his colleagues is a simple example, but it clearly illustrates the main issue: there is, as a function of the experience the program has in solving the problem, an alteration of a set of parameters that is fundamental to the solution. In this case the adaptive features were built into the alteration of the set of comparison records. The coefficients of each of the thirty-one samples varied with experience. Yet, in some more sophisticated adaptive systems, the rules for making the comparison might also have been adaptively altered.

Analytical techniques for short-duration transients

So far we have discussed continuously fluctuating signals and transients lasting long enough to make the details of shape interesting and measurable. There is, however, a class of bioelectric potentials which may also be called transients but which are usually so brief that the investigator is interested only in the simplest measures, such as amplitude and time of occurrence. The most typical example of this class of signals is the spike action potential recorded from single neurons. Ordinarily the potentials are recorded with microscopically small electrodes, but careful dissection techniques and unusual anatomical configurations often allow several individual potentials to be recorded simultaneously from groups of neurons by relatively large electrodes.

The investigator encounters several general problems in dealing with this type of signal. First of all, he may simply require a statement of the statistics of the response he is studying in order to define the pattern of activity generated by a standard stimulus condition. On the other hand, he may be faced with analyzing a mixed response into its individual components.

In an important paper, Cox and Smith (1954) described the formal limitations on the analysis of superpositioned processes such as a mixed pool of neuronal action potentials. The process of superpositioning is defined by Figure 8-17. Here the outputs of a group of pulse generators (neurons in this particular instance) are mixed on a single information channel so that only information concerning the time of occurrence of the individual responses is conserved. All amplitude data are lost, as are all data concerning the association between a single response and any particular one of the individual pulse generators. Cox and Smith have described some important properties of superpositioned signals that are relevant to any discussion of the processing of nerve action potential data. First, they demonstrated that even if the pulse generators contributing to the pooled population of responses

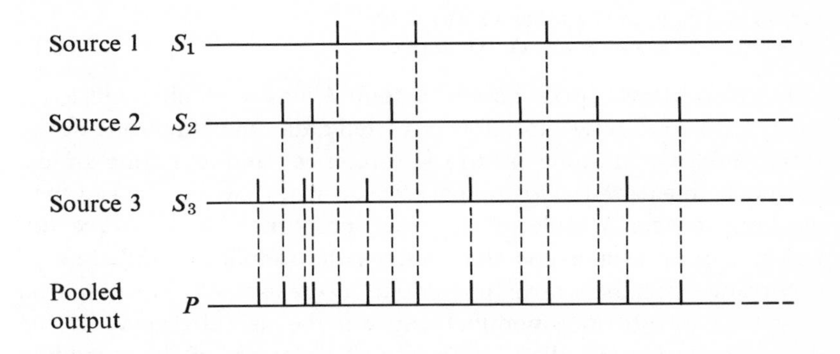

Fig. 8-17. *A schematic drawing of the pooling of responses from three different sources as depicted by Cox and Smith. (From D. R. Cox and W. L. Smith, "On the Superposition of Renewal Processes,"* Biometrika, *41, 1954, p. 91. Fig. 1)*

are perfectly periodic, the intervals between successive responses tend to become randomly distributed as the number of generators increases. This is a major finding, because it says there is no possible technique that, using interval alone, allows us to subdivide the pooled signals into their constituents. For that matter, it also says there is no way to tell anything at all about the statistical properties of the generators themselves when their number gets large. However, for smaller numbers of fibers we can at least describe the general statistical nature of the family of generators that contributed to the pooled response. For example, using their technique, we would be able to distinguish between a set of perfectly periodic generators and a set of randomly firing generators.

The important conclusion to be drawn from the Cox and Smith paper is that a general analysis of superpositioned or pooled nerve impulses is not possible on the basis of interval alone. Moreover, the conclusion of nonanalyzability may be true even if amplitude is added as a separation criterion for large numbers of pooled neurons. The surgical dissection technique and the multiple microelectrode, therefore, remain powerful tools for the study of complex patterns of neural activity. For less complex mixtures of neural impulses, however, simple statistical manipulations are useful, and in one or two cases ingenious techniques have taken advantage of special properties of specific neurophysiological situations to perform actual subclasses of the general analysis excluded by Cox and Smith. The following sections describe some of the simple techniques that have proved especially useful.

SIMPLE STATISTICAL MEASURES OF NERVE SPIKE POTENTIAL ACTIVITY

A given nerve spike action potential has two characteristics easily measured from digitally converted data: the amplitude of the spike, relative to some arbitrary reference, and the time of occurrence, measured with some sort of real-time or elapsed-time clocking device. A table of the basic properties of the nerve impulses can be established that defines the amplitude and time of occurrence for the entire population of responses. Since tables, however, are an uneconomical and not too useful display of the data, the simple expedient of forming histograms of the responses has evolved. The amplitude histogram, the most direct, is a plot of the number of nerve impulses that occur at any one of a set of amplitudes.

Figure 8-18 is a typical computer print-out of an amplitude histogram. In this case the responses were recorded from a gross electrode hooked about the ventral nerve cord of a crayfish (Uttal and Kasprzak, 1962). This analysis is particularly useful for the pooled type of recordings described by Cox and Smith. As a matter of fact, for relatively small numbers ($n < 5$) of involved neurons, the amplitude histogram provides a basis for making the analysis that was impossible with interval alone, because impulses generated by larger neurons or those closer to the electrode tend to be larger than impulses generated by smaller neurons or those farther from the electrode. Thus a rough discrimination can be made within the ensemble of neurons contributing to the pooled response. The record of Figure 8-18 shows the results of stimulating the last ganglion with white light. Incidentally, these last responses are obtained because there happens to be a photosensitive receptor in the terminal ganglion.

From the histogram it can be seen that this photoreceptor activates a number of medium-sized cells in the nerve cord. An automatic scaling feature has been built into the computer program, so that the horizontal scale (in this case the number of responses rather than the amplitude dimension) is appropriate to the maximum number of responses in the most active amplitude class.

The second type of histogram that is often used is a derived

```
                                   Number of peaks

        0         10        20        30        40        50        60        70        80
        •         •         •         •         •         •         •         •         •

    0  I  0
    1  I  0
    2  I  0
    3  I  0
    4  I  0
    5  Ixxxxxx  6
    6  Ixxxxx  5
    7  Ixxxx  4
    8  Ixxxxxxxx  8
    9  Ixx  2
   10  Ix  1
   11  I  0
   12  Ixxxx  4                                    Distribution of amplitudes
   13  Ixxxxx  5                                      photic stimulation
   14  Ixxx  3
   15  Ixxxx  4
   16  Ixx  2
   17  Ix  1
   18  Ixxxxx  5
   19  Ixxxxxxxxxxx  11
   20  Ixxxxxxx  7
   21  Ixxxxxx  6
   22  Ixxxxxxxx  8
   23  Ixxxxx  5
   24  Ixxxxxxxxx  9
   25  Ixxxxx  5
   26  Ixxxxx  5
   27  Ixxxxxxxx  8
H  28  Ixxxxxxxxxx  10
e  29  Ixxxxxxxxxxxxxxxx  16
i  30  Ixxxxxxxxxxxxxxxxxxx  19
g  31  Ixxxxxxxxxxxxxxxxxxxxxxx  23
h  32  Ixxxxxxxxxxxxxxxxxxxxxxxxxxxxxxxxxxxxxx  38
t  33  Ixxxxxxxxxxxxxxxxxxxxxxxxxxxxxxxxxxx  35
   34  Ixxxxxxxxxxxxxxxxxxxxxxxxxxxxxxxxxxxxxxxxxxxx  44
o  35  Ixxxxxxxxxxxxxxxxxxxxxxxxxxxxxxxxxxxxxxxxxxxxxxxxxx  50
f  36  Ixxxxxxxxxxxxxxxxxxxxxxxxxxxxxxxxxxxxxxxxxx  42
   37  Ixxxxxxxxxxxxxxxxxxxxxxxxxxxxxxxxxxxxxxxxxxxxxxxxxxxxxxx  55
p  38  Ixxxxxxxxxxxxxxxxxxxxxxxxxxxxxxxxxxxxxxxxxxxxxxxxxxxxxxx  55
e  39  Ixxxxxxxxxxxxxxxxxxxxxxxxxxxxxxxxxxxxx  37
a  40  Ixxxxxxxxxxxxxxxxxxxxxxxxxx  26
k  41  Ixxxxxxxxxxxxxxxxxxxx  20
   42  Ixxxxxxxxxxxxxxxxxxx  19
   43  Ixxxxxxxxxx  10
   44  Ixxxxxxxxxxxxxxxxx  17
   45  Ixxxxxx  6
   46  Ixxxxxx  6
   47  Ixxxxxxxxxx  10
   48  Ixxxx  4
   49  Ixxx  3
   50  I  0
   51  Ixx  2
   52  Ixx  2
   53  Ixx  2
   54  Ix  1
   55  Ixxx  3
   56  I  0
   57  Ix  1
   58  Ix  1
   59  I  0
   60  Ix  1
   61  Ix  1
   62  Ixx  2
   63  Ixxxxxxxxxxxxxxxxxxxxxxxxxxxxxxxxxxxxxxxxxxxxx  45
```

Fig. 8-18. *A histogram of amplitudes of nerve action potentials recorded from the ventral nerve cord of the crayfish when light impinges on the caudal photoreceptor. (From W. R. Uttal and H. Kasprzak, "The Caudal Photoreceptor of the Crayfish: Quantitative Study of Responses to Intensity, Temporal and Wavelength Variables,"* American Federation of Information Processing Societies Conference Proceedings, 21, *1962, p. 166.)*

measure. Derived histograms are formed from the intervals between successive responses or from the latencies between the stimuli and the responses. An excellent example of the latency histogram (and an important application of it) is found in the work of Fox and O'Brien (1965). They tabulated a latency histogram for responses picked up from single cells in the visual cortex of a cat following stimulation with a light flash. A sample of their record is given in Figure 8-19. The result was very signifi-

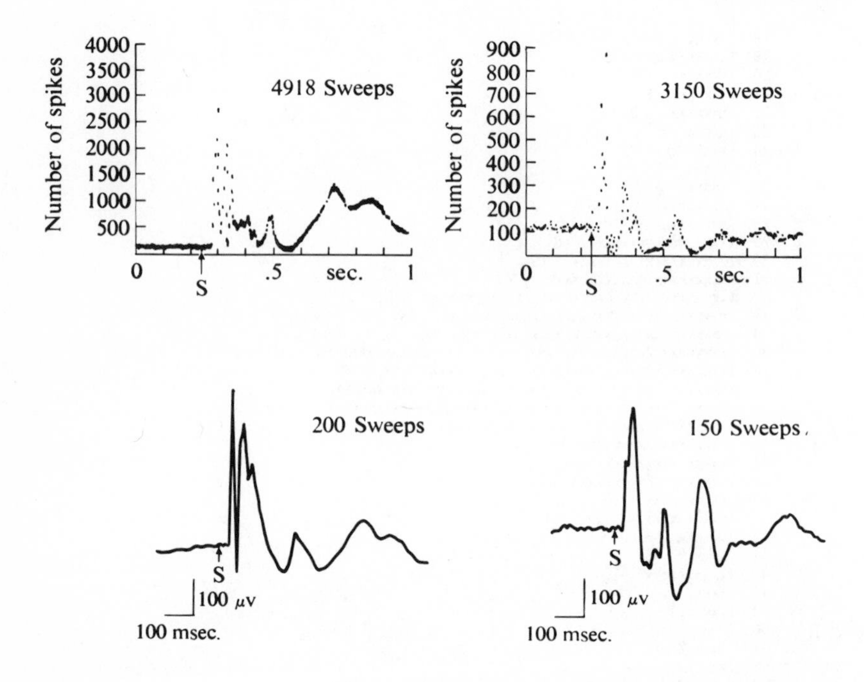

Fig. 8-19. *The data of Fox and O'Brien showing the similarities of the histogram of intervals and the compound evoked potential from the visual cortex of a cat. The upper traces (A and C) are interval histograms and the lower traces are the compound evoked potentials. (From S. Fox and J. O'Brien, "Duplication of Evoked Potential Waveform by Curve of Probability of Firing of a Single Cell,"* Science, 147, *1965, p. 888.)*

cant because it suggested a relationship between the probability of firing as evidenced by the latency histogram and the time course of the averaged evoked potential. This is an important correlation for it illustrates an interpretation of a complex waveform in terms of the response probabilities of a single structure rather than in terms of the effects of deterministic firing of several different anatomical structures. This completely new insight into the physiological mechanism has emerged from the analysis and the display techniques used in their experiment.

Another similar derived measure that has proved to be useful is the instantaneous frequency plot. Schoenfeld (1964) has described its historical development in his laboratory and its significance. The technique is simple but has turned out to be extremely important in the pursuit of the classic studies of the horseshoe crab compound eye carried out over the years by H. K. Hartline and his colleagues. The technique is essentially an interval measurement between successive nerve impulses. The reciprocal of the interval is computed for each interval and plotted as a function of real time on a graph or other display. The plot is, therefore, a running measurement of the rate of firing of the individual neuron being studied.

CORRELATIONAL TECHNIQUES FOR NERVE IMPULSE STUDIES

Let us now return to the problem of analysis, specifically to the problem of meaningfully separating a pooled or superpositioned group of responses into its constituents. We have pointed out how this can often be done on the basis of amplitude alone, but another technique has also demonstrated its worth—a cross correlational technique. Casby, Siminoff, and Houseknecht (1963) implemented such a technique on an analog device. (It is, however, a straightforward process to implement the procedure on a digital computer.) Gasser and Erlanger (1937), who were concerned with the classic problem of the compound action potential, had used single electrical shocks, a most unnatural stimulus condition, to evoke the compound action potential from peripheral nerves. The problem considered by Casby and his colleagues was whether the evoked potentials were true measures of the statistics of nerve action potentials or represented an abnormal response generated by the unnatural stimuli.

The most direct way to answer this question was to use natural stimuli and to record the individual neuronal responses from the nerve trunk on a single recording channel, as was done in Figure 8-18. But then they had also to analyze the responses to see whether the same pattern of activity found by Gasser and Erlanger was replicated. The analysis was done on the basis of conduction time. They cross correlated the signals picked up from two electrodes, one close to the point of stimulation and the other more distant, in accordance with the generalized correlation equation. The delay,

τ, between the two functions was varied in systematic steps, giving one point on the cross correlation function after another. This technique depends upon the development of high correlations between signals that are delayed by an amount equal to the conduction time of a given set of fibers. The correlogram so produced reproduced the form of the classic response recorded by Gasser and Erlanger but did so without using pulse electrical stimuli.

The results of the experiments of Casby and his colleagues were encouraging from a number of points of view. First of all, they were able to verify the data of Gasser and Erlanger and therefore to show that there was no serious artifact introduced into the analysis by the unnatural electrical pulse stimuli. Later, Siminoff (1965) was able to apply the technique to the general problem of neural coding and to demonstrate patterns of activity produced by natural stimuli, a long step forward in understanding how neural signals represent sensory information.

This chapter has surveyed a number of analytical and technical procedures for handling electrophysiological signals that are of special interest to physiologically oriented psychologists. But electrophysiology is not the only realm of measurement for psychologists and others concerned with behavior. Chapter 9 will survey other techniques that have been used in various psychological experiments to reduce the work load on the experimenter and enhance the quality of his data in more behavioral situations.

9: COMPUTER APPLICATIONS IN THE PSYCHOLOGICAL LABORATORY

Introduction

We have previously introduced the computerized behavioral sciences laboratory as a natural development, one that grew out of the complex needs of the psychological experiment and the resources offered to such problems by the new technology. In this chapter we will specify the computer operations that are particularly relevant to the automation of laboratory procedures and will illustrate, by research examples, how these features have been used by several behavioral scientists.

The general functions of an automated laboratory are described by the same paradigm that describes any general information-processing system. Computers have input, processing, storage, and output capabilities, and the computerized laboratory is no exception. However, in the computerized laboratory, each computer function must be considered in the context of its relationship to the human or animal subject. Thus, computer outputs must be regarded as inputs of stimulus materials to the subjects. The functions a computer can perform in an experiment are diverse, and limited mainly by the ingenuity of the experimenter and the programmer to implement a particular experimental design. These functions can, however, be classified in the following way.

Computer functions

PREPARATION AND DISPLAY OF STIMULUS MATERIALS

Computer programs can be written to generate more or less complex stimulus materials, which may or may not be contingent upon previous responses. Simple programming algorithms can be constructed that allow the computer to generate, in a few milliseconds, stimulus patterns it would take hundreds of hours to do manually. The generation of visual displays from dot matrices on a cathode ray tube in which the dot patterns are generated by probabilistic rules is an example of visual stimulus generation that has opened up a whole new field of research on human pattern and depth perception. This work literally had not been possible to perform previously. Julesz (1960), for example, has studied the stereoscopic depth effect generated by showing slightly displaced dot patterns to each eye, thus creating a retinal disparity. Such stimuli allow depth perception to be studied in a very pure form, since only one cue for depth—stereopsis—is present. All other depth cues have been eliminated by using patterns in which no figures emerge until the disparate images actually fuse. In a similar investigation also employing computer-generated displays, White (1962) generated stimuli that were used to study the perception of depth on the basis of intersection cues. The "bent wire" drawings used in his experiments were plotted on the face of an oscilloscope in such a way as to eliminate stereopsis and other contaminating cues.

These two examples rely heavily upon the ability of the computer to draw figures on visual displays. It is not, of course, an absolute limitation, because computers are able to produce complex stimulus patterns for the other senses as well. Swets, Millman, Fletcher, and Green's work (1962) is an ingenious study of computer teaching methods used by the computer to generate tones that were contingent upon the student's previous responses. Yntema, Wozencraft, and Klem (1964) recently discussed the use of the computer to easily generate large vocabularies of speech signals by a process analogous to the old cut and splice techniques. This procedure works according to rules that shortened the duration of the vocalization but did not, as would be the case with a simple speedup of the tape-recorded message, increase the component frequencies. Norman (1966) has applied the technique to problems in short-term memory. Furthermore, we (Uttal and Krissoff, 1966) routinely use the computer to generate patterns of electrical stimuli that are used to stimulate the human somatosensory system.

Computers can also be employed for simple preparation of more conventional stimulus materials. In many laboratories stimulus materials that have been prepared on computers are simply presented in a predetermined serial order. Thus, lists of printed alphanumeric materials and punched paper tapes of some complexity can be made available for conventional noncontingent experiments.

Scheduling of stimulus materials often involves the use of random number tables. The tables can be stored in a computer, but since it is generally wasteful of computer memory to keep them there, much interest has been expressed in simple algorithmic techniques for generating pseudorandom numbers. Both multiplicative and additive techniques have been developed that generally involve trimming or rounding operations on prior products or sums. (See Green, 1963, Chapter 9.) An often overlooked opportunity in experiments with human beings is actually to use the least significant digits of response measures as *quasi*-random numbers. For example, the least significant digits of reaction times, which are measured to fractions of milliseconds, make excellent sources of these numbers. As another example, events with specific choice probalities are easily generated by filling a register with the appropriate proportions of 1's and 0's and rotating it a random number of positions, possibly even determined by the response latency itself. The computer program could then select the part of the resulting term that appears in a given part of the register. This term will appear with a probability determined by the proportions of 1's and 0's originally loaded into the register.

The types of display devices available on conventional business computers are relatively limited, but the simple and flexible input-output systems on newer computers make it possible to adapt any coded input display technique to real-time computer control. Relays may be set, dials twisted, and electronic gear triggered; alphabetic and numerical characters can be printed and punched; figures can be drawn on cathode ray tubes.

One of the most underrated and best developed tools for psychological research is the computer-controlled typewriter. In a wide variety of applications in which verbal materials must be manipulated, it has proved to be a powerful and flexible tool. We shall discuss it in greater detail in Chapter 10, "Computer Teaching Machines."

COLLECTION OF RESPONSE DATA

Just as the computer is helpful for the display of stimulus material to human subjects in an experiment, it is also useful for collecting information about the responses of the subjects. Responses from human and animal subjects may be of many different kinds, but as far as the computer is concerned, they fall in two major classes. In the first class are responses that are primarily discrete in form and suitable for almost direct input from the subject to the computer. These are responses, for example, that involve the depression of a key to indicate an event or a choice by the subject. An example is the simple reaction time, which is terminated by the depression of a key. Any typewriter keyboard manipulation belongs to this class of response. The information is generally of a very low data rate, for people push only a few keys in a second, even for complex and preprogrammed operations such as piano playing or typing. *Event occurrence* is a suitable term to define this class of response.

The other class includes responses that are, in general, transduced from some other physical variable to electrical analog signals. We have already discussed this sort of signal in Chapter 8.

Some recently developed devices can accept more complex graphic responses from humans and feed them directly into a computer. The "RAND Tablet" (Davis and Ellis, 1965) is such a device. A very finely photoetched matrix on the surface of a flat pad is the drawing medium, and a hand-held stylus picks up time-encoded signals from the matrix by a capacitive coupling technique. Thus there is no necessity for a direct connection between the stylus and the etched lines carrying the coded signal. The signal is coded in time and depends upon the position of the probe at any given moment. Once inserted into the computer, a series of these signals can be used directly as an indication of the path taken by the stylus. As the stylus moves, the computer follows the position and stores sufficient information to allow the track to be retraced and manipulated as desired by the user.

A similar device capable of serving the same function is the combination of a computer-controlled cathode ray tube—to be discussed in detail shortly—and a light pen. This input system depends upon a synchronization of the output from a photocell mounted in, or optically connected to, a penlike pointer and a particular step in the computer program. When the photocell is activated by the momentary phosphorescence of the cathode ray tube (CRT), it indicates to the computer that a spot of light has been "seen" at a particular place on the face of the scope. Thus, by scanning the face of the oscillograph with the cathode ray beam, one is able to pick up a set of coordinates showing the current position of the pen. Programs may be written to follow the light pen and even to leave tracks on the face of the CRT indicating where the light pen has been. This is accomplished by retracing those points for which a previous record had been made.

On a simpler level, there are a number of extremely useful devices for acquiring discrete responses for computer input from a subject participating in a psychological experiment. For example, information from two-position switches can be fed almost directly into a digital computer in the form of a coded 1 or 0. Other multi-position devices may have their outputs encoded, and the technology of connecting such devices is well established. We spoke of the details of the required circuitry for the inputs in an earlier chapter. The position of sliders and pointers, as further examples, may be entered into the computer by means of analog-to-digital converters that encode position directly, rather than on the basis of the voltage-encoding process described in Chapter 8.

DECISION MAKING AND ANALYSIS

Although a machine may have sensors and effectors, it is not very useful unless it can also perform integrating operations, transforming and manipulating the input data into an appropriate form of output. Modern digital computers can serve both as logical manipulators and as arithmetic processors; both features are extremely important in the automated laboratory. We have described the contingent experiment as one of main evolutionary steps in the experimental methodology of psychological research. Clearly such a technique depends upon the ability of the control system to make sophisticated judgments of both a logical and an arithmetic nature.

An effective real-time use of the computer is the presentation to a subject of the results of a complex calculation reflecting the influence of his response almost immediately after he responds. Edwards (1966) has been studying the ways human beings deal with "soft" information, such as verbal statements about hypothetical political situations. After reading a sample paragraph describing some new development, the subject is asked to make a set of probability estimates of the possible international conflicts that could ensue. His responses are fed directly into the computer from positional control levers. The computer determines the joint probabilities of five different estimates made by the subject and then displays these probabilities as a bar graph on a cathode ray tube monitor. The subject is therefore able to see the effects of his estimates graphically displayed and can observe the interactions that occur between different sets of estimates. The computer is also able to introduce perturbations in the calculation of the probabilities by means of programmed rules unknown to the subject, thus influencing future decisions by the subject in subtle ways. This is a relatively straightforward expression of an important experimental technique—the contingent selection of stimuli on the basis of previous responses.

Smith (1961), discussing the general idea of the contingent experiment, points out that in the history of psychophysics there have been a number of contingent techniques. One of the most famous is the Bekesy audiometer, a device for testing auditory thresholds. The subject constantly adjusts a control so that the acoustic signal is just detectable. As soon as he hears the signal, he turns the sound down; when it is no longer detectable, he turns it up. The process goes on continuously as the frequency of the sound waves is scanned. Thus recording the position of the dial on an appropriately calibrated scale can automatically generate a permanent audiogram or contour of detectability without the experimenter's intervening in any way. For the reader interested in the formal mathematical treatment of this problem, Wald's (1947) treatise on sequential analysis is an elegant and thorough foundation.

An analogous psychophysical method is called the up-and-down method. It differs from the Bekesy system in that the stimulus intensity is not continuously adjustable but rather is adjusted only in discrete steps. For example, in a study of visual thresholds, the experimenter would change filters, decreasing the opaqueness if the subject had given a negative response and increasing it if he had given a positive response. For our discussion the important point in both these experiments is that they are simple illustrations of the *contingent experiment.* The next stimulus in a sequence was not completely predetermined before the experiment had begun; each sequential stimulus was dependent or contingent upon the previous responses.

Difficulties in performing a contingent experiment in the conventional laboratory are based upon the fact that the decision rules for selecting sequential stimuli can quickly become so complex that there is insufficient time for the experimenter to determine the conditions of the stimulus for the next trial. Similarly, for complex stimuli, even the adjustment of the new stimulus pattern can be a time-consuming task. However, if a computer is connected on line to the experimental system, these decisions and the generation of complex stimuli can be relatively easily implemented. The permissiveness of the computer response repertoire, therefore, allows us the opportunity to expand greatly upon our earlier methodologies.

Smith has also suggested the general category of the *Markov experiment*—just such a computerized expansion of our experimental technique, which though simple in concept, is clearly beyond the technology of the nonautomated laboratory. A Markov experiment of the type he proposes is one in which the probabilities of a set of sequential responses are dependent upon the previous response, and in which a random process generator uses these probabilities to select an appropriate stimulus from the list of acceptable stimuli. Other similar methods are available. Smith also refers to the *Robbins-Munro* modification of the up-and-down method, in which the step size is decreased as the number of stimuli presented to the subject increases.

Perhaps the most highly developed form of this type of contingent experimental control is that proposed by Taylor and Creelman (1965). They developed a set of rules known as Point Estimation by Sequential Techniques. The PEST routines specify a set of rules for certain actions to be taken when a given response situation occurs. For example, upon a reversal from a *yes* answer to a *no* answer, the size of the step is halved. On the other hand, the size of the step is doubled if two sequential *yes* or *no* responses occur. Among all of the PEST rules, perhaps the most significant is the exit rule, which terminates the experiment if a step of sufficiently small size has been achieved. The utility of the rules is that data collection can be made to be very efficient so that data points are concentrated around the value of especial interest, such as the threshold, and that, once this point has been zeroed upon, the experiment is terminated. This is quite a different approach from, for example, the shotgun approach of the classic method of constant stimuli. Pollack and Headly (1967) have analyzed the ability of the Taylor and Creelman routines to withstand arbitrary decisions on the part of the experimenter. They report the techniques to be remarkably resistant to diverging influences.

In general, these methods and others that will shortly become available have significant advantages for the economic design of experiments. For instance, they concentrate data collection in the region of most active interest and in some cases can provide criteria for deciding when an experiment can be appropriately terminated. In addition, of course, are the efficiencies of automatic stimulus generation and data analysis.

Above all else, the on-line research scientist needs a tool that increases his freedom to explore new and important avenues of research as promptly as possible after the idea has formed. Computers provide rapid and flexible reprogramming of complex procedures, and often such manipulations may be implemented far more quickly with a computer than by the development of special-purpose equipment. This is a subtle issue of efficiency that cannot be settled for all instances, but it is clear that, even though the initial cost of a general-purpose computer is quite high, it may quickly prove to be truly economical when compared with the total cost of special-purpose equipment. A suitable program may be written to simulate the behavior of a complex system of discrete electronic instruments in far less time than it takes to finance, order, assemble, and use the noncomputerized components.

The fully automated laboratory

So far we have discussed in a very general way the specific functions computers can perform. We have given examples of some special functions that can be made available to psychological research by the new computer technology. In addition to this piecemeal application for special subtasks, there has been progress in automating the total laboratory operation. The present section will deal with this topic and will also introduce further technological concepts important for such a laboratory.

In the past, because of the difficulties involved in setting up a computerized laboratory, some psychologists found themselves being drawn away from the substantive matter of their investigations and required to become experts in computer systems design or programming. In one sense this was a loss for the research, but in another, these pioneers have done much to champion an idea that many believe will ultimately be crucial to the development of psychological research techniques.

Small computer systems ideally suited to use in automated laboratories have been announced, offering simple input-output systems and appropriately powerful languages. The extreme commitment of time and energy required in the past is no longer necessary, and it is obvious from the literature already published that the idea of automation is making great headway in the laboratory.

The ultimate breadth and significance of these new techniques are by no means clearly established, but they are suggested by the multifunction capability of systems like the one described by Nickerson in 1964. He lists the following applications of a special-purpose laboratory-control computer developed under his supervision:

1. Presentation of verbal information on a cathode ray tube to instruct subjects, to provide stimulus materials, and to give periodic feedback to subjects concerning their performance.
2. Recording of responses made by subjects with light pen, typewriter, or telegraph keys.
3. Measurement of response latencies with millisecond accuracy.
4. Scheduling of temporal order of events or spatial arrangements of display elements, according to programmed rules which may include randomization with or without forcing constraints.
5. Modification of experimental parameters on the basis of performance.
6. Adjustment of the difficulty of a judgmental task to match the capability of the individual subject.
7. Production of a record of the trial-by-trial progress of the experiment.
8. Performance of statistical analyses on data as they are collected, thus providing the experimenter with the results of the analyses immediately at the termination of the experimental session.

Let us now look at the hardware system that accomplishes all these functions. While it is not at all necessary that a system, to be useful, be as elaborate as the one described here, our example does illustrate many of the different instrumentation aspects of the computerized laboratory.

Shuford (1964) discusses the organization of the facility. Built around a medium-sized computer, the system is diagrammatically represented in Figure 9-1. Among its many features is a mass memory capacity consisting of a magnetic drum and a bank of magnetic tape units. (It should be pointed out that some other experimenters have found it necessary to utilize the intermediate characteristics of magnetic disks, which have better access time than tapes and larger capacity than drums.) The system also has the usual input-output devices, such as paper tape punch and reader, a control console typewriter, and printers and plotters, for reading in programs and reading out data. But the most interesting features for the purposes of our discussion are the special units designed for interaction with subjects.

Among these special units is a group of relays, driven by a register of flip-flops, that control external equipment requiring high voltage levels or otherwise unusual power conditions. For input, a register of switches is used to allow the experimenter to communicate a desired state to the computer. Such switches are often called *sense switches* and can be tested periodically by the computer to determine which of the two alternative courses of action is to be undertaken at a particular stage in the experiment. A switch in one position would indicate to the machine that the program route should be different from what it would be if the switch were in the other position. This function is usually implemented by a "branch on sense switch" instruction, which tests the state of the switch and branches the program accordingly.

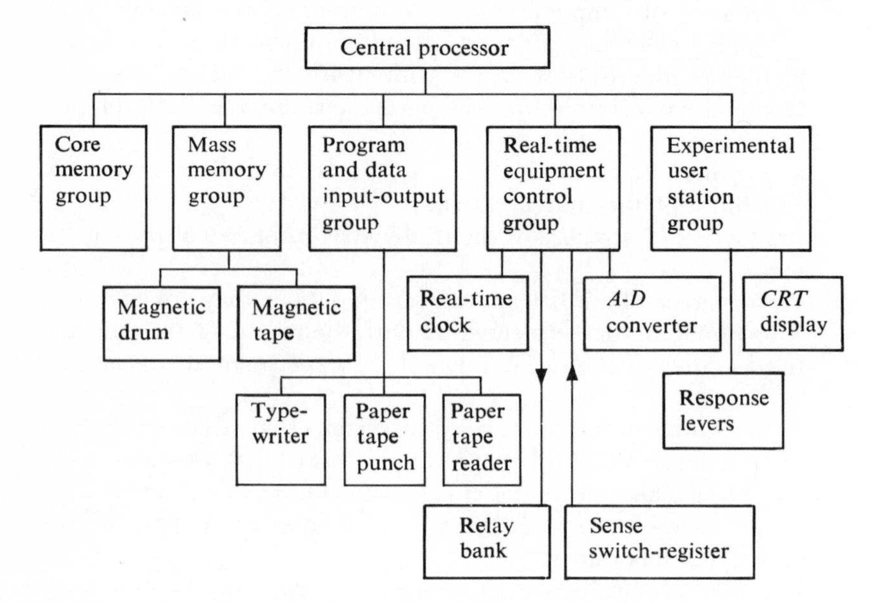

Fig. 9-1. *A digital computer system, which has been especially equipped to handle several different kinds of psychological experiments. (Modified from E. H. Shuford, "The Decision Sciences Laboratory Program of Techniques and Facilities for Automating Research," Technical Documentary Report No. ESD-TDR-64-553 (September, 1964), Office of Technical Services, Department of Commerce, p. 20.)*

The laboratory system described by Shuford includes an analog-to-digital converter, like that described in the previous chapter, as well as a multiplexer to allow selection of various inputs. The capability to interrupt the computer on the basis of external operations is also present in addition to a real-time clock (see below).

Perhaps most relevant to this discussion are the terminals or experimental stations that interact with the subjects. In the system described, such terminals include a battery of cathode ray tube displays with light pens, which are connected to the computer, and a group of computer-controlled typewriters.

This brief outline of a multipurpose behavioral science research computer can serve little purpose without an elaboration upon the uses to which it is placed. Later in this chapter we shall present some examples of recent research utilizing these kinds of terminals in ways that illustrate the powerful potential of computer-controlled experiments.

CLOCKING AND TIMING

We have already spoken of the important general functions of a program interrupt capability in defining the temporal order of events in computers. Time measurements are also of much consequence in the context of real-time psychological experiments. The elapsed time between a computer output and a subject's response is often a significant dependent variable—for example, if reaction time measurements are desired. Occasionally, too, it is necessary to be able to restimulate a subject if he has not responded and a given period of time has been exceeded.

Several kinds of timing devices can be attached to computers for such timing operations. All are based upon a *clock*—the general computer term for a highly periodic event generator. A precision astable multivibrator, such as that discussed earlier in this book, is one example of a device that can be used to generate regular events. For psychological experiments, a one-millisecond clock has proved to be a reasonable compromise between the precision of time measurement required and the potential overload of the central processing from too-frequent time markers.

On the other hand, many real-time systems take advantage of the easily available and very regular clocking obtained from the 60 cps. power line that feeds electrical power to the computer. The sinusoidal oscillation of the power line is amplified and clipped, thus providing a more or less square wave alternating at 60 cps. The edge of the rising or falling waveform is then used to trigger a pulse generator, which emits a standard pulse 60 times a second. Clocking intervals as infrequent as 1/60 of a second are often useful in applications involving verbal responses from the subject, although they would not satisfy the higher precision needs of, for example, a motor reaction time type of experiment. One-sixtieth of a second is also frequently used in time-sharing systems as the time quantum allotted to a given program before it is interrupted and displaced by the next program in the queue.

Clocks may be used to time computer operations in several ways. One of the most economical in terms of additional hardware is to allow the repetitive clock pulse to interrupt the computer each time a pulse occurs. The computer then spends a few instructions incrementing a special core memory location, which is subsequently referred to whenever time measurements are required. However, this is somewhat wasteful of computer time, since a one-millisecond clock interrupts frequently enough to take an appreciable amount of time away from the operation of the ongoing programs. The advantage of such a system is that it can be inexpensively implemented with a simple multivibrator connected to the existing interrupt system of a computer.

On the other hand, a counting register, which is incremented directly by the clock pulses, can be set up external to the computer. Elapsed time can be determined by reading the contents of this register upon demand from the computer. The advantage of this system is that it does not take up any central processor time for processing time counts. One disadvantage, though, is that the latter type of clock requires a considerable amount of additional circuitry. External register clocks can be used in some interesting ways that the simple clock interrupt scheme cannot. The counter could, for example, be in the form of a decrementing register preset to a specific count. After the preset number of time pulses had been counted and a count of zero obtained, the counter would then emit an interrupt signal. The computer program would accept this interrupt and perform the required control operation.

Some engineers compromise between these two timing devices in the following way. A single word in the core memory matrix of the computer is used as the counter and is incremented by each clock pulse automatically without the execution of any computer instructions. Thus, only a small amount of additional external circuitry is needed, and the computer does not lose any significant amount of computing time during the accumulation of time counts.

CATHODE RAY TUBE DISPLAYS

Since man's visual capabilities are extraordinarily good for collecting information from spatial displays, an intense effort has been made to provide interface equipment for visual communication between computers and men. Currently, one of the most useful devices for psychological research is the general-purpose *cathode ray tube*, or CRT. The CRT is an evacuated glass envelope with a source of electrons (the electron gun) at one end and a fluorescent material at the other end, which glows when hit by the electrons. Figure 9-2 is a diagrammatic representation of a typical CRT showing its various components.

The electron source is a heated filament similar to that found in a radio vacuum tube. The heating action, produced by a current, tends to boil off the outer electrons of the atoms of the metal making up the filament. These electrons are then attracted, by a strong positive potential, toward the face of the CRT, which is covered with the fluorescent materials. The focusing and collimating of the diffused bundle of electrons emitted by the filament are accomplished by placing an appropriate voltage on a special set

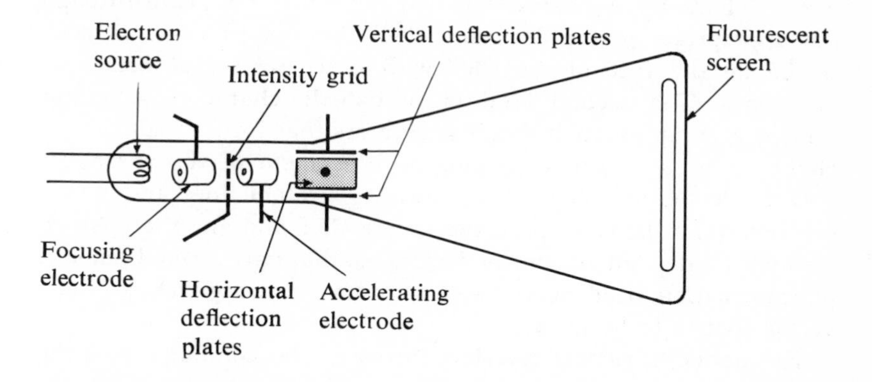

Fig. 9-2. *A typical electrostatic cathode ray tube, which can be used as a visual display under the control of a digital computer.*

of focusing electrodes. It is also possible to control the brightness of the fluorescence on the face of the oscilloscope by means of a grid electrode interposed in the elctron beam pathway. Finally, it is necessary to be able to position the electron beam on the face of the CRT. This can be accomplished in two ways—by either magnetically or electrostatically deflecting the beam of electrons as they move from the electron source to the fluorescent material. Often both techniques are used simultaneously in a single tube. When electrostatic deflection is employed alone, two sets of deflection plates are used—one for horizontal and one for vertical positioning. Similarly, electromagnetic control requires two sets of coils, but since the coils may be external to the CRT a simpler construction technique can be applied to the evacuated tube itself.

It should be noted that a simple CRT is capable only of producing a spot of light on the fluorescent face at a particular place, determined by the voltages on the horizontal and vertical deflection plates. But obviously with such a point plotter it is possible to draw any figure desired. Any alphabetic character can be generated by selecting an appropriate matrix of dots. A straight line can be generated by placing a long row of dots between the initial and terminal points defining the line. However, CRT's have developed far beyond the simple point plotter. Devices have been designed to plot alphabetic characters automatically and to draw curved lines by tracing out a continuous vector.

There are two main kinds of automatic alphabetic character generators. The first utilizes a masking technique in which a metal sheet is perforated with cut outs in the shape of alphabetic characters. A character is next selected by deflecting the beam through the appropriate perforation, and then the shaped beam is positioned on the face of the CRT with a second set of deflection electrodes. The second kind of alphabetic character generator utilizes a group of small vector generators that form an alphabetic character by sequentially tracing each segment of the character.

Other techniques devised for drawing straight lines and curves go far beyond the concept of the simple CRT and are often associated with independent control devices, so that only a small amount of information need be transferred from the computer for each vector that is to be drawn.

The actual electrical interface between the computer and the control circuitry of the CRT must be a digital-to-analog converter that converts the digital code of the computer to the voltages necessary to deflect the cathode ray beam to the desired position.

Another important factor in the selection of CRT's is the nature of the phosphor or fluorescent material. Very-short-persistence phosphors can be used to reduce the amount of time a given spot will glow after the bombarding electrons are removed. Short persistence may be advantageous for certain types of applications in which extreme persistence would cause interference between subsequent displays. On the other hand, in the usual application with a digital computer, a relatively long persistence is usually desired, so that there will be a minimum amount of flicker as the display is repetitively rewritten. The time required for the computer to recycle a display completely may be quite short; however, since it is not infinitesimal, the improper choice of phosphors may lead to an unsteady image.

It is possible to eliminate completely both the problem of flicker and the necessity of rewriting the message on the face of the oscilloscope by use of a *storage* CRT. A storage CRT simulates an infinitely long persistence by the addition of special circuitry to the CRT. Any signal drawn on the face of a storage CRT will be retained undiminished in brightness until intentionally erased by some action of the user (or the computer program). Thus it is necessary to write the pattern desired on the face of the oscilloscope only once—the computer is then free to go on to some other part of its task.

In many applications this may be a particularly powerful means for reducing the load on the computer. Storage tubes, however, usually do not have the ultrafine resolution of a conventional CRT and do have a considerable amount of background fluorescence. Their disadvantages may limit the use of these very practical devices.

THE COMPUTER-CONTROLLED TYPEWRITER

Perhaps one of the most often used yet most often underestimated devices for human interaction with a computer is the electric typewriter. A computer-controlled electric typewriter is capable of both transmitting information from the subject to the computer and displaying information from the computer to him. Many of the early experimental real-time installations used typewriters successfully and demonstrated their wide applicability for communicating alphanumeric information. For the low data rates encountered in alphanumeric interaction between a human and a computer, the typewriter is eminently suitable, not imposing undue restrictions on the computer as do some more powerful all-electronic displays. Many of the alternatives to a keyboard-driven device also deprive the user of the opportunity to construct alphabetic responses fully.

Some recent devices are compromises between the typewriter and the cathode ray tube. These new *electronic typewriters* have typewriter-like keyboards, with simple CRT displays replacing the platen of the typewriter. The special CRT's are often very limited in scope in order to maintain simplicity and can only display alphanumeric characters. Electronic typewriters have the advantage of electronic reliability and silence but functionally are indistinguishable from a typewriter. They should, however, be distinguished from the full-capability CRT's, which allow full geometric display and the use of the light pen.

Examples of psychological research projects using automated laboratories

In a sense this section may be premature. The idea of the truly automated laboratory—with closed-loop control of the experiment and with appropriate modification of the stimulus contingent upon the subject's performance—is in its early stages of development. The technology is so new that there are few published examples of the approach. Although the following experiments are not completely mature developments, they do illustrate various aspects of the automated behavioral sciences laboratory.

A COMPUTER-CONTROLLED EXPERIMENT IN DECISION MAKING

In recent years, Bayesian statistics has become an important tool for psychologists interested in the subjective processes underlying human decision making and probability estimates. The basic idea of this system of statistics is that there are two probability distributions—one that exists before the presentation of the stimulus and one that is formed after the stimulus is presented, as a combination of both new and old information. Amnon Rapoport (1964) has applied Bayesian statistics in a study of human probability estimation, using a computer to control the entire experimental procedure. The small digital computer used in his experiment communicated with the subject through a standard typewriter.

The problem Rapoport was investigating was the development of sequential probability estimates by the human observer in a highly abstracted situation. Specifically, the subject was asked to estimate the portion of 1's in a 10×10 matrix composed of 1's and 0's. The first guess in each trial was simply that, a completely unfounded hunch based upon no information. After the subject made his guess, a small amount of information about the matrix was presented to him. This information was in the form of a 3×3 submatrix that was supposed to be part of the larger 10×10 matrix about which he was guessing. The subject was then given the opportunity to make another estimate, based on the additional information. If the probability estimate made by the subject still was not correct, he was allowed two additional guesses before this particular trial was terminated. A monetary reward was used to keep the motivational level of the subject high.

The computer performed a number of important operations in this experiment. First, it generated all of the 3×3 submatrices that were transmitted to the subject. (The 10×10 matrices were really only mathematical fictions and were represented by a single stored number.) The parameters of the 3×3 matrices were altered from one experiment to another. Second, the computer acquired the subject's responses. Third, it made the immediate calculations necessary for deciding to continue or to terminate the trial. Finally, it accumulated the statistics of the subject's response. Rapoport states some of the important but less obvious arguments for the automated laboratory:

Special mention is warranted concerning the use of a computer in the present experiment. Much has been written lately about the accuracy and speed of computers, and about their use for simulation purposes. Undoubtedly, the inference of the parameters for each subject, the construction of Model II, and the simulation of estimates and predictions of individual subjects would prove to be a very time-consuming task, if a computer were not available. In addition to the use of computers in analyzing data we would like to emphasize the value of the computer as a technique for experimentation. In the present study, the computer succeeded in doing well something that many experimenters do not do very well: taking and giving orders. This was done quickly, accurately, and reliably. Furthermore, it was the author's impression that the use of a computer for instructing the subject, for evaluating his responses, and for providing him with immediate feedback changed something very basic in the experimental situation. It seemed that subjects were ready to trust and to obey the computer much more than they would believe a human experimenter. The subjects did not think the computer would make mistakes or cheat them, as they often think the experimenter does in psychological experiments. This impression was conveyed from the subjects' attitude and comments while being instructed prior to the experiment, from spontaneous remarks throughout the experiment, and particularly from an informal talk with each subject after the experiment was completed. As the extent to which this phenomenon might influence the behavior of decision-makers is not known, further investigation is needed, particularly within the context where subject-experimenter interrelationships are extensive. For our purposes, by using the computer and thus eliminating the experimenter from the experimental situation, a further step was achieved toward a better control of extraneous variables. We would not actually be surprised if it could be shown that in part the consistent results obtained in the present experiment were due to the use of a computer-controlled task [Amnon Rapoport, 1964, p. 369].

The major goal of the Rapoport experiment was to test a specific Bayesian model of human decision making. It is well to note that the accomplishment of this task might not, in fact, have been possible without the dynamic control of the computer, since sequence effects played such an important role in the subject's behavior.

A COMPUTER-CONTROLLED EXPERIMENT IN CONCEPT FORMATION

Concept formation has long been one of the major areas of psychological inquiry that is difficult to investigate quantitatively. The categories or concepts into which items were to be classified often could not be numerically defined, and the significant stimulus dimensions of the individual items of a given class were hard to measure. Weinberg (1965) has devised a computer-controlled task with a highly metricized stimulus set that overcomes many of the difficulties, bringing the resources of the computer to this area of inquiry.

The display configuration used in Weinberg's experiment employed a cathode ray tube display to present the stimuli. A light pen was used by the subjects to respond. A typical set of stimulus patterns is illustrated in Figure 9-3. The stimuli, as can be seen, are

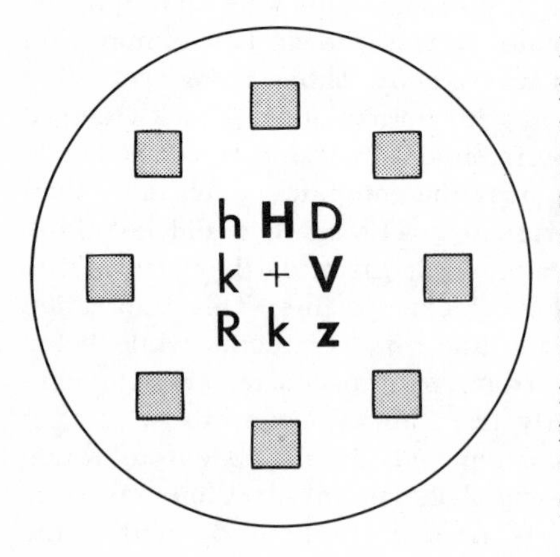

Fig. 9-3. *Weinberg's display (as plotted on the face of a cathode ray tube) for use in the concept formation experiment described in the text. The ring of squares are the response media which, when touched with a light pen, indicate the subject's answer to the problem. (From G. M. Weinberg, "Experiments in Problem Solving," Unpublished doctoral dissertation, University of Michigan, 1965, p. 35.)*

3 × 3 matrices of alphabetic characters. Each position in the matrix can differ in character, case, and brightness. The small cross in the center position is merely a fixation point and is constant from trial to trial. Varying the parameters of each character position allows a large number of stimulus matrices to be displayed that are rather complicated, yet precisely specifiable. Specifically, each matrix is defined by a pattern such as that shown in Table 9-1.

Character Position	1	2	3	4	5	6	7	8
Intensity	A	NA	B	NB	A	NA	3	B
Case	NB	A	1	NA	B	NC	NA	A
LTRA	A	2	C	NA	C	A	B	N1
LTRB	C	NA	A	4	NA	N1	C	B
LTRC	1	NB	NA	NC	N2	NB	NA	A

Table 9-1. *The character coding matrix used by Weinberg to introduce some redundancy into an otherwise too-complicated stimulus design. (From G. M. Weinberg, "Experiments in Problem Solving," Unpublished doctoral dissertation, University of Michigan, 1965, p. 29.)*

The character positions are numbered clockwise from the upper left-hand corner. In Weinberg's system, an *N* preceding a given table entry means that the complement of the indicated bit is to be used rather than another freely chosen bit. From the table we see that one bit represents intensity, one bit represents case, and three bits are used to select a particular character from a subset of our full alphabet for each character position. Therefore, each position on the display matrix is fully represented by a five-bit digital code. Since there are eight character positions in the matrix, 2^{40} different stimulus patterns can be defined with this algorithm.

This is, however, far too many patterns, and Weinberg has reduced the number of potential stimuli to 2^7 by a selection rule that defines the particular stimulus set. The selection rule is called a *designator word* and consists of a seven-bit word defined with each bit labeled in the following order: *ABC*1234. Thus, for example, each time the letter *A* appeared in Table 9-1, the computer program would inspect position *A* of the designator word to determine whether 1 or a 0 should be placed in the position. Since the letter *A* occurs in several places, an element of redundancy is added to the stimulus patterns and the number of independent stimuli is greatly reduced.

The questions asked in the experiment concerned the nature of the subject's strategies in classifying the characters—just which of the redundant informational features were used and how did this selection change as a function of experience with the task?

The display shown in Figure 9-3 has another feature. The concentric ring of brightened spots was, in fact, part not of the stimulus display but rather of the response mechanism. Remember that in CRT displays like these, figures are traced out sequentially in time. It is therefore possible to use a light pen to indicate into which one of the eight possible categories or "concepts" a particular display has been classified by the subject. Weinberg had the computer acquire the responses and compile a considerable amount of information about each trial on a magnetic tape. In this particular experiment the data were then transferred to a larger computer for analysis; but conceptually, if the machine used in the experiment had been powerful enough, it could have performed the data analysis on line equally well.

It would be well to consider a flow chart (Fig. 9-4) of the logical processes involved in presenting a single stimulus trial in the Weinberg experiment. This will help to elucidate further some of the capabilities of the computer-controlled laboratory. First, the computer chooses the values of the stimulus matrix by a selection

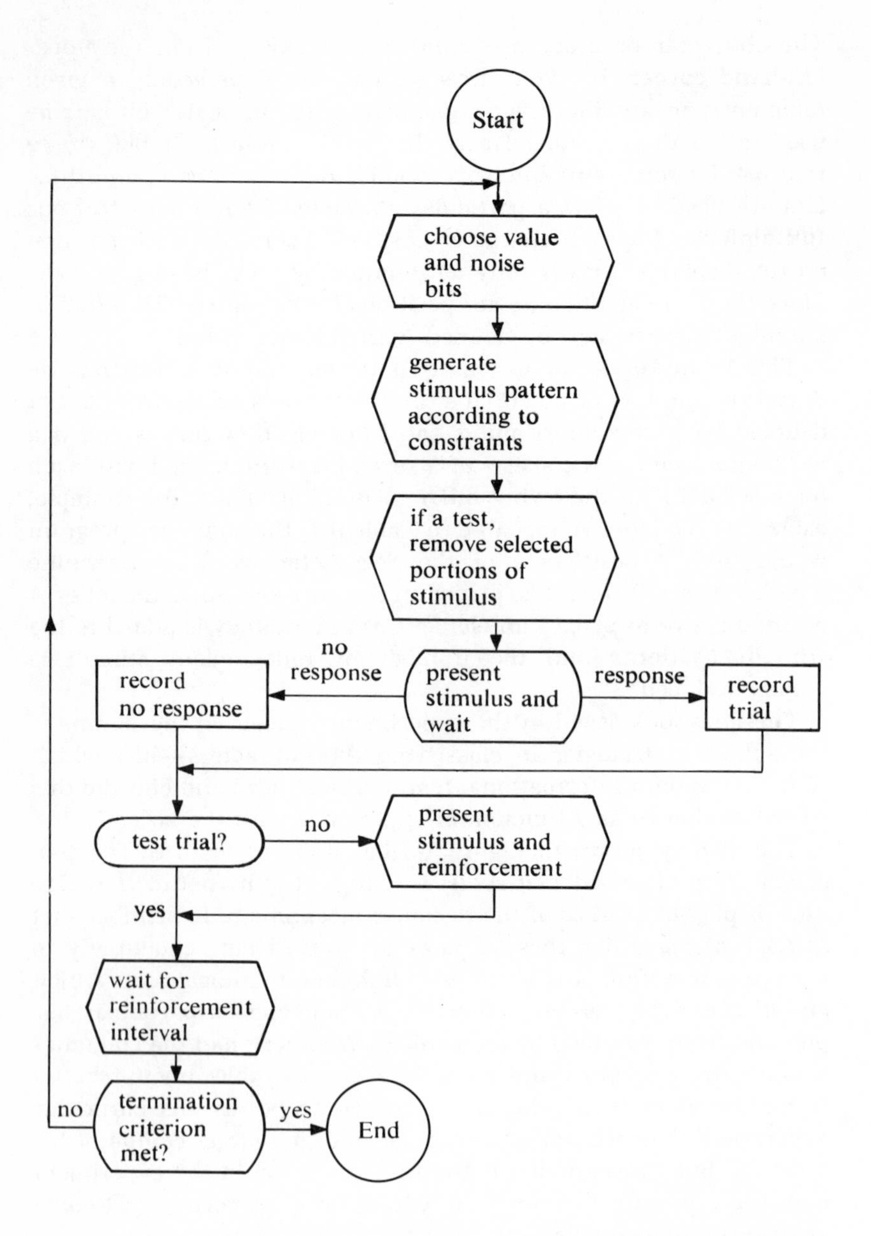

Fig. 9-4. *The flow chart for one trial in Weinberg's concept formation experiment. (From G. M. Weinberg, "Experiments in Problem Solving," Unpublished doctoral dissertation, University of Michigan, 1965, p. 18.)*

rule specific to a given experiment. After these rules are established, the computer branches into a routine that actually presents the display to the subject. On training trials the entire generated display might be presented to the subject; but if the trial were to test the development of a concept, selected portions of the figure might be left out of the total display. This is a means of identifying critical cues that if eliminated would lead to deterioration of the response in a way indicative of the strategy the subject is using.

The reinforcement Weinberg used was a transient brightening of the correct answer and a more limited brightening of the square the subject had pointed to. A final test, generally twenty correct sequential responses, was made to see whether the subject had achieved a termination criterion.

When coupled with the automatic operation of the experiment, the detailed data collection and the highly structured nature of the stimuli allowed a close investigation of the strategies adopted by subjects in developing the concepts or categories into which the stimuli were placed. In Weinberg's opinion one of the major results of the experiment was that subjects were able to learn the task at all, for at first glance it appeared to be a difficult and complex one. Even more significant was the fact that the individual strategies could be inspected in detail. One important set of results dealt with the choice of the elements of the matrix that were used by the subject for the classification. The pattern of this set of choices appeared to be relatively individual, each subject displaying certain predispositions that were reflected in his results. In sum, the experiment is a prime example of a type of research that is impossible to consider without real-time computer control. It also represents a major step forward in the quantitative analysis of what had been a predominantly qualitative subject—the psychology of concept formation.

A COMPUTER-CONTROLLED PSYCHOPHYSICAL EXPERIMENT

Chapter 8 described electrophysiological analysis methods that might have been applied to the problem of the neural encoding of sensory phenomena. Of course, it is also possible to approach the problem of sensory coding from the point of view of the psychophysical experiment. One of the most convenient methods for exploring sensory encoding is to apply electrical pulse stimuli to the skin. Brief electrical pulses have the advantage of producing responses that are of the same duration as the natural nerve impulses and therefore can drive a pattern of nervous activity that is precisely known. We used a computer-controlled psychophysical technique (Uttal and Krissoff, 1966) to explore the effects of the pattern of the electrical pulses on the detectability of an asynchronicity in a train of stimuli. We were interested in the ability of subjects to detect microtemporal fluctuations in repetitive stimuli as a test of the availability of time as a neural code.

A small computer was programmed to serve as a general-purpose pattern generator, a response acquisition system, a data analyzer, and a modifier of the stimulus patterns on the basis of the subject's past responses. The amplitudes and intervals of a train of constant current stimulus pulses varied in accordance with the specific experimental problem being studied. The stimuli were applied to the subject through two test tubes containing saline solutions into which he had dipped the first joint of the index and middle fingers. The subject's task, in all cases, was to report whether or not he felt an asynchronicity or a gap in the "buzzlike" stimulus. He responded by depressing either a *yes* or a *no* key. The keys were connected directly to the computer and interrupted the computer when they were depressed. After logging the response information, the computer presented another stimulus pattern, altered in accordance with the up-and-down method of limits described earlier in this chapter. Figure 9-5 is a block diagram of the experimental apparatus, showing the feedback loops from subject to computer to subject.

At the end of each experimental block a complete statistical analysis of the accumulated data—including the mean, the standard deviation, and the response range—was made. Two decisions were then made about the parameters for the next block. The length of the gap in the initial stimulus in the next block was selected on the basis of the mean gap threshold for the previous block. In addition, the step size for the unit change of the gap was reset to one-tenth of the range of the stimulus variation in the previous block. The temporal pattern of the stimuli themselves was produced by a programmed pattern-generator subroutine that timed the intervals between the various stimuli.

The specific experiments conducted explored the effects of the stimulus amplitude, intervals and numerosity, and the position of the discontinuity on its detectability. The most interesting result concerned the position of the discontinuity. The threshold was elevated whenever the stimulus pattern became asymmetrical.

The psychophysiological significance of this result is not particularly germane to our present discussion on computer applications. In sum, time appeared to be a weaker code than we might have

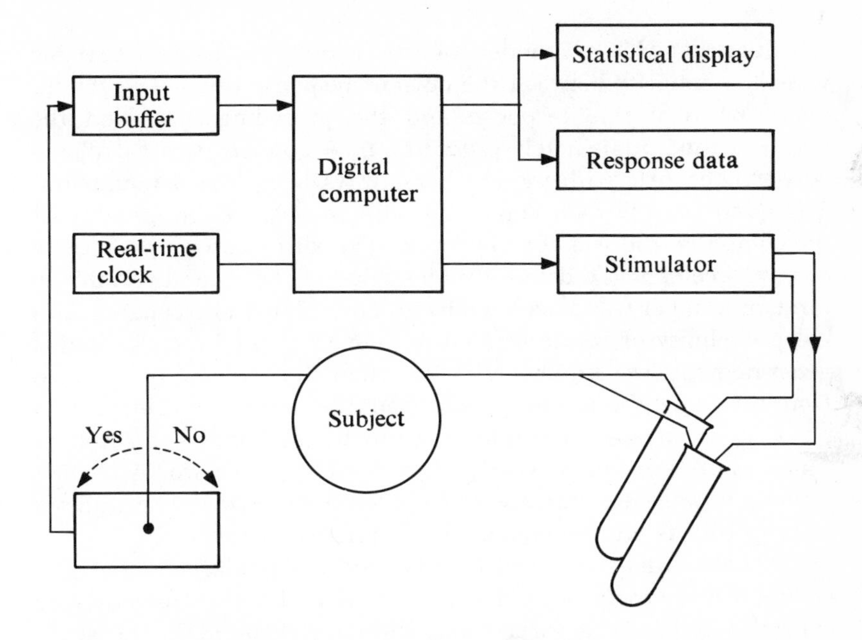

Fig. 9-5. *Block diagram of the apparatus used by Uttal and Krissoff, showing the feedback loops from the computer to the subject to the computer required for contingent experimental control.*

expected. We are more concerned with the computer's role in the experiment. It proved to be a very important one, contributing greatly to the solution of the problem as well as to the efficiency of the experimental procedure. In spite of the initial cost, the small general-purpose digital computer provided an economical way of implementing the many timing, counting, and manipulative functions required in an experiment of this sort. The computer completely automated a complex experimental design with a minimum of auxiliary bookkeeping and off-line statistical manipulations.

A COMPUTER-CONTROLLED INSTRUMENTAL CONDITIONING EXPERIMENT

Weiss and Laties (1965) have used a small digital computer to control an experiment in instrumental conditioning. They were interested in reinforcing a constant interval between successive bar-pressing responses. The rhesus monkeys used as their subjects could close the contacts of a switch ad lib. A small amount of fruit drink was given as a reinforcement, but the schedule of reinforcement was interestingly complex. The animals were not reinforced each time they pressed the lever but received a drink according to a schedule that was a function of two variables. The first variable was the similarity between the current response time—i.e., the interval between this response and the preceding one—and the response time immediately preceding it. A quotient was calculated between the two, with the smaller always being the denominator. The quotient was then compared with a table in the memory of the computer and was thereby associated with a certain probability of reinforcement. To determine the value of the second variable, a random number was calculated by an algorithm and compared with the probability of reinforcement developed from the table. If this generated random number was less than the probability obtained from the table, the reinforcement would be presented. Thus it was not only the degree of similarity between the successive response times that determined whether the reinforcement would be presented; it was also influenced by a random factor. The authors refer to this as an *autoregressive reinforcement schedule*.

The calculations involved in this contingent reinforcement procedure were clearly beyond the capability of a noncomputerized control system. As it turned out, the data reported in the study show that a monkey in such an environment tends to respond with a mean interval between successive responses of about .45 second, clearly eliminating any possibility of manual calculation of the reinforcement schedule.

In addition to the calculation and decision-making use of the computer in the experiment, it is interesting to note that the computer was used in more conventional ways for analyzing the data. One of the very important ways in which conventional data analysis was accelerated involved utilizing the computer to plot the results of the experiments in the form of graphs and on the face of a cathode ray oscilloscope. By plotting the data in a number of different ways, Weiss and Laties demonstrated long-term serial effects in the response times that were displayed as fairly regular drifts of long duration in the averaged interval. To smooth the data to show these more effectively, a moving average, $\overline{X}$,

$$\overline{X} = x_{n-1} + 2x_n + x_{n+1}$$

was computed and the results of the calculation were often plotted instead of the raw data.

Another interesting display of many successive responses showed that, although the average response interval was about .450 second, the animal did not really respond periodically but was strongly influenced by the reinforcement schedule to respond more nearly as he had before. As the authors point out, here was a result that is somewhat redundant with the preceding one showing long-term drifts, but it does point up the same important outcome in a different manner.

This experiment is another interesting application of computer control of a psychological experiment that could not have been executed without the fully automated capabilities of a general-purpose digital computer.

In this chapter we have attempted to demonstrate by example a methodological trend in behavioral science research. There is at so early a stage little, in a formal sense, that could be more usefully presented. The capabilities of a computerized laboratory are best understood in terms of the tone they set for such research rather than in that of a strict set of rules. Other writers have responded in the same way in discussing the problem. The reader is specifically directed to Miller, Bregman, and Norman's (1965) related handling of the issue.

Since it is not possible to present any formal rules, it is immediately obvious that the ways in which computers can best be put to use for a given experiment depend mainly upon the nature of the experiment. Methodology, however, clearly contributes to our perception of the possible range of experiments. It seems that the new methodologies can significantly widen the currently conceived range of behavioral science research. Perhaps this point can nowhere be made plainer than in the notion of the computer teaching machine, which we will discuss in Chapter 10.

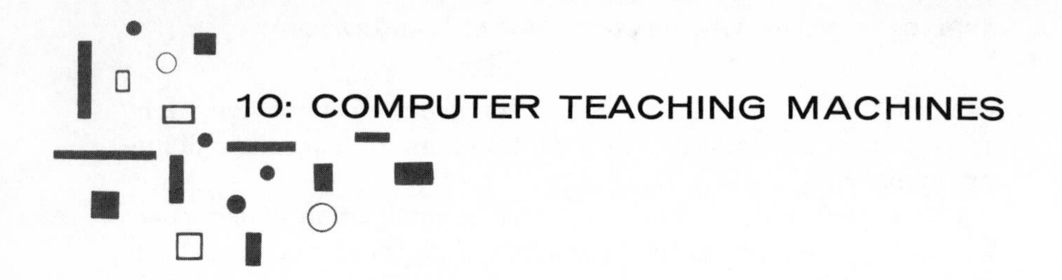

10: COMPUTER TEACHING MACHINES

Introduction

Of all the proposed applications of real-time computers, perhaps none has attracted so much popular attention, or promises to make such a direct impact on the development of human society, as the use of computers to tutor. The reasons for this impact of a still relatively undeveloped and untested idea, of course, are found in the retarded condition of education both in the less affluent countries and in the most modern Western cultures. It is somewhat startling to have to admit that we still know very little about the learning process. In its most complicated form, the conceptual transfers between a young child and an adult tutor, teaching can at best be said to be an art. Yet, if any single fact is obvious to even the casual observer, it is that a large class of students listening to a teacher lecture represents a teaching situation far less effective than the adaptive conversation of a tutor and a single student.

The hope expressed in the current enthusiasm for computer teaching machines has been that the computer's ability to process natural languages will ultimately allow at least a partial simulation of the natural tutorial conversation. A certain amount of progress has been made toward this goal, but the art and science of computer teaching machines is still in its infancy. The purpose of this chapter will be to describe the computer teaching machine as an example of real-time computing, and to assess both the sources of the idea and the degree to which it might be expected to contribute to our educational technology. We shall also attempt to categorize the classes of computer teaching machines that we believe are significantly different from one another. The categorization is necessary because the fact that *not all teaching machines that use computers are computer teaching machines* is often overlooked in the general enthusiasm for the machines and the idea.

Further, we shall discuss the types of utility programs that have evolved out of the need to simplify the author's role in the preparation of programs. Finally, the relation of the computer teaching machine to other natural language processing applications will be examined.

Psychological foundations of computer teaching machines

At this early stage in its development, the idea of computer teaching machines is regularly being challenged. There is a constant repetition of the basic question "What advantages does the computer teaching machine have over conventional means of education that justify the investment of funds which might be used equally or even more fruitfully in other ways?" The question is complex because it implies an underlying base of agreement that may be only superficially valid. First, it implies that the general question of validity can be answered in a specific and scientific fashion, not only for computer teaching machines, but for any educational or communication technique. Indeed, if one looks at past events, with the exception of psychological test standardization one is hard pressed to find any example of a validation of such complex techniques. Second, it presumes that there *is* an enormous economic disadvantage to computer tutoring, an assumption that may not be valid if all the consequences of more efficient utilization of student time are also taken into consideration. Furthermore, even if there is some immediate economic trauma, it assumes that this is worse in the long run than the misutilization of lesser funds on outmoded—but currently accepted—forms of education.

Obviously, then, the question is a loaded one. We shall deal later in the chapter with a few of the technical details, such as multiplexing, that reduce the cost of computer teaching machines; but the economic factor will ultimately be determined by the technical progress made in the development of new techniques and procedures. However, we mainly leave this question to the accountants and salesmen who will decide the answer over some conference table of the future. Our chief concern will be with the methodological and psychological details of the idea.

Perhaps the simplest, and therefore the most elegant, proposition attempting to justify computer teaching machines is a statement made by Sidney Pressey (1959). Originally concerned with the noncomputerized teaching machine, it nonetheless retains its power in this new context. He said, "Almost any reasonable method involving pupil activity and adjustment to individual differences will show gains." The two essential aspects of this expression are thus seen to be motivation and practice. Implicit in it also is a criticism of classroom lecture techniques in which student participation and individual attention are greatly reduced.

But reduced from what and by what? Education for the masses —from some points of view, that means two or more students—is a relatively new concept. In earlier stages of cultural evolution a family head would pass on to his sons the basic information necessary for sustaining life. Guiding the child's hand with his own, the father would respond immediately to deficiencies in the performance of the youngster. Such an individual approach was possible because there was little division of labor; since most of the parents of a community were masters of a small number of basic skills, all were potential tutors. But as civilization became more intricate, additional layers of complexity and specialization of labor allowed individuals to achieve higher levels of performance in a smaller number of skills as they were relieved of other duties. Most important was the development of nonmanual skill educational requirements. Rather than learning a handicraft, students began to learn patterns of thought or conceptual skills. In these cases, they no longer had to "practice" overtly a manual art to achieve mastery, but thinking as such and contemplative manipulations assumed increased prominence. It seems certain that this development was related to the cultural evolution of specialization of labor, which allowed part of the population to do something else with their time than simply work to meet the needs of survival. Thus a group of "students," more or less free from the needs of sustenance, began to replace the individual apprentice. Furthermore, as society became more complicated, the utility of education became obvious to those who could profit from an educated populace. Business, armies, and government particularly began to appreciate and to support educational activities that trained citizens in useful skills such as reading, writing, and arithmetic. I shall not labor the point. The interested reader is referred to Sebastian de Grazia's (1962) treatise *Of Time, Work and Leisure* for a thoughtful analysis of this phenomenon.

The utility of education was only one of many forces adding impetus to the spread of education to a wider and wider audience, and thus to larger and larger classes. This democratization of education has culminated in social schemes in which education has come to be considered a "right" of each individual, basic to his exploitation of equal opportunity. More recently, the technological environment has provided an enormous number of mechanical aids to supplant human toil and thus has added even further opportunities for mass education. Nowadays, how very small a proportion of the population is really necessary to provide the necessities of life for all the others! We have witnessed an enormous proliferation of "service," managerial, and other luxury activities as major occupations in our mid-twentieth-century culture.

Foremost among those luxury activities is education. It is a luxury, however, that may evolve into a necessity—as the only way meaningful occupations can be given to "unnecessary" persons not involved in sustenance vocations. Furthermore, education holds a unique promise for solving, if not in this generation, then ultimately, the social problems of our world. Yet today some speak of education, in the jargon of the marketplace, as the fastest growing "business" in America. This absurdity, this looking upon knowledge and its dispersal as just another commodity to be exploited, may return to haunt us in the centuries to come.

For the moment, let us again consider the historical expansion of education. Free from the requirements of manipulative practice, groups congregated to learn of concepts where before only individuals could practice skills. What had been engaged in infrequently in leisure time, such as verbal histories (stories) or religious ceremonies (music and dance, philosophy, astronomy, psychology, etc.), became the activities of a more frequent, often full-time commitment. Teachers could now lecture rather than individually guide. Thus there has been an enormous divergence of educational opportunity. Whereas primitive societies primarily taught survival skills that could be learned on an individual handicraft basis, modern societies primarily teach conceptual skills that can be transferred by voice or, even more dramatically, by the printed word. It is almost too obvious to point out that the invention of printing allowed the trend toward mass education to explode into a worldwide revolution.

One practical effect of this revolution was that the master-apprentice relationship gave way even more to the lecturer-student relationship, and specifically one in which the spoken word became the major tool of tutorial "action" ("interaction" is especially inappropriate in this context). From a one-to-one relationship, education had evolved into a one-to-many relationship. The powerful interaction between master and apprentice was thus replaced by a weaker, one-way communicative process between teacher and class.

The two emphases of Pressey's statement now become clearer. First, it suggests the importance of learning by practicing. While this importance is overt and obvious in teaching handicrafts, there is often the mistaken assumption that practice can be minimized in the more conceptual curricular materials. Thus, for instance, reading without writing takes up too much of our curricular effort. Second, the statement expresses the necessity of adjustment or adaptation to individual differences in a local and immediate manner for the optimization of learning.

In an earlier paper (Uttal, 1962*a*), I formulated a slightly different statement, encompassing some of the same concepts expressed by Pressey. I pointed out the intrinsic motivating properties of a two-person conversation, drawing analogy between some engineering concepts used in control theory and certain education processes. A control engineer distinguishes between *open-loop* systems, in which no feedback from the output exists to modify the input, and *closed-loop* systems, in which feedback is used. The technological history of the past three decades reflects the increasing realization that closed-loop systems are not only quantitatively superior to open-loop systems but differ from them in fundamental qualitative ways owing to the nature of the dynamics of feedback.

A repeated comparison of the present state of a system with the desired end state is necessary to arrive at that end state economically. The model for a closed-loop kind of system in human education is, of course, the tutor-student dialogue, the *conversational interaction* that is now well employed to remedy some of the unfortunate effects of our classrooms. As we have said, conversation is a highly motivating and only modestly fatiguing process. The reasons are as simple as Pressey's statement. The conversant is actively participating in the dialogue, and the responses he receives are adaptive to his stream of thought and understanding. It can be seen that human learning by tutoring meets more of the basic requirements for the optimization of learning, while education by class and lecture continually violates these criteria.

Why, then, has the classroom lecture process become so dominant in our educational technology? We have already suggested one historical reason. The changing nature of society and, therefore, the changing nature of the curriculum fostered it. But the chief reason is not a rational one based upon a critical evaluation and test, but rather one based on logistic convenience. It is administratively simple to congregate a class and present an open-loop lecture. A lecture is superficially efficient in the sense that information is "transmitted" to a large class by a single lecturer. And we must admit that, in the absence, until now, of any practical alternative to "mass open-loop" education, it has reigned supreme for hundreds of years.

Being an analytical race, we are not satisfied with these global statements and yearn for a more detailed expression of the individual factors that influence the educational act. To search the literature of experimental psychology appears initially to be a fruitless task, for the isolated and abstracted examples of classic, instrumental, and nonsense-symbol learning seem unrelated to the complexities observed, for instance, in a child's learning to read. Yet like all scientists, experimental psychologists have learned about the complex by studying the simple, and a second look does begin to enlighten. In this primarily technologically oriented book, it would be inappropriate to attempt a completely documented statement of emerging principles. It is, however, useful simply to list those "principles" that are relatively self-evident. They can serve as a basic outline of the features that should be built into the the ideal teaching machine.

The following categorization is not to be construed as a rigid ordering. It is neither exclusive nor exhaustive, and similar organizations presented by other authors may be more satisfying to some readers. We have attempted to order some of the variables—or, more properly, groups of variables—as an *aide-mémoire,* rather than as a scientific taxonomy.

MOTIVATIONAL VARIABLES

As we shall see, each item in this scheme might, from one point of view or another, claim precedence over the others. The category of motivation is easily expanded in meaning and scope but refers here to a relatively restricted concept. It is closely related to the term *trapping* used by Licklider (1962) to describe the tendency of students interacting with the computer teaching machine to persevere in the tutorial process almost unaffected by fatigue or external environmental distractions; the student's attention and energies are "trapped" by the computer to an astonishingly successful degree. Also reported elsewhere are instances in which students became quite angry if interrupted during their lesson. Licklider attributes these effects to the continuity of the stimulus material. The student, by virtue of the rapid response of the computer, never has time to drift off on a side stream of consciousness. But this highly motivating state probably has other causes too. We would suggest, for example, that stimulus uncertainty is one of them. The analogy may be drawn betweeen tutorial activity on a computer and a game like bowling. The responses emitted by the mechanism are, a priori, unknown. Small differences in the response of the student or the bowler may result in large differences in response from the mechanism—a correctly interpreted answer, or strike, on the one hand, and a wrong answer, or "gutter ball," on the other. The uncertainty adds an element of surprise and adventure that may be as powerful as temporal continuity in maintaining "trapped" attention.

This has also been called the "pinball effect": a highly stereotyped response (withdrawing and releasing the plunger) has a wide variety of results, each with a relatively high uncertainty of occurrence. Uncertainty may, therefore, be very effective in motivating performance. But it must be a modest kind of uncertainty. It must be partially, but not completely, dependent upon the player's responses. A game in which the response was completely determinable by the player would be uninteresting, as would a game in which his responses merely triggered the random occurrence of members of a large family of responses. The behavior of the addicted pinball player who spends hours engaged in this intellectually impoverished pursuit suggests that games share some such motivational force. The issue is: can we transfer this force to activities that are more profitable for the player?

MEANINGFULNESS

The statement that educational material should be meaningful is a tautology. Even so, it is observed as such only on a gross level. Many lower levels of meaningfulness are violated constantly in the classroom situation. Material must be meaningful not only in the large but also in detail. New material, that is, should be relevant to the immediate state of understanding of each student. Implicit in this statement is a requirement for a constant and immediate evaluation of individual differences. While one student may be stalling, waiting for a lecture to catch up to his level of understanding, another may be swamped by the same set of materials. Though brilliantly executed, a lecture may serve the needs of only a very small percentage of the members of the class. How small the percentage is, is open to conjecture, but the wide spreads in examination scores (which themselves are adapted to some intermediate level of comprehension) suggest that meaningfulness is not being achieved on this microscopic level in most lecture situations.

Meaningfulness is related, of course, to vocational goals and differences in interest patterns as well as to the intellectual differences of the students. Thus, the determination of what is meaningful for any given student is a complex and difficult task. There are, however, indirect but useful signs of individual meaningfulness. They are often expressed in current performance and comprehension tests of the student's understanding. The fact that, in the conventional educational process, tests of performance and comprehension are likely to be too infrequent and too long delayed minimizes their utility.

TEMPORAL CRITERIA

Perhaps the single most important result gleaned from studies of learning in the psychological laboratory is that learning is greatly influenced by temporal variables. This result is shown in many ways, but generally it can be seen that there is an optimum time, specific for each of the various kinds of learning, between the presentation of the stimulus (or fact or question) and the validating reinforcement. Less strongly established, but with a higher level of face validity, is the precept that the student should proceed at his own optimum speed. Self-pacing of educational sequences can be shown to be closely related to both of the preceding factors, motivation and meaningfulness, since they can be seriously reduced in effectiveness if the student proceeds too slowly or too rapidly. In most kinds of human learning, the more immediate the validation, the greater the effectiveness of the learning, so pressure has been exerted to make reinforcement "immediate." *Immediacy*, a vague term, seems to be on the order of a fraction of a second for motor skills and perhaps a couple of seconds for the more complex verbal skills. Slight lags in tracking tasks can seriously inhibit the level of performance, while a delay of a second or two in a mathematics course following the completion of a long calculation seems to be not too important. The delays of days, weeks, or months prevalent in conventional education must be compared with these estimates with a sense of frustrated horror.

Self-pacing must not, on the other hand, be overdone, for—again this is an opinion rather than a rigorously confirmed fact—challenge adds to the motivational level of the student. The rhetorical question is the human tutor's embodiment of this idea. A satisfactory teaching mechanism should, therefore, attempt to stimulate sufficiently by forcing the pace slightly, so that the student is optimally challenged.

PRACTICE AND SPECIFICALLY CONSTRUCTED ANSWERS

As we shall see later, the available technology of computer teaching machines has often been dominant in defining the educational tools they use. One of the most serious effects of this technological dominance has been the minimization of the importance of practice by overt construction of answers. In some of the noncomputerized teaching machines, in which an unfortunately high level of redundancy has been used to reduce student errors (itself a reflection of a technological rather than a psychological criterion), overt responses naturally would be ineffective. On the other hand, in a dynamic situation in which a variability of response is encouraged, simple multiple-choice selection of an answer can, we believe, much reduce the effectiveness of the tutorial interaction.

STEP-BY-STEP CONTINUITY AND MASTERY

Computer teaching machines did not spring full-blown from nothing. They are the logical outcome of the ideas embodied in noncomputerized teaching machines. We refer here specifically to the work of Sidney Pressey and B. F. Skinner. What was the contribution of these workers that has persisted even though their technology is now practically superseded by the computer teaching machines? It was the concept of partitioning the educational materials into a set of steps or, in their terminology, *frames*, and of requiring mastery of each frame before the student could progress. Other educational processes deal with lectures, chapters, and similar large blocks as the conceptual unit. Although such syntheses are important to the development of overall interpretations, they are particularly weak pedagogic tools when the subject matter is one in which there are strong sequential dependencies. All teaching machines, both computerized and noncomputerized, strive toward reduction of material into small frames that can be analyzed individually. Thus, they can be dealt with on a level of analysis far deeper than that allowed in the above-mentioned procedures. In this light, one wonders how a subject matter such as mathematics could ever have been taught with a mass lecture. In later analyses we may decide that it probably was not, but rather is the sort of material that is, fortunately, susceptible to self-tutoring.

Unique features of computer teaching machines

The computer teaching machine, as it has evolved so far, has not yet implemented all these criteria or guides. Barring some completely unexpected barrier, however, it can be expected to come much closer to simulating the interaction between a human tutor and a student than does the methodology of the classroom or any other current teaching procedure. It clearly shares certain unique features with the human tutor that distinguish it in extremely significant ways from other types of teaching machines and non-automated teaching techniques.

The first of these unique features is that the processes of the conventional classroom, which are usually separated by necessity into relatively unrelated parts, are unified into a single, homogenous, smooth, two-way flow of information between the tutor, human or machine, and the student. Conventionally the presentation of information, practice and drill, recitation, testing, and evaluation are separate functions, called up more or less sequentially and at widely spaced intervals. The effects of evaluation, therefore, cannot influence the teacher's presentation until the critical time—now—is long past. Recitation or practice, rather than coming at each step in a meaningful manner, often comes after such a long delay that much of its utility is lost.

The situation is quite different with the computer teaching machine or the human tutor. In this context, all the processes are merged. The presentation of information, practice or recitation, individual study, and, finally, testing are all taking place in a manner that, from one point of view, can be regarded as simultaneous and, from another, can be considered the optimum sharing of the student's time and effort.

The next unique feature emerges immediately from this dynamic and smoothly flowing process. It is, of course, the fact that since "tests" precede the presentation of each new step, a failure on a given test precludes that presentation. This critical, though simple, idea means that the student stays with each step of the curricular sequence until he has mastered it. Since each student is free to proceed at his own pace, the final effect is that the entire schedule and pace of the educational process, as well as the criteria for success, are altered. In a conventional classroom a group of students spends a constant amount of time to learn an amount of material varying from student to student, but in a computer teaching machine situation each student spends a variable amount of time to learn a constant amount of material. The especially important fact is that there is no a priori reason that this variable amount of time should not be the amount associated with complete mastery.

This fundamental difference in the organizational effects of the two types of teaching suggests that the full implications of computer teaching are not appreciated by the large group of apologists who, for one reason or another, regard the computer teaching machine as but "another weapon in the educational arsenal." It also suggests that there may be fundamental and therefore truly irreconcilable differences in the two processes that will lead to future conflicts over issues far removed from simple tests of validity or efficiency. One potential social and cultural impact of this difference is not frequently enough considered. What will it mean to world society to have suddenly thrust upon it the possibility of educating enormous numbers of people to relatively high levels of mastery, perhaps in a shorter time than previously? This question supersedes the trivial issues of the limitations of current computer teaching techniques. But then, man has never adequately planned for such cosmic trauma to the status quo in the past; unfortunately, there is little reason to expect him to do so now.

From a practical point of view, the computer teaching machine can be seen to be unique in other ways. Quite conceivably some of its unique features could be achieved by human tutors, but here the logistic problem seems insurmountable. There simply are not enough masters to serve the needs of the army of apprentices now eager and available for study. The computer teaching machine, like educational television and other audio-visual devices, performs the useful task of amplifying and diverging the information from the single master, so that it may be directed to a very large number of students. With the exception of the computer teaching machine, however, all of these information amplifiers do so at a terrible cost: the loss of the flow of information from the student to the teacher. We have already expressed, in several different ways, the importance of feedback to the final mastery of the subject matter.

Without feedback, the one-way information systems, such as films and television, become simply communication systems. The model provided by the human tutor suggests that education is not simply communication but is, rather, an information-processing activity in which substantial adaptation, interpretation, and generation of new specific material from general classes make the communication issue rather insignificant. Unfortunately, many current research and development efforts are emphasizing the communication aspects of the computer teaching machine, with a resulting neglect of the information-processing or concept-manipulative aspects. Similarly, the emphasis on educational television merely enhances the already demonstrated limitations of the conventional lecture. I believe this to be a misemphasis, based upon a lack of awareness of the real meaning of computer teaching machines and the related dynamic educational processes.

That true meaning has its genesis in the nature of the modern digital computer as originally set forth by Burks, Goldstine, and von Neumann (1947). The essential feature, the very foundation of the cultural impact that computers are having, is the ability of the computer to deal with prestored instructions and addresses in the same way it deals with numbers. Thus, on the basis of tests and branches, the sequence of the computer program is alterable as a function of what conditions are met. This internal manipulation of instructions made it meaningful to strive for higher-speed technologies and huge programs that could execute millions of instructions. But these are only secondary consequences of the essential feature of digital computers. Internal manipulation of instructions also makes it possible to attempt to use computers for programs simulating the human intellectual process implicit in tutoring, or, for that matter, in thinking. All the other ingenious innovations in hardware pale beside the basic brilliance of this truly influential idea—the stored, internally modifiable program. This is the one reason that an emphasis on the communication aspects of computer teaching machines represents a major misdirection at the present stage of their development. Rather, we should be studying the logical foundations of the process and how they may be best simulated.

Finally, it should be pointed out that the computer teaching machine shares other features with other pedagogic procedures. They are, therefore, not conceptually unique to computer teaching. In a practical sense, though, often the realization of features such as immediacy and depth of analysis becomes effectively unique, or, at least, explicitly manipulated, solely in the computer-oriented teaching environment.

Types of computer teaching machines

Because of these formal and practical features unique to computer teaching machines, it is particularly distressing to see the astonishing lack of appreciation, among many workers in the field, of the significance of the stored-program computer. All too often there is both an apparent unwillingness to probe deeply into the full capability of the computer as a teaching tool and an expedient exploitation of less-than-adequate systems that seriously obstruct imaginative progress in some of our most heavily financed ventures. Such a sweeping generalization requires that we give a more detailed analysis of the various types of computer teaching machines.

As stated before, not all teaching machines that are connected to computers are computer teaching machines. The major intended implication is that many of the so-called computer teaching machines fail to embody a sufficient portion of the full range of potential capacities of the computer. At the lowest level, we see computers weakly attached to more or less independent, or "free standing," teaching terminals. Here they are performing no other function than a slightly elaborated bookkeeping. We shall refer to such devices as *degenerate computer teaching machines*.

At a more sophisticated level, a dichotomy can be used to classify two other major divisions of computer teaching machines, on the basis of the logical process underlying their operation. The first of these we shall call *selective computer teaching machines;* the second, *generative computer teaching machines*.

DEGENERATE COMPUTER TEACHING MACHINES

We would consider a computer teaching machine degenerate when it does not allow the teacher to utilize a large number of the dynamic advantages potentially offered by a computer in his tutorial program. This inhibition on the development of a truly effective tutorial conversation is frequently a result of an ineffective use of computer technology. For example, one of the most important bases of effective education, as we pointed out previously, is practice. We refer here specifically to that capability that allows the student to construct his answers. Many terminals for computers permit answers to be constructed; the most important is the relatively dependable and economical computer-controlled typewriter. Some computer teaching machines, however, use a small set of multiple-choice buttons as the only response mechanism allowed the student. I submit that this expedient to reduce the demands on the central processor disastrously decreases the effectiveness of the tutorial process. Such an input medium is a prima facie sign of a degenerate computer teaching machine. The repertoire of responses allowed the subject is too small and stereotyped, and, more critically, the types of analyses that can be applied to this type of highly restricted response are minimized. In such a case the skeptical question "Why do you need a computer at all?" is reasonably well justified and extremely difficult to answer, for little sophisticated branching and much less detailed analysis of student response are possible.

Another technological constraint leading to degeneration lies in the area of bulk storage of textual material. We have frequently seen investigators turn to some conventional form of storage medium such as microfilm. Bulk storage on microfilm, however, has a number of serious disadvantages. First, a frame of microfilm is capable of storing too large a block of material. Or, from another point of view, too few individual addresses are available for each block of information. Thus, there is a strong tendency to make the step-by-step sequence one in which the steps are so large that it is not possible to distinguish the details of student deficiencies. Instead, the analysis program must revert to responses that are not specific to the individual student's performance but are more general. This leads directly to a minimization of the need of specific analysis and, therefore, of the development of specific analysis routines comparable to the analyses carried out by the human tutor.

Microfilm also has the disadvantage of being a nonerasable form of data storage, unlike the magnetic media of other types of computer memories. It is more difficult to change a section of a microfilm record as new insights into the education process are obtained. Finally, since most microfilm devices are designed to display their contents to a single subject, the advantages of pooled information storage are lost.

Degenerate computer teaching machines can thus be identified with extremely limited input media and output display devices that are relatively static and often too unrefined in step size. Associated with these features has often been an inadequate ability to process alphabetical as opposed to numerical information. In general, the "free standing" teaching machine, in which a small amount of special-purpose logical circuitry is associated with a simple multiple-choice keyboard and a microfilm (or equally limited audio response mechanism), must be considered as an automated conventional teaching machine, rather than as even a degenerate computer teaching machine. We shall speak later of the inhibiting forces introduced, on the other hand, by terminals of too great electronic sophistication.

SELECTIVE COMPUTER TEACHING MACHINES

We can now turn to the more serious attempts at utilization of the computer's logical power to provide solid tutorial aid. If one strives to find a single discriminating difference between the conventional teaching machine and the computer teaching machine, he may be somewhat confused. As we have pointed out, there are several unique features. But one operational or logical principle does help to unify the preceding ideas by virtue of its fundamental significance to all of them. This is the concept of *branching.*

Conventional teaching machines by and large, because of their technological limitations, are necessarily relatively nonadaptive. Operationally the result is a sequencing of the student's progress that is essentially linear. On the other hand, the computer teaching machine, if effectively programmed, is capable of adapting to the student's progress. It does so by allowing a large amount of decision making at critical points in the instructional sequence on a detailed and microscopic basis.

Branching, though reaching its highest stage of development with computer teaching machines, developed elsewhere. The term was originally used to describe logic embodied in the scrambled textbook or equally simple microfilm tutors by Crowder (1959). Both of these technologies, however, allow branching only at the grossest level without any detailed analysis of the student's responses. Perhaps, then, a more definitive term to apply to computer teaching machines would be *microscopic branching.*

Nevertheless, the basic idea of branching is exemplified in the scrambled textbook, and certain subsequent noncomputerized teaching machines, and should be so acknowledged. In sum, branching is a sequencing procedure in tutoring in which any one of several alternative statements may be presented to a student; the specific decision of which alternative is determined by the student's most immediate response. The types of *branching trees* or *decision logics* possible constitute a large family of hypothetical alternatives. In a *main trunk* type of tree, after a short remedial digression, the student is always returned to some central sequence. In a *fully branched* tree, once having left a given sequence, the student never returns to that point. These are but two of a large number of logics that could be devised.

The actual implementation of branching structures in most current teaching machines has been through a process involving storage, comparison, and, finally, selection. This is the set of activities that characterizes the class of computer teaching machines we call *selective.* All possible questions, statements, and remedial hints and queries (indeed, any action of the computer) are prestated by the author of the teaching machine program. They are then prestored in a large and, hopefully, randomly accessible memory. The student's answers to questions are analyzed by simple processes in which, perhaps with some slight editing, they are compared with a list of possible alternative correct answers and anticipated incorrect answers. If a match is obtained between any answer in the list and the student's answer, this match specifies and thus selects one of the prestored statements from the computer memory, which is now displayed to him. The analysis routines in such a process are very simple. A simple comparison is made of input with members of a set of alternative answers; a match completely determines the next statement.

Most computer teaching machines dealing with general verbal materials appear at present to be members of this category. These applications take advantage of the capability of a computer to compare and to store small chunks of material. They also greatly benefit from the author's freedom to change easily and nearly instantaneously the contents of a single statement or question. As quickly as improvements become apparent to the human author, they can be added to the existing program.

Many current selective computer teaching machines allow only a single type of selection process or branching criterion. Programs are written in such a way that a skeleton logic is made available, upon which the author may hang a large number of verbal statements. The steps may be small, and complex sequences can be generated on the basis of a large lexicon of simple statements and a few simple selection rules. Thus, the selective computer teaching machine can, superficially, present a good imitation of the tutorial dialogue.

To illustrate, we have chosen to concentrate on the work of a single laboratory, rather than to attempt a global analysis of the many prototype computer teaching machine projects now under development. Swets and Feurzeig (1965) have described a program that is used to teach medical diagnostics to physicians. In their program they have tried to allow a great deal of flexibility in the tutorial sequence. They go so far as to let the student divert the course by typing in one of a list of "vocabulary" items, specially coded items sensed by the computer as a cue for digression to some other routine. Their goal was to develop, in the sense described above, an adaptive conversational interaction between a simulated master pathologist and a student diagnostician. They achieved the goal by an ingenious and energetic utilization of the selective techniques.

The following excerpt from their published protocol stands as an outstanding example of a high level of selective programming. The capitalized phrases are inputs from the student, while the longer sentences represent displays of the stored tutorial materials to the student. The excerpt begins in the middle of a longer conversation as a student makes a tentative diagnosis. At various points (phrases terminating with a question mark) the student asks for laboratory test results.

PULMONARY INFARCTION

Yes, I remember you liked this diagnosis before. There's no question of the need to account for this possibility. . . . But rule it out, won't you, on the basis of the history of shaking chills, high temperature, and somewhat excessive WBC.

ACUTE PYELONEPHRITIS

Very good. You should think of acute pyelonephritis. It's consistent with many of your patient's signs and symptoms—but not all. Wouldn't you want some signs of dysuria to support this diagnosis? And what about the respiratory symptoms in the history and findings? You'd better reevaluate the evidence.

FRIEDLANDER PNEUMONIA

A wise thought—but off the mark. You don't have the usual Friedlander pneumonia gelatinous type sputum nor the Klebsiella organism—do you? Hold off on this diagnosis for awhile.

(Deleted: interchanges concerning some physical examinations and vital signs, and some diagnostic assertions that were off the mark.)

PLEURAL EFFUSION

A good contender, but let's be careful. What evidence would rule it in or out?

POSITIVE EVIDENCE OF ANOTHER DISEASE

Is there such evidence?

POSSIBLE EVIDENCE THOUGH INCONCLUSIVE

Since you aren't sure, continue the examination until you have conclusive evidence one way or the other.

RBC?

An RBC is not indicated at this time. It's an unnecessary expense for a poor patient.

WBC?

22500.

STAPH PNEUMONIA

Fair enough. But where is the guilty organism? When you have isolated staphylococcus aureus in significant numbers in your samples of this patient's fluids or excretions, let me know.

PNEUMOCOCCAL PNEUMONIA

Are you absolutely sure?

YES

You can't be until you have irrefutable evidence. What would help you nail down the diagnosis?

EVIDENCE FROM SPUTUM SMEAR AND CULTURE

Good. Anything else?

NO

I think you might also want evidence from x-ray findings. Go ahead and we'll see what happens.

X-RAY?
Not ready yet. Try the blood lab.
DIFFERENTIAL?
Marked shift to left. Even though all the lab reports aren't in, you have enough information to make a presumptive diagnosis. If you care to make one go right ahead.
ACUTE PYELONEPHRITIS
It's getting hard to hold on to this diagnosis with neither history nor signs of dysuria. Moreover, the pain is getting away from the flank region into the lower belly. Still thinking of a renal problem? Reconsider.
TB PNEUMONIA
Any other thoughts as to diagnosis? The sudden high rise in WBC and differential is against it and you don't have tubercle bacilli in the sputum.
URINE EXAM?
The urine test shows presence of albumen, few hyaline casts, few WBC, occasional RBC.
X-RAY?
The x-ray shows: area of consolidation, right lower lobe, consistent with pneumonic process. This is a good time to review the total findings and to make another tentative diagnosis—if you like.
EVIDENCE OF FLUID?
No evidence of fluid.
SPUTUM SMEAR?
Gram-positive rods.
STREP PNEUMONIA
Fine, but how can you distinguish this from any other bacterial pneumonia? Wait until you have an irrefutable case.
VIRAL PNEUMONIA
But what about shaking chills, rusty sputum, elevated WBC, etc.—all the evidence of an acute febrile bacterial process? You are in error, doctor.
SPUTUM CULTURE?
Presence of pneumococci.
STREP PNEUMONIA
Incredible! You have disregarded the positive findings that should clearly have established the correct diagnosis.
PNEUMOCOCCAL PNEUMONIA
Very good. It's obvious now, though there were some confusing signs and symptoms in the picture. You've seen your way through to the correct diagnosis.[1]

[1] Reproduced from John A. Swets and Wallace Feurzeig, Computer-aided instruction, *Science*, Oct. 29, 1965, *150*, 574–575, with the permission of the editors of *Science* and the authors. Copyright 1965 by the American Association for the Advancement of Science.

The dominant influence on the sequencing of the instructional program can be seen to be the pressures exerted by the computer program, which reflects the selection of sequential statements by the author. The existence of a dictionary for student-controlled branches suggests that the basis for such decisions is a simple comparison. The number of items that can be matched and appropriately responded to, however, is apparently fairly large, illustrating a thorough and careful approach to the production of selective computer teaching machine programs.

In the protocols the signs of the comparison and selection process are clear. Answers to questions are either *yes* or *no* or are limited to one of the items of the vocabulary list. The richness of the program evolves directly from the tutorial ability of the original program author to ask rhetorical, probing, and informative questions and to anticipate possible queries initiated by the student. Alternative sequencing for a specific remedial or tutorial side path is provided by a very large prestored dictionary of dialogue.

Swets and Feurzeig's work is an excellent example of how close to the ideal of a conversational tutor one can come with the selective techniques that are practiced now. But the dialogue discussed here is only the tip of an iceberg. Late in their paper they point out that the example shown, which in its totality took an hour for a rather poor student to complete, required over *sixty* hours of author and programming time to prepare. The unseen portion of the computer teaching process—the preprogramming effort underlying the sequencing rules and the logistical effort underlying the preparation of the lexicon of statements—can now, perhaps, be appreciated as of prime importance to the ultimate utilization of this new idea of computer teaching machines.

GENERATIVE COMPUTER TEACHING MACHINES

Selective computer teaching machines represent the current level of development of the teaching machine art. It should be clear that this can be but an early stage of development; there is much progress yet to be made. The reason is that the logistical limitations of selective devices have begun to interfere with their theoretical effectiveness. The predetermination of the full contents of a complete tutorial dialogue is tedious, to say the least. Worse, it is constraining and inhibiting, since it requires the author to restrict the student's digression to irrelevant—that is to say, unanticipated—materials.

It is clear also, as Walter Reitman has pointed out in a personal communication, that the human tutor's role is not one of selection and comparison.

. . . rather he analyzes the deficit in the response, using a general model of the task structure, the possible points of difficulty, and a model of the learner. Then he constructs probes for analysis and new exemplars to teach. What are stored are not specific branches, outcomes and responses, but general purpose models of the task and the student with heuristics for the use of these models for the instruction of specific individuals.

Obviously a computer that simulates this kind of behavior internally is very different from one operating on a selective basis, even though the two may appear overtly to the user to be identical. Such a computer teaching machine would also be an extremely economical means of achieving powerful teaching programs, since the tedious and exhaustive authoring of all the steps in the teaching program would, hopefully, not be required.

We have chosen to call the devices that produce the steps in a teaching program by a process of analysis and construction *generative computer teaching machines*. Only a few examples have been reported so far. With one exploratory exception (Uhr, 1964), even these have been in special forms of education which, for one reason or another, happen to be particularly appropriate to this type of programming. In fact, most of the devices we shall describe are essentially analog, dealing with continuous signals easily generated by simple algorithms. Nevertheless, we feel that some form of generative programming must also be the future direction taken by the computer teaching machine development projects dealing with verbal materials. As will be seen later, the recent development of the "information-processing languages" provides a possible entry in the generation of verbal programs.

One of the first examples of a generative teaching machine was Licklider's (1962) imaginative use of a computer and a cathode ray oscilloscope to allow a powerful tutorial interaction to be developed for the subject of analytical geometry. Like the human tutor, this technique used no fixed, prestored dialogue but had a small number of algorithms that could perform generally useful functions. For instance, it could *plot* a graph on the face of an oscilloscope, or *substitute* parameters presented by the student in the algebraic expression of some geometrical curve. In this way, with a small library of standard equations for various two-dimensional curves, the student could explore the effects of changing intercepts, slopes, and other parameters that defined one or another curve. He could also, because of the ability of the computer program to track a photoelectric pointer, alter the geometry of the curve itself and observe the effects on the various parameters of the analytical expression corresponding to that curve. Furthermore, as

Licklider so insightfully pointed out, the visual display of a cathode ray tube allows additional rhetorical tools to be brought into play, such as enhancing or circling a critical point.

Another example of a generative computer teaching machine, in which the special analog properties of the subject matter allow algorithmic generation of an almost unlimited number of computer responses, is illustrated by the work of Buiten and Lane (1965). Their computer teaching machine was designed to teach students how to pronounce foreign language words. The student, presented with an audio recording of a given word, repeated that sound into a microphone. The microphone was connected to an analog-to-digital converter that fed a digitized representation of the speech sound into the computer. The computer analyzed the speech sound for certain gross characteristics, namely, pitch, amplitude, and rhythm. It then responded to the student by means of a set of meters indicating how far he had deviated from the sample sound. It is not yet clear whether these particular dimensions are optimum or even adequate to train a student in foreign language pronunciation. Nevertheless, the important feature of this computer teaching machine is that, unlike the usual "language laboratory," it does not leave to the student's untrained ear the decision whether or not his performance meets an acceptable standard. Instead, an analysis and evaluation is made on an individual word basis by an impartial, though discriminating, attendant—the computer.

As a further specific example of generative programming we can point to the use by some laboratories of random number generation as a means of varying the terms of mathematical problems. In this way new problems can be generated in great numbers for a variety of students or for different attempts by a given student at the solution of different members of the same class of problem. Claims have also been made for editing routines that are able to recognize nearly equivalent spellings or phonetic equivalents. This sort of input to the computer is, of course, a very important part of the generative computer teaching machine concept.

Ultimately the direction real-time generation of programmed materials must take is that suggested by the work of Weizenbaum (1966) on a program for the synthesis of conversational interaction. His programming system (called ELIZA) analyzes inputs from the user and responds to him in a nondirective fashion with sentences generated by utilization of critical phrases from the human input. Unlike the directed dialogue of the Swets and Feurzeig material, Weizenbaum's dialogues are strongly directed by the human conversant. Weizenbaum's programs—briefly—work by detecting key words and context and then transforming the human message into a responsive phrase by fitting certain key words into prestored sentences, much as a teaching machine with sentence substitution might work. In general, it appears from his report that extensive scripts of prestored material are still necessary, but Weizenbaum's programs do have the rudiments of a generative system.

Another intriguing representation of a true generative teaching program is that described by Uhr (1965). Uhr attends directly to the problem of the generation of tutorial programs from formal definitions of the problem area and the responses made by the student. His current programs are designed to handle well-defined problem types such as elementary arithmetic and word-for-word language translation. They do so by using prototype problem formats like "How much is A plus B?" which have been previously stored in the computer and which are filled with numbers either generated by some random number calculator or derived from a history of the student's performance on previous problems. Uhr goes on to suggest that there is really no limitation on the prototype characterization of many different problems; almost any problem that can be formally stated can be presented. The difficulty in most cases is the analysis of the answer. For example, the presentation of a theorem proof to a student would require the computer to be able to deal with the many possible paths that might be equivalent. This is a problem going far beyond the simple statement that 3 + 4 is, indeed, equal to 7.

Another generative approach may prove useful in the development of teaching machine programs. It would entail the generation of computer teaching programs from preexisting texts written for other purposes. (See the discussion of Uhr's work later in this chapter.) Such a process, of course, also requires highly sophisticated language-processing techniques and therefore demands a much higher level of information-processing skill than that satisfying the needs of the specialized examples given above. This approach would be halfway toward a real-time generation of computer responses, in the sense that, although program steps are generated automatically by a computer, it is done before the student sits down at a teaching terminal. The teaching program is thus selective in operation and internal logical design, but generative at its source. It could not constantly maintain the same high degree of adaptability to be expected of an algorithmic generative program, but a successful text processor would help to solve the logistic problem of program generation.

Equipment requirements for computer teaching machines

Five years ago the first major meeting on computer teaching machines was held in Washington, D.C. In the published volume of the proceedings of that symposium (Coulson, 1962), one can read of the problems faced by some of the early workers in this field, and of some of the insights that grew out of their experiences. Several of them recognized that there was but one area of equipment deficiency at the time—terminal devices. All expected the deficiency to be quickly resolved. Their expectations were not to be unfulfilled, for the technology of remote terminals existed, and the multiprogramming procedures that have gained so much attention in more recent years received one of their first public presentations at that meeting (Teager, 1962). It is interesting to note that an advanced example of current selective computer tutoring (Swets and Feurzeig, 1965) is actually being carried out on the same computer used by Licklider (1962) for his work reported at the symposium. In short, the hardware technology for selective computer tutoring exists and has existed for years. Later developments, while allowing certain practical advantages, have added little to our fundamental understanding of the nature of computer tutoring.

The situation is not quite so self-evident when we discuss generative computer teaching machines. Considering only the specialized type of tutoring such as that illustrated by the work of Licklider in analytical geometry and Buiten and Lane in the field of language tutoring, we see that the small machines perform quite adequately for a small number of students. On the other hand, if we consider the extreme requirements of generative techniques for general verbal discourse, such as those suggested by Uhr, it is obvious that some of the largest computers may be necessary to service even a single student. Most of the high-level natural language processing studies carried out have required extensive computer capability to handle the requirements of the appropriate compilers. Nevertheless, the current technology does include such resources, and although future developments may produce computer hardware more naturally suited to the processing of words rather than numbers, there appear to be few current technological limitations on conceptual exploration. At least it seems that current studies in natural language processing have rarely been inhibited by any missing technological development other than local availability.

In some senses, there have perhaps been substantial steps backwards. One area in which progress seems to be from the selective to the degenerate form of computer teaching machines is in the bizarre development of superelaborate terminal devices. Some "computer terminals" are so complicated that they represent financial investments greater than the computer controlling them. Many are glorified microfilm readers suffering from the limitations described earlier for this class of terminal. Others have response modes that are completely redundant with the capabilities offered by the simpler typewriter-type terminal. The computer in these instances becomes merely a controller or a testing device for the "superterminal," in which some restricted form of logical control is invested. Often whatever special features are offered could also be found among the wide range of decision-making instructions available from the general-purpose computer and an imaginative use of its simple terminals.

What, then, are the equipment requirements for a computer-based teaching system? For obvious reasons we must frame the answer to this question in the context of selective computer teaching machines.

The *sine qua non* of a selective computer teaching machine is a large random-access memory file. It is central to all of the existing computer teaching machines that do not belong in the mediocrity of the degenerate classification.

The reasons for the primacy of this portion of the hardware of a computer teaching machine are obvious. Most of the educational materials that need be dealt with are verbal. Words are stored in computers in coded forms that are relatively poorly condensed. There are no algorithms for storing a paragraph. Each character in a word must be stored. Each sentence must be not only properly placed in that memory but also tagged with sufficient addressing uniqueness so that it can be accessed at the proper time. Currently, as we have said, in selective computer teaching machines an exhaustive prestorage of the entirety of all anticipated dialogue is required. This alone would specify massive memory capacity. On the other hand, the branching concept and the ability of the computer to go from one step in a given sequence to a large number of other steps specify that there be no rigid sequential links between the various steps. Rigidity can be allowed neither in the logic of the branching nor in the physical instruments that store these dictionaries of dialogue. Magnetic tapes or similar microfilm reel devices, with their serial structure and long access time, are therefore unnatural embodiments of the selective computer teaching machine concept and may be considered to represent another sign of a trend toward degeneration. Magnetic drums and disks, the latter predominant because of their greater capacity and the modest access time requirements of computer tutoring, come closer to meeting the specific needs of the computer teaching machine function.

As already noted, the real-time requirements of the computer teaching machine are relatively modest. The "immediacy" of reinforcement in a verbal and conceptual learning situation is usually not severely damaged by a delay of a second or two between student input and computer response. This fact has an important hardware implication: it removes from active argument a controversy over which of all available types of computer central processing units is most suitable. When coupled with an appropriate random-access memory and a reasonable number of terminal devices, almost any modern computer is capable of providing the necessary processing power. Comparing the simplest control computer to the largest and most powerful general system, we see little real advantage for selective devices as long as adequate random-access bulk storage is available.

The other significant issue then remaining is the controversy surrounding the teaching terminal itself. Apparently it must be simple and flexible, require little pretraining to operate, allow construction of answers, and demand a minimum amount of maintaining control by the computer for retention of the display.

In the symposium proceedings mentioned above, two important instrumentation trends may be discerned. The first is a trend toward the use of the typewriter, both as an input and as an output device. The second is the imaginative exploration carried out with cathode ray tube displays for special instances in which they were particularly useful. Today, a number of other technological advances may or may not contribute to computer teaching machine terminal power. One of the most important is an alternative to the printed output of the typewriter. Several manufacturers have now marketed cathode ray tube terminals that are capable of displaying a matrix of alphabetic characters in the same way a typewriter does on a piece of paper, but much faster and with the additional advantages of erasability of previously presented materials. There is little conceptual advance in such a development. The material is displayed in much the same form, but certain advantages of convenience suggest that this type of display will gradually replace the typewriter as the most useful terminal for general verbal interaction.

Another new idea is the graphic input terminal. Described in greater detail elsewhere in this book, it allows the computer to accept drawings and handwritten letters as direct input rather than combinations of keypresses. Our impression is that although such terminals may become useful in special instances, they will probably not come into widespread use for a long time, if ever. The reasons for this pessimism lie not only in the economic realm (the devices themselves are expensive and require extensive computing power to control and interpret their input) but also in a fundamental coding characteristic of the system. Codes serve the important function of reducing the variety of distinct symbols that must be stored to express a given concept. But the graphic input devices produce essentially uncoded symbols. Their outputs, in this sense, are much like Chinese pictographs or Egyptian hieroglyphics. Thus, they generate symbols that are relatively difficult to process and to store, and they require enormous preprocessing before decoding. There is no way to break this barrier. It is a basic limitation specific to uncoded forms of information.

The use of such terminals, therefore, minimizes the possibilities for implementing the very important technological advance of time sharing. Selective computer teaching machines, with their extensive stored dictionaries of dialogue, achieve practical utility by virtue of their ability to service many students individually but apparently simultaneously. Thus, the idea of a computer teaching machine is intimately related to the idea of multiple-terminal or time-shared operation. Sufficient computing power exists for handling a large number of typewriter terminals, but does not, and, as suggested above, may not exist for handling an equally large number of uncoded graphic input devices.

A similar set of problems is revealed when one considers the graphic displays designed to draw extremely complicated figures. These devices either require enormous amounts of computer central processor time or must themselves be so elaborate that they, indeed, are almost whole computer systems. In the first case, the application of time-sharing techniques, so fundamental to an economic realization of the computer teaching machine, is thwarted. In the second case, the cost of the individual terminal rises so fast that it becomes impossible to maintain a widespread application.

From another point of view, however, certain special applications may be able to afford such a luxurious utilization of computer services. One can imagine situations in which the graphic display is both extremely useful and economically feasible. Some engineering training programs, particularly at universities that are interested in computer design as such, have had remarkable opportunities to experiment with training techniques utilizing graphic displays. Sutherland (1963) reports the development of a noteworthy computer-graphic display system (SKETCHPAD) that allows the student to gain manipulative experience in structural design unsurpassed by any other experience than, for example, building a bridge itself. In some instances the student has opportunities for experimentation and observation of effects that are not possible in real life, such as stressing the bridge beyond its load limits and observing the results.

In sum, the notion of graphic displays has great promise but is confounded by the complexities of the instruments themselves. Some researchers have successfully used pseudographic displays, which have the capability of displaying a modest number of geometric figures. This has usually been accomplished by taking the type of alphabetic character generator that uses a punched-out stencil to form the character and substituting a few forms for a few of the special characters. This very limited use, however, should not be confused with that of the general-purpose vector generators mentioned in the previous chapter.

In sum, the selective computer teaching machine, the archetype of current computer teaching machines, depends upon large random-access memories and multiple alphabetic input-output terminals. Specifically, we suggest that a typewriter keyboard and a cathode ray tube, capable only of displaying matrices of alphabetic information, may be the most reasonable terminals for the foreseeable future. Special purposes will call for additional visual and auditory display, but care must be taken not to destroy the capability for adaptive conversational interaction when it is integrated into the system. The responsiveness of the terminal to the student is critical. The equipment serves only to maintain the fullest possible adaptive capability. Licklider (1962) was right when he observed that one quickly passes the point of diminishing returns with more and more elaborate terminal technology.

Special-purpose compilers

We turn now from the hardware implications and requirements of computer teaching machines to a discussion of the programming systems that have been evolving to meet the needs of this particular application area of real-time digital computers. Again we shall be mainly constrained to considering the techniques called for by selective computer teaching machines, since the frontier area of generative programming is still so poorly developed.

The task is, then, well defined. The simulation of a conversational interaction by a selective technique requires that there be a large store of statements from which to select. The compilation of the statements has become the great obstacle to widespread use of this type of teaching machine because of the enormous effort necessary to produce a small amount of programmed material that can truly be said to be adaptive.

Two major approaches have been suggested to overcome this logistic barrier. In the first, the human author preparing the set of statements can be provided with a programming system that acts as an administrative assistant for him. A *teacher's compiling language* plays the same role as does, for example, *Fortran* (an algebraic compiling language) for the mathematician. It reduces the need for the detailed machine language coding actually required to make a computer operate. It does so by acting as a translator that accepts information in a language similar to the "natural language" of the mathematician—algebraic formulas—and converts it into the language required by the computer—a family of highly specific instructions.

The teacher's compiling language likewise translates the natural language of the author into a machine storable, selectable, and addressable form. Though the final disposition of a given statement may leave it in apparently the same form in which it was entered, it has, in the interim between input and output, undergone a number of manipulations and transformations.

The second approach to overcoming the difficulties of statement generation is far more complicated. It involves the processing of statements that were not originally partitioned and segmented for computer tutoring into a sequence usable for that purpose. Thus it has been suggested that an existing textbook might be interpreted by a computer program into a usable set of statements. This subtle and difficult processing of natural languages has not yet attained a sufficiently high level of development so that we can point to an exemplary teaching system. Some progress, however, has been made on an experimental level.

TEACHER'S COMPILING LANGUAGES

In the basic source document to which we have referred so often (Coulson, 1962), many of the authors expressed the need for programs that could act as clerical and administrative assistants to the authors of selective teaching machine programs. See, for example, the papers by Uttal (1962) and Licklider (1962). Huskey (1962) described what is the essential framework of such a programming system when he discussed his idea of *procedure communication language* for use "among humans, among machines or between humans and machines." Since 1962, teacher's compiling languages embodying the utilitarian concept of the assistant to the author have been developed, perhaps most highly in the "Coursewriter" language conceived by Mrs. Lenore Selfridge at the IBM Research Center.

Teacher's compiling languages ideally provide another level of man-machine conversational interaction by allowing the author to communicate efficiently with the computer. The author, after performing some simple sign-on manipulations, creates a sequence of statements to be used in his course. Assigned to each statement is a meaningful code identifying it as a member of a particular category. Thus a presentation of new information might be identified, for example, as FACT, implying that this particular statement, when selected, is to be presented to the student and followed by another statement without a student response. The following statement may be presented after a certain elapsed time or after the student has indicated that he has read the statement. In any case, the choice of the next statement is not determined by any characteristic of the student's response. On the other hand, another statement might be tagged QUES, indicating that it is a question. A question, however, is not a complete instructional unit in this type of dialogue. The complete instructional unit in a totally selective computer teaching machine includes a comparison between a student's answer and several anticipated responses.

Therefore, no question is complete without a comprehensive set of alternative anticipated answers. The latter may be divided into three categories. The first is the group of alternative correct answers. Thus the answer *1* might appear in the alternate forms *1*, *one*, *1.0*, or even *wun*. The second is the set of incorrect answers that can be anticipated on the basis of previous experience, intuition, or some obvious and likely flaw in the logical processes leading to the student's response. This category might include 2, *two*, *Men*, or *men*, each of which is a response that, for one reason or another, might be expected. The third category includes all of the unmatchable responses. No anticipatory process can possibly be assumed that will completely encompass the wide variety of responses available to an enthusiastic and fumbling student. There is always, then, a catch-all category required to handle responses that have not otherwise been anticipated. In each case an address is associated with the response. It is the address of the next appropriate statement, which itself might be tagged FACT or QUES, or any one of several other functions. Thus, a chain is formed of sequential responses by means of which a student can be adaptively tutored.

This illustration of some of the rudiments of a hypothetical teacher's compiling language displays both the great strength and also what is probably to be the fatal weakness of the selective computer teaching machine concept. The strength derives from the fact that the selective tutor is the best way so far developed to allow a group of students to pass actively through a common chain of statements, but each apparently along a different sequence. The weakness derives from the fact that the list from which sequential statements are to be selected can never really be large enough to allow truly free and complete selective branching. Such an anticipatory process would be, even with the assistance of the teacher's compiling languages, a task of an enormous magnitude.

Therefore, not unnaturally, a compromise has been reached. All selective computer teaching machine programs are not capable of full branching, but rather have been programmed with strong restorative tendencies. That is to say, outside of remedial loops and diagnostic tests, the tutorial sequence is usually far more linear than many computer teaching enthusiasts are willing to admit. The naturalness of this compromise is sharply illustrated by noting that a fully branched program with but three branches at each nodal point would have at least 3^n statements required after the nth branchable statement had been presented. Over 88,000 statements ($3^{10} + 3^9 + 3^8 + \ldots + 3^1$) would thus be required to support a ten-step sequence. This calculation easily demonstrates the absurdity of completely free branching. The result is that branches must be truncated, either by the dead-end termination "Call your teacher —the computer can take you no farther," or by the less traumatic process of branches bending back into the main trunk of the course.

TEXT ANALYSIS

There has been some effort to develop compiler techniques for partitioning a paragraph of ordinary text material into a series of statements suitable for a selective computer teaching machine program. Uhr, who developed an advanced form of teacher's compiling language (1964), has experimented with techniques capable of analyzing text into a rough form that could subsequently be smoothed by practical testing with human subjects. In this way a mechanism for the compilation of lists of anticipated correct and incorrect answers was provided, as well as a means for editing out the irrelevant or trivial items that such a procedure would undoubtedly produce.

Uhr uses two other methods for the manipulation of verbal materials. The first is the technique of partial match features. An answer is compared not only *in toto* to a prestored answer but also in parts with elements of the list of alternative anticipated answers. Thus, if there is an amount of congruency exceeding some predetermined percentage, the answer may be considered correct. Those parts of it that are matched correctly can then be extracted for presentation as a reinforcement to the student.

The means by which partially correct answers are presented to the student represents the second method used by Uhr. We have mentioned it previously and called it *sentence substitution,* though he does not use that term. The matching portions of the student's answer were inserted into an incomplete sentence with the leading phrase "Yes, you are right to say . . . ," thus adding an element of individuality and pertinence to the particular answer. In a sense, this process is primitively generative. The sentence substitution technique is possible because of the capability of some of the modern computer languages to substitute items from one list in another. These list-processing languages, of which we shall speak in greater detail later, thus act as surrogates for the semantic processing performed by the human intellect. They substitute propinquity within a list for the so-far-undefined nature of human semantic association. Verbal sentences are typical lists, which can be handled in this way.

The relation of computer teaching machines to other forms of natural language processing

Up to now we have considered the computer teaching machine as a relatively isolated real-time computer development. This is necessarily an oversimplification based upon the comparative newness of the field and the lack of an analytical expression of its relevance to other new computer applications. Nevertheless, the act of education—education in the most important sense—is not limited to the tutorial function. Libraries and critical analysis both are major tools for enhancing the education of the student. The kind of education exemplified by library usage and contemplative exploration is not confined to advanced graduate studies but must be regarded as important at all educational levels, once a basic reading skill has been instilled.

Education, therefore, demands more from our technology than

simple tutoring. Computer teaching machines cannot be considered complete educational machines until they also provide an opportunity for a student to explore the literature. The development of computer information retrieval techniques has occurred simultaneously with the development of computer teaching machines and has been, perhaps, even more intensive. We shall briefly discuss the functional similarity of library automation and the computer tutor.

A related series of developments in the field of "information processing" promises to have a considerable impact on our analysis of the educational process. *Information processing* is a term used in many different ways. We are referring here specifically to the techniques created for the semantic analysis of alphabetically coded material. The problem is a massive one, since computers have been primarily designed to handle arithmetic or numerical information. When computers are applied to alphabetic processing more profound than simple storage, the unnaturalness of their logical design requires programming gimmicks of a kind probably quite different from the semantic manipulations the human intellect seems to use in processing similar data.

INFORMATION RETRIEVAL AND COMPUTER TEACHING MACHINES[2]

Consider the interaction process between a computer teaching machine and a student. A statement is fed from the computer memory to a display. When the student responds, the computer program selects another appropriate statement, on the basis of some evaluation of the characteristic of the response. The chain of dialogue is *directed* mainly by the computer tutor, constantly forcing the student along a sequence dictated by the educational goals of the teaching program.

Consider now how a hypothetical information retrieval system might work in a library. A student arrives and indicates a field of interest. Let us assume that our hypothetical information retrieval system is organized to help him search by carrying on a question-and-answer game. The dialogue might then be in the form of a series of directive and selective statements by the student and questions by the retrieval system. For example, the student might be interested in references discussing the biochemistry of lipids in the brains of cats. Having been previously instructed in the use of the system, he makes his first statement to the computer:

[2] I am grateful to Professor Manfred Kochen for discussions that elucidated this relationship.

BIOCHEMISTRY

The computer might then respond with a classification table reducing the field of biochemistry to a next lower level of classification:

BIOCHEMISTRY 500,000

PROTEINS
GENETIC MATERIALS
LIPIDS
CARBOHYDRATES
ETC.

In each case, the number appearing with the main category would indicate the number of references available in the field. The student then would select the most appropriate subcategory and indicate that to the computer system:

LIPIDS

to which the computer would reply:

BIOCHEMISTRY OF LIPIDS 20,000

NERVOUS SYSTEM
VISCERA
INTEGUMENTARY
CIRCULATORY

The student, being most interested in nervous system lipids, would select:

NERVOUS SYSTEM

The computer would then respond:

BIOCHEMISTRY OF LIPIDS OF THE NERVOUS SYSTEM 5,000

BRAIN
SPINAL CORD
BRAIN STEM
PERIPHERAL NERVES
ETC.

Once again the student could indicate his choice of category by simply specifying:

BRAIN

to which the computer might reply:

BIOCHEMISTRY OF THE LIPIDS OF THE BRAIN 200

DIFFERENT PARTS OF THE BRAIN 175
DIFFERENT SPECIES 50
DIFFERENT LIPIDS 135

Our hypothetical student might now also receive a hypothetical output from the hypothetical computer indicating that the category of biochemistry of brain lipids classified with emphasis on species differences represented the lowest level of classification available to the computer and had only fifty references. The student could then ask for a scan of titles and select those that seemed to be of greatest relevance to study in detail.

This example is not presented to suggest an efficient mode of conversational information retrieval. Rather, it is intended to point out that the dialogue so generated is very similar to the dialogue generated by a computer teaching machine interaction. In fact, the goals of both are clearly seen to be identical, namely, to transmit information and understanding to the student. There is, however, an apparent difference: in the case of the information retrieval activity, the course of the dialogue is directed by the student, not by the computer as it is in the case of the computer tutor. Still, the similarities are profound. In both cases a branching structure is used, and individual responses from the student help to determine the choice of the next statement.

The difference between the computer teaching machine and the computer information retrieval system, we submit, is but a quantitative one. They vary along a dimension representative of which of the two conversants, the computer program or the student, is more actively directing the conversation at any given time. Qualitatively the two processes appear to be identical. They represent a common methodology with common goals, each of which could substantially benefit from a merger of the two heretofore separate research traditions.

THE RELATION OF COMPUTER TEACHING MACHINES TO INFORMATION PROCESSING

The term *information processing*, as we have said, has taken on a specific meaning to the psychologists and computer specialists who are particularly concerned with the simulation or modeling of thought processes. To them, information processing does not mean computation in its most general sense, or information processing as it is used in the information retrieval field. It describes the techniques of simulation most obviously, though not exclusively, carried out on a digital computer using a special set of compiling languages called *list processors*. List-processing languages were designed to provide a means of simulating the semantic relations so that this type of information can be processed as well as the specific manipulation of numerical terms. They allow such processing of semantic relations by substituting common occurrence in a list of terms or interlist comparisons for the complicated associational processes of human cognition and thought.

Thus, the list-processing languages provide a formal method of describing these relationships, without any attempt at reduction to the underlying mechanism. In this sense, a list- or information-processing model is more like a mathematical model than an explanation of a set of phenomena in terms of physical reductionism.

The complete details of the list-processing languages and the achievements of workers in supplying a rational description of human thought are outside of the purpose of this chapter. The reader is referred to the eloquent discussion by Reitman (1965) of the development of this field and of its relevance to the emergence of what probably will become a major psychological tradition. Here we are concerned, however, with the aspect of information-processing languages which suggests that they may have a special relevance to the development of computer teaching machines. This aspect lies in their potential contribution of a powerful means of generative computer teaching machine programming.

The list-processing languages offer, by virtue of their ability to deal with the semantic relations between a set of items, a means of generating verbal strings (sentences) in the same way geometric strings (diagrams) could be generated by means of algebraic algorithms. In the latter case, a set of components—x and y coordinates—was ordered by means of a formal relation. Operations can also be conceived that would act upon the formal relation itself to alter its form and thus affect all later geometric figures generated by that relation. In the same way, the relations among lists and sublists can be manipulated so as to produce different verbal sentences. Since we may assume that the operations performed on the relations among the lists can be functionally determined by the requirements of the system in which they are embedded, namely, the student-teacher relationship, it is clear that this approach has many potential implications for our problem. It could provide a means of generating adaptive conversation with verbal elements, just as the special analog cases of generative teaching machines generate nonverbal adaptive responses to meet their needs.

The other point of interaction between the information-processing techniques and those of the computer teaching machine lies in the basic importance of our understanding the acts of teaching and learning. The information-processing languages provide a theoretical framework that can be used for the analysis of the processes spoken of by Reitman as being the essence of human tutoring. To understand such interactions is to afford an opportunity to simulate them. This has been the theme of the present chapter, for computer teaching techniques have much yet to gain from an approach that maximizes the simulation of these particular cognitive processes. Formal models would then be of inestimable value, even if they did not prove completely satisfactory as a means of actually generating program elements.

A FINAL NOTE

We have tried to point out the interrelationships between computer teaching machines and other forms of natural language processing. It is clear that there are many other interactions which we have not mentioned. The development of the computer teaching machine is intertwined, to an astonishing degree, with the general notion of the time sharing of central processors on the one hand and large bulk memories on the other. The developments of which we spoke in Chapter 6 may, in some sense, be more of a practical influence on the evolution of computer teaching machines than the logical developments we have stressed.

The debate continues on many of the questions discussed in this book. What seems to be the best answer today may be invalidated very shortly by some new technological or programming advance. We could speculate about what form the advance will take, but in a certain sense it is impossible to speculate constructively at this point. The real-time developments we have spoken of are still in the state of ferment characteristic of a new idea. Surely they will become routine in a far shorter time, however, than that required for some of the older techniques. Our communication techniques are also increasingly efficient. Furthermore, as the organization of this book attests, the notion of real-time computers is an empirical one. Thus the controversies that are so vigorous today are going to be solved by practical tests, not by rhetoric or theoretical discourses. The important thing is that this information be made widely available. That is the purpose of this book.

III: APPENDICES

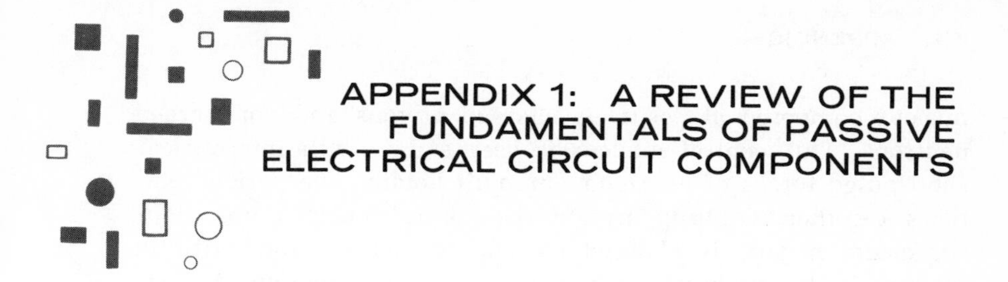

APPENDIX 1: A REVIEW OF THE FUNDAMENTALS OF PASSIVE ELECTRICAL CIRCUIT COMPONENTS

To utilize computers fully in their direct on-line role, the behavioral scientist must be familiar enough with the basic principles of electricity to understand not only the operation of the logical elements of the computer but also their basic circuit components. This appendix is intended to be an introduction to the fundamental concepts of electricity and magnetism. It will not explore all the ramifications of electricity and magnetism but provide a useful and practical point of view and a depth of knowledge such that the operation of the more complex parts of a computer system may be understood.

Basic electrical properties

Modern ideas of electricity are rooted in the supposed action and interaction of the basic particles of matter. During the last two decades monumental strides have been made in the definition of the nature of matter. All of the new developments, however, are generally in agreement with the orbital model of the atom proposed by Bohr in 1913. The Bohr model suggested that each chemical element was in the form of a planetary system surrounding a central nucleus composed of positively charged protons and noncharged neutrons. This central nucleus is very stable, with internuclear short-range forces of enormous strength holding the various particles together. Orbiting around the central nucleus are, Bohr suggested, negatively charged particles called electrons, tied in their paths by weaker long-distance forces of attraction. A basic principle of atomic structures is that the orbital electrons can orbit only at certain specific distances from the central nucleus and that all other orbits are "excluded." Since the radius of the orbit of the electron is determined by the amount of kinetic energy (energy of movement), the orbital concept is intimately related to the development of the quantum theory of energies. This extraordinary theory states that energy comes only in certain discrete packets and that the packets, or quanta, cannot be divided into smaller units. Further investigation by many distinguished physicists has shown that these acceptable orbits can contain only a specific maximum number of electrons at a given time and that the number varies from one orbital level to the next. Furthermore, the maximum number of electrons differs if the orbit is more or less close to the nucleus. In general, at room temperatures, the electrical properties of materials are determined by the outermost, or valence, orbit and the number of electrons it contains. For this reason, the system of electrical units that has developed is defined in terms of the electron and its electrical charge.

CHARGE

Charge is rather inadequately defined as the state of electrification of an object. Simple experiments demonstrate that there are two kinds of charges, positive and negative, which obey the well-known laws of repulsion between like charges and attraction between unlike charges. The unit of charge has been associated with the electron, one of the basic particles out of which matter is formed. The mass of the *electron* has been measured repeatedly; there is general agreement now that it is a particle with a mass of 9.1×10^{-28} grams, and that its charge will be considered the basic reference for a unit negative charge. Unfortunately, the charge on an electron is very tiny compared to the practical levels of charge dealt with in electrical circuits. A large, more useful unit of charge, the *coulomb*, has therefore been defined. It is a charge equal to the charge on 6.28×10^{18} free electrons.

POTENTIAL DIFFERENCE (VOLTAGE)

The familiar laws of attraction and repulsion are an expression of the fact that a force is acting between charges that can result in mechanical action. This force has been shown to be in the form of an inverse square law:

$$F = \frac{kq_1q_2}{r^2} \tag{A1-1}$$

where F is the force acting between two objects, k is a constant dependent upon the units chosen and the material in which the charges are distributed, q_1 is the charge of the first object, q_2 is the charge of the second, and r is the distance between the two objects. If a charged object is moved a distance X by a force F, then work, W, is said to have been done:

$$W = F \cdot X \tag{A1-2}$$

From these two relations (equations A1-1 and A1-2), we can define the *volt*, the practical unit of potential difference or driving force used in electrical circuits. It is important to maintain the idea of a force capable of doing work in electrical circuits. This driving force is called *potential difference*, is measured in volts, and is defined in the following way in terms of the basic idea of charge:

1. One volt of potential difference is equal to 10^8 absolute volts.
2. A potential difference between two points is one absolute volt, when 1 erg of work is done moving a charge of 10 coulombs from the more negative to the more positive point.

The volt is a unit of practical size and represents a convenient unit of electrical driving force in electrical and electronic circuits. Voltage may be generated not only by the accumulation of electrical charges but also by chemical power sources (batteries) or electromechanical devices that convert the energy of movement of mechanical objects, such as rushing water, to various forms of electrical energy.

It is very important to remember that the concept of voltage or potential difference always must be expressed in terms of two points. Thus, a voltage exists between two different points in an electrical system; it is not possible to measure the voltage of a point without referring that measurement to some other point. The voltage between point A and point B may be different from that between A and C or between B and C. Usually in electrical systems a common reference point to which all voltages are referred is established. This point is frequently made common to many systems by connecting it to the earth, which is locally equal in potential. Such a connection is ordinarily called a "ground" reference and is useful, but it is not necessary; in many systems the voltages are not referred to ground but are isolated from it.

In some systems such isolation is desirable and would be indicated by a zero voltage measurement between individual test points and a ground reference, even though a considerable voltage may exist between two test points.

Voltages also may have the property of changing in amplitude as a function of time. Thus while some voltage sources are constant in amplitude, others may be varying in either a regular or an irregular fashion. In general, temporal fluctuations are determined at the source of the voltage. Batteries and power supplies that produce a constant potential difference between two poles are said to be direct current (or DC) voltage power supplies. Figure A1-1*a* is a plot of the output of a DC power supply. As time passes, the voltage from a DC power supply is relatively constant. On the other hand, rotating machinery that is used to transform the kinetic energy of moving water or steam to electrical power usually produces alternating current (or AC) voltage, in which the waveform of the voltage is sinusoidally varying in time. Figure A1-1*b* is a plot of a typical AC voltage.

Electrical power is now commonly transferred over power lines from the place of generation to the user's location as AC voltage because of the ease with which voltages are changed from one amplitude to another by transformers. The complete story of how alternating currents are produced by rotating machinery would be inappropriate in this book, but the reader is referred to any basic physics text for greater detail.

In most electronic equipment it is necessary to convert the AC voltage to a DC voltage in order to avoid unpredictable performance as a function of which value of the cyclic AC voltage happens to be present when a circuit is utilized. Conversion from the varying AC voltage to the steady DC voltage is carried out by means of circuits called DC power supplies. DC power supplies are usually built into the specific equipment to be powered and produce DC voltages according to the special needs of that equipment.

Figure A1-1*b* also shows some of the critical parameters used to specify the characteristics of an AC voltage. Unlike DC voltages, which are completely specified by the single parameter, voltage amplitude, AC voltages may vary in ways other than amplitude. An AC voltage may vary in the length of time it takes to pass through one complete cycle, i.e., to produce one complete wave. This time is called the period and is usually signified by the Greek letter tau (τ). Tau is the length of time it takes for the variation in voltage to pass through a single *cycle*. Alternating

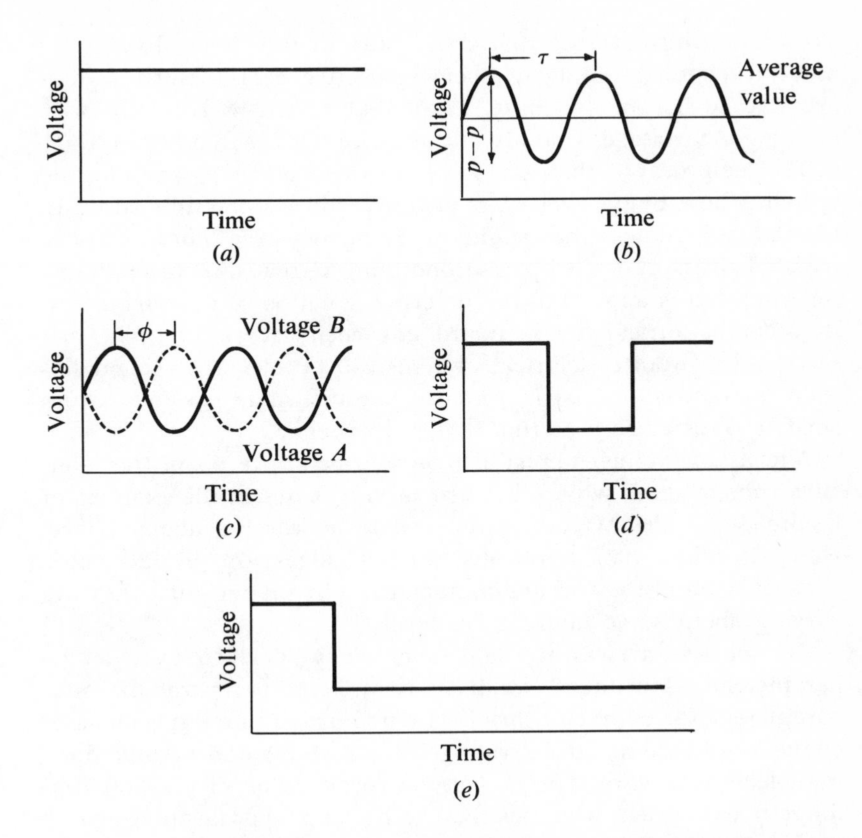

Fig. A1-1. *Voltages can have many different waveforms. The most common are shown in this figure.* (a) *The form of a DC voltage is constant over time.* (b) *The form of AC voltage varies sinusoidally in time. This particular sine wave has some average value other than zero, indicating that it is produced by the sum of both DC and AC voltages.* (c) *Two sinusoidal waveforms that are out of phase with each other.* (d) *A negative-going voltage pulse. A pulse is a change in voltage that is transient and followed shortly by a return to the original level.* (e) *A negative-going level change. A level change is a shift in voltage that is maintained for a relatively long period of time.*

current is periodic, since it is usually produced by rotating electromechanical machinery. Each complete rotation of the machinery produces one cycle of alterating current.[1] Thus a single cycle is also said to be composed of 360°. This angular representation is important in specifying the relations between two otherwise identi-

[1] This is not completely accurate. Complex rotary AC generators can produce many cycles of AC voltage for each rotation.

cal alternating currents that differ only in the times they arrive at corresponding points of their respective cycles. Such signals are said to be out of phase. Figure A1-1*c* shows two otherwise identical AC voltages that are out of phase with each other by 180°.

The reciprocal of the period (τ) is called the frequency (f) and specifies how many cycles are being produced per unit time. In the United States the standard frequency for power-line-distributed AC is 60 cycles per second, and a great deal of engineering attention is applied to the precise regulation of this frequency. In other countries, the standard has been set at 50 cycles per second. In aircraft electrical systems, 400 cycles per second has been chosen as standard, primarily because it is possible to use smaller transformers at this higher frequency.

Alternating voltages must also be specified in terms of the reference voltage about which they are varying. Thus in the example of Figure A1-1*b* the AC voltage is seen to be varying about a level which is other than zero volts. Such voltages are, in fact, mixtures of AC and DC and are characterized by the fact that they are varying about some nonzero DC level.

DC voltages are, as we said, completely specified by a single parameter. AC voltages, we have seen, require several different parameters for a precise specification. Furthermore, specification of the amplitude of an AC voltage is not simple and may be done in at least two ways. The first is the specification of the potential difference between the positive going and the negative going peaks. Peak-to-peak voltages are easy to measure with an oscilloscope. However, a 100 volt peak-to-peak voltage, for example, does not have the same power-carrying or heating capability as a 100-volt DC. For this reason an alternative means of specifying the amplitude of AC voltages is often used. It is the root-mean-square (rms) voltage measure, which is equal to the square root of the average value of the squares of the voltage taken instantaneously at a large number of equally spaced points on the AC waveform. It can be calculated that the rms voltage is equal to 70.7 percent of half of the peak-to-peak voltages for a purely sinusoidal waveform.

Other waveforms are frequently found in electronic circuits, but in digital computers two are of special interest. A *pulse voltage* is a short transient change in the voltage either from a more negative level to a more positive level (a positive going or a positive pulse) or from a more positive to a more negative level (a negative going or a negative pulse). See Fig. A1-1*d*. The width of a standard pulse in a computer system is usually defined by the specific electronic circuitry in that system. On the other hand, longer-lasting voltage shifts are referred to as *level changes*, even though the change in level may last only a few microseconds longer than a standard pulse (see Fig. A1-1*e*).

Voltages may be combined in two ways. They may be interconnected in series so that the positive pole of a power supply is connected to the negative pole of the next supply, and so on. Figure A1-2*a* shows such a circuit. The figure also introduces the first

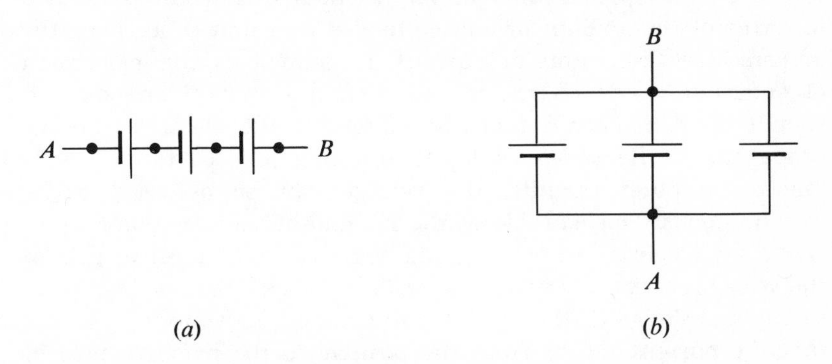

Fig. A1-2. (a) *Voltage sources connected in series to increase the available voltage. No increase in current is produced by such an arrangement.* (b) *Voltage sources connected in parallel to increase the available current. No increase in voltage is produced by such an arrangement.*

of the symbolic forms representing the various electronic and electrical circuit components. This symbol, —|⊢—, represents a DC power source, and although it evolved from the electromechanical battery, it is now used generally to refer also to electronic sources of DC power. The longer bar signifies the positive side; the shorter bar the negative side. In a series circuit as shown in the figure, the voltages are additive, and the voltage between *A* and *B* is the sum of the voltages of the three power sources.

On the other hand, in the parallel circuit, illustrated in Figure A1-2*b*, all the positive poles are connected together and all the negative poles are connected together. The total voltage, therefore, is equal to the voltage of only one of the power supplies. There is a further constraint in that each of the power supplies must be equal in voltage to each of the others in the parallel circuit in order to avoid the transfer of charge from one of the power supplies to another without useful work being done. Parallel voltage sources are useful for increasing current capacity over that available from a single unit.

CURRENT

When a voltage is applied to a conductor of electricity, a stream of electrons tends to drift through the conductor from the more negative pole of the voltage to the more positive pole. The stream is called a *current.* Just how large the current will be is determined by the characteristics of the voltage, as well as by the characteristics of the material through which the stream is being forced by the applied voltage. The amount of current is defined in terms of the amount of charge moved in a unit time. Thus the *ampere,* the basic unit of current, is defined as the movement of one coulomb of charge in one second past a given point. It should be remembered that the effects of the electrical energy propagate at the speed of light, and that, except for the very fastest computer circuits, the voltage can be assumed to be instantaneously measurable at the far end of the conductor.

We say electrons move from the negative to the positive pole of the voltage source. However, for historic reasons that evolved prior to our knowledge of the electron, a common convention is to say that the current moves from the positive to the negative pole of the voltage source.

Current may also be defined in another manner. Current-carrying conductors are surrounded by magnetic fields. If a wire loop with a radius of one centimeter is constructed and, by the application of an appropriate voltage, a current is produced in it, and if a magnetic field of two oersteds[2] is produced, the current is by definition equal to ten amperes. Since amperes are relatively large amounts of current, a smaller unit, the milliampere (1/1000th of an ampere), is regularly used as a practical unit in electronic circuitry. In most computer logical circuits the current levels are measured in milliamperes. Some modern circuits are able to measure and respond to currents in the order of micro-micro or "pico" amperes. On the other hand, the DC power supplies for all the circuits in complex systems usually are capable of providing currents measured in tens of amperes.

Impedance

So far we have talked about connecting a conductor between both poles of a voltage source and the resulting current in the con-

[2] An *oersted* is the unit of magnetic field strength. The strength of a magnetic field at a point is defined as one oersted if one dyne of force is produced on a unit magnetic pole placed at that point.

ductor. The amplitude of the voltage determines, in part, the amplitude of the current in that a higher voltage tends to drive greater current through a given conductor. Other factors, however, contribute to the determination of the amount of current that will flow. They include characteristics of the conductor itself, as well as the temporal properties of the applied voltage. Some materials, *conductors,* naturally allow a large current flow, while other materials, *insulators*, allow only a small amount of current flow. Thus applying a given voltage to a good conductor results in a large amount of current, while the same voltage applied to a poor conductor results in only a small amount of current.

The general term for the property of conductors to obstruct the free flow of current is called *impedance*. The impedance of a conductor is determined by two factors: the nature of the materials from which the conductor is made and the geometric arrangement of the parts of the conductor—as well as, in some cases, by the characteristics of the applied voltage. Even though this statement may sound as if it hides a multitude of mysteries, all impedance is of one of three types: (1) resistive impedance, (2) capacitive impedance, and (3) inductive impedance.

RESISTIVE IMPEDANCE

It is well known that different materials have different resistive impedance (resistance), and that this property can be explained on the basis of the number of electrons in the outer orbit of the atomic structure. Materials with atomic structures in which the outer orbit is composed of only one or two electrons (generally metals) are usually very good conductors with resistances of the order of 10^{-6} ohms per cubic centimeter.[3] In these materials the electrons can relatively easily break free from the orbit and become available to participate in the flow of current.

In contrast, materials having a complete or almost complete outer orbit with seven or eight electrons (eight is the maximum for outer orbits) are exceedingly reluctant to release their electrons. The electrons are said to be bound tightly in their orbital paths. This property is also called the *octet rule,* and we shall have much more to say about it later. Materials with more nearly complete outer orbits have resistances of the order of 10^{12} to 10^{16} ohms per cubic centimeter and are considered very good insulators. The element sulphur and materials like mica and polyethylene are examples of nonconductors. A third group of materials, about

[3] For a definition of an ohm, see below.

which we will speak later, are composed of atoms in which the outer orbit has three, four, or five electrons that are intermediate in their freedom to leave their orbital pathways. These materials are called *semiconductors* and have resistances of the order of 10^4 to 10^5 ohms per cubic centimeter. Germanium and silicon are typical semiconductors.

The *ohm* is the unit of resistive impedance. One ohm is defined as the resistance of a conductor such that a current of one ampere is generated by an applied potential difference of one volt. There is a simple formal relation among current, resistance, and voltage, known as Ohm's law, that is widely used in electrical circuit design and theory:

$$I = \frac{V}{R} \tag{A1-3}$$

where I stands for current in amperes, V for the applied voltage in volts, and R for the resistance in ohms. This law states that the current produced in a conductor is directly proportional to the applied voltage and inversely proportional to the resistance of the circuit.

As we have stated, the resistance of a circuit is determined not only by the nature of the material but also by the physical geometry of the conductor. The resistance of a conductor is directly proportional to the length of the conductor and inversely proportional to its cross-sectional area. The constant of proportionality is the resistance per cubic centimeter or the *resistivity* of the material. These statements may be summarized by the following equation:

$$R = K\frac{L}{A} \tag{A1-4}$$

where R is the resistance of the conductor, K the resistivity, L the length of the conductor, and A its cross-sectional area.

Thus, material and geometry completely define the impedance of a purely resistive circuit. Unlike capacitive and inductive impedance, which we will describe, resistance is not affected by the characteristics of the applied voltage. Constant empirical testing over many years has failed to show any nonlinearity in equation A1-4 for resistance or any sensitivity to the frequency of an applied AC voltage that can be attributed to the resistive impedance of a conductor.

As a practical consideration, almost all materials have a measurable resistance. Under certain extreme conditions, such as ultralow temperatures approaching absolute zero, some materials appear to have a nearly zero resistance. This phenomenon is called *superconductivity* and has been considered a possible method of forming computer memories. Current once started in a circular superconductor will continue to be conducted, in an apparent violation of Ohm's law, even after the applied voltage is removed.

It can be seen, then, that the smaller the resistance, the more current will flow for a given applied voltage. On the other hand, large resistances tend to allow small currents when the same voltage is applied. Large resistances are, therefore, small loads on the voltage source, while small resistances are large loads. The *load* on a voltage source is defined in terms of the current being drawn by all of the conductors connected to it. Practically, the limit of a given voltage source is best thought of in terms of its capacity to provide current. For example, a good power supply may be able to provide ten amperes of current, but when this limit is exceeded, the voltage will tend to become distorted in one way or another. A power supply should be adequately fused so that it may turn itself off when the load limit is exceeded.

As another example of the concept of load, a particular circuit element in a computer may be able to drive or provide ten milliamperes of current to other units. When this limit is exceeded, the usual result is that the voltage presented to various parts of the total load is reduced or distorted. In this case the logical or arithmetic function of the circuit may not be achieved. Most circuit components are designed to provide a certain current, and care must be taken to avoid attaching a larger load than that specified.

A practical matter often overlooked by the novice experimenter with electrical circuits is that the potential difference of a voltage source is meaningful only in terms of the difference between its positive and negative poles. Thus a conductor or a load must make a complete circuit between the two poles. A wire that is connected to just one side of a voltage source does not really exist in the electrical system and for all practical purposes can be ignored (except as a potential safety hazard). The exception to this rule is that high-frequency signals are often able to pass between conductors by means other than the direct resistive circuits. Capacitive and inductive parasitic paths allow this type of interaction.

Power and wattage. Passing a current through a resistor expends energy, and the rate of energy expenditure is defined in terms of the electrical parameters of the circuit. Thus:

$$P = VI \qquad \text{(A1-5)}$$

where P denotes the power in watts, V the applied voltage in volts, and I the resulting current in amperes through the conducting pathway. Applying Ohm's law, we see that P for electrical circuits is also defined by

$$P = RI^2 \tag{A1-6}$$

since

$$V = RI \text{ (Ohm's law)} \tag{A1-7}$$

Much of this power is transformed into heat, which must be dissipated by the resistor without overheating beyond its design specification. Small resistances, therefore, have a tendency to be physically large compared to larger resistances through which less current flows for a given voltage. Before a resistor is introduced into an electrical circuit, it is always a good practice to make the simple power calculation and to pick a unit rated for at least that power dissipation capability.

Combinations of resistors. We can now consider the effects of connecting voltages in various combinations. We can intuitively see from an examination of equation A1-4 that adding resistances in series will increase the total resistance of the combined circuits, while adding resistances in parallel actually reduces the total resistance of a combination by providing alternative pathways (i.e., additional cross-sectional area) for the current. Figure A1-3 shows

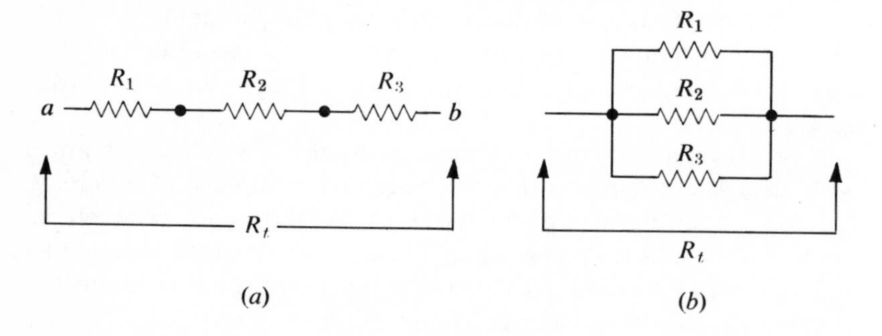

Fig. A1-3. (a) *Resistors connected in series. The effect of such a circuit is to increase the total resistance.* (b) *Resistors connected in parallel. The effect of such a circuit is to reduce the total resistance of the circuit.*

resistors combined in series and parallel. It can be derived by means of Ohm's law that the total resistance of a series resistance combination as shown in Figure A1-3*a* is equal to the sum of the individual resistances, or, expressed formally:

$$R_t = R_1 + R_2 + R_3 \tag{A1-8}$$

If a voltage between A and B is applied in the series situation, a current will then flow through the total circuit which is equal to

$$I = \frac{V}{R_t} = \frac{V}{R_1 + R_2 + R_3} \qquad \text{(A1-9)}$$

Parallel circuits, rather than adding to the total resistance, actually decrease the effective resistance of the total circuit. Once again we can use Ohm's law to derive a formal relation for parallel combinations of resistors such as that illustrated in Figure A1-3b:

$$\frac{1}{R_t} = \frac{1}{R_1} + \frac{1}{R_2} + \frac{1}{R_3} \qquad \text{(A1-10)}$$

Many computer circuits involve networks of resistive elements through which the current must be calculated.. Two important rules, Kirchhoff's laws, can be used to set up a system of simultaneous algebraic equations that can be solved to compute the total and partial current through any given part of the network. Kirchhoff's laws are as follows:

1. Current flowing into a junction is equal to current flowing out of a junction.
2. The sum of the voltage drops around a closed loop is equal to the applied voltage in that loop.

The first law is relatively obvious. A resistive circuit has no place for electrons to be stored and therefore to accumulate. Hence, any current going into a wire or a junction of several wires must be equaled by the amount of current flowing out. In effect, that is, total amount of current flowing through a series circuit is equal to the current flowing through each of the resistors. This leads to another important concept, the *voltage drop*. When a voltage is applied across a resistor, the potential difference is applied to the two ends of the resistor. The voltage may be assumed, therefore, to have dropped from the higher level to the lower through the resistor. On the other hand, the current flowing through a single resistor in a complex resistive circuit will be determined not only by its own resistance but also by the resistance of the other components of the circuit. Thus, it is as if a voltage has not been applied to that particular resistor as such, but rather that a current of a certain magnitude has been run through the resistor. Ohm's law can be rearranged to the following form to look at the resulting voltage from this point of view.

$$V = IR \qquad \text{(A1-11)}$$

Thus we may calculate a voltage that exists across a resistor by knowing its resistance and the current through the resistor. The resistor is therefore said to have a voltage drop across it, and if we measure with a voltmeter between the two sides of the resistor, our meter will show that potential difference between the two sides.

In a series circuit, the sum of the voltage drops through the whole circuit is said by Kirchhoff's second law to be equal to the sum of the voltages applied to the series circuit. But the voltage drop across each resistor, consequently, can be only a smaller proportional part of the total applied voltage. This idea is extremely important in defining a very useful application of the series circuit called a *voltage divider*. The voltage divider shown in Figure A1-4 can be used to provide a lower voltage from another source of voltage that is too high to be used in the particular application desired. The voltage between points *a* and *c* (V_{ac}) is equal to

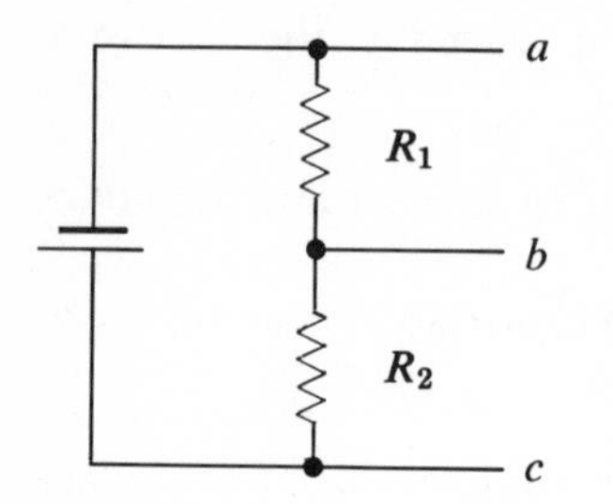

Fig. A1-4. *A voltage divider illustrating the way in which a smaller voltage can be produced from a larger one by tapping off only a part of the voltage drop of the total circuit. (See text for full description of operation.)*

the applied voltage and by Kirchhoff's second law is equal to the sum of the voltage drops across the two resistors. However, the voltage drop (V_{ab}) across one of the resistors can be shown to be equal to

$$V_{ab} = V_{ac}\frac{R_1}{R_1 + R_2} \tag{A1-12}$$

Thus, if the two resistors are equal in their resistance, half the voltage would appear across each of the resistances. If the two are not equal, the voltage drop across each would be that proportion of the total resistance represented by each.

Kirchhoff's laws may also be applied to determining the currents through more complex combinations of parallel and series resistive elements. As an example, let us determine the currents, I_1, I_2, and I_3, through the network shown in Figure A1-5 for which all resistances are equal to 10 ohms and the applied voltage is equal to 10 volts. By Kirchhoff's first law, the total current I_t must be equal to the sum

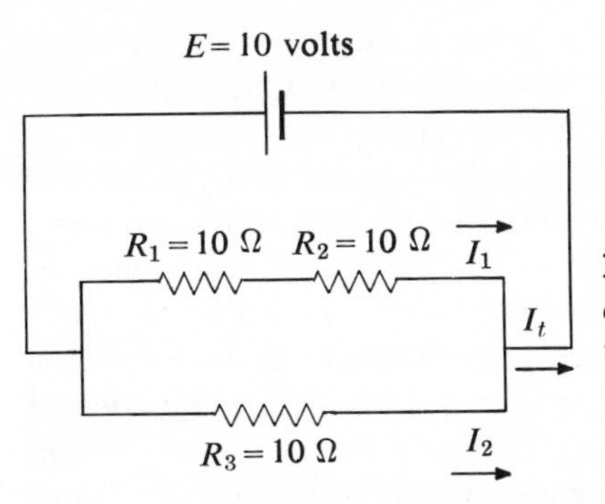

Fig. A1-5. *A combination of parallel and series resistors for the text problem.*

of the two partial currents in the two parallel arms in the circuit. Therefore

$$I_t = I_1 + I_2 \qquad \text{(A1-13)}$$

By Kirchhoff's second law, the voltage drop around each of the two closed loops is equal to the applied voltage. Using Ohm's law to compute the voltage drop across each resistor:

$$V = R_1 I_1 + R_2 I_1 = 10 I_1 + 10 I_1 \qquad \text{(A1-14)}$$

and

$$V = R_3 I_2 = 10 I_2 \qquad \text{(A1-15)}$$

These three simultaneous equations may now be solved for the three unknown currents: $I_1 = ½$ amp, $I_2 = 1$ amp, $I_t = 1½$ amp.

Although we have developed the idea of Ohm's law and Kirchhoff's laws in terms of purely resistive circuits, they also expand to somewhat more complicated forms that are strongly frequency-dependent for capacitive and inductive circuits. We shall describe the general properties of these other two types of impedances, but the special problems of phase shift and frequency sensitivity put the calculation of these useful laws beyond the intended scope of our book.

CAPACITIVE IMPEDANCE

If two conducting objects are brought in proximity to each other but are not connected by means of a conducting pathway, it is possible to store charge on the combination by accumulating electrons on one object while depleting the electron supply on the other. The amount of charge that can be stored is a function of both the geometry and the material separating the objects. Because the voltage produced by the stored charge opposes the applied voltage, the flow of current tends to be impeded. The word *capacitor* is used for the circuit components used, and the tendency to restrict current flow is called *capacitive impedance* or *capacitive reactance.* In order to describe clearly the property of capacitive impedance, we shall frame our discussion in terms of a device in which the two objects are parallel plates separated by a *dielectric* (insulating) material. There are other forms of capacitors, but the analysis of the parallel plate capacitor is simplest, and most commercially available units for use in electronic systems are of this type.

Parallel plate capacitors are constructed as shown in Figure A1-6. Two conducting plates face each other, separated by an in-

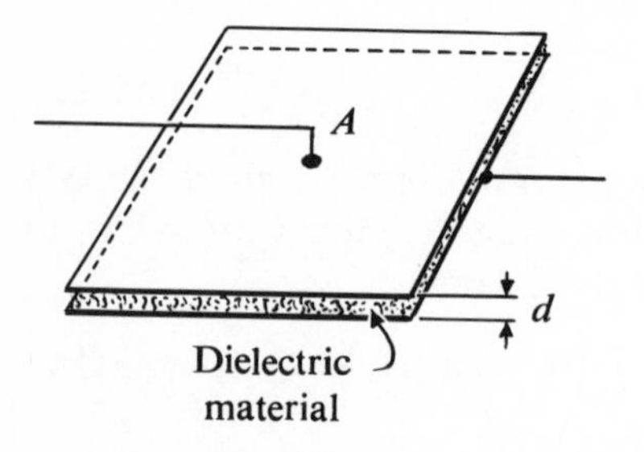

Fig. A1-6. *A schematic sketch of a parallel plate capacitor.* A *is the area of the plates and* d *is the distance between the plates. The gap between the plates is filled with some dielectric material.*

sulating material. Capacitors have the property of storing a certain amount of charge for a given applied voltage. After the voltage is removed, if there are no paths for the capacitor to discharge, the charge stored on the capacitor remains indefinitely, discharging only by leaking through the dielectric material or the surrounding environment. Different amounts of charge will be stored by different sized capacitors. The ratio between the stored charge Q and the applied voltage V is defined as the *capacity* (or *capacitance*) of the device:

$$C = \frac{Q}{V} \tag{A1-16}$$

It is important to note that the capacity of a capacitor is not the same as the impedance in ohms that the capacitor will offer to the flow of current when a voltage is applied. Capacity is, rather, a measure of the ability of the device to store charge. Capacity is measured in *farads,* one farad being defined as the capacity such that an applied voltage of one volt will store one coulomb of charge. It turns out that the farad is also one of those enormously large units that do not occur in usual practice, and as a result the microfarad has become the standard unit of capacity. Useful capacitive elements can be constructed with capacities measured only in micromicrofarads (picofarads).

As we have said, the capacity of a capacitor is a function of its geometry and the nature of the insulating material separating the two plates. The capacity of a parallel plate capacitor is defined by the following equation:

$$C = \frac{k\,A}{4\pi D} \qquad \text{(A1-17)}$$

where C is the capacity in farads, A is the area of one of the plates, D is the distance between the plates, and k is the so-called *dielectric constant* of the insulating material. The constant 4π occurs in the equation because its derivation is based upon spherically shaped charged bodies.

Because capacitors store charge, they act essentially as voltage sources equal to and opposite the applied voltage. When a voltage is applied to a capacitor (see Fig. A1-7), the unit charges until the voltage across the capacitor is equal and opposite in polarity to the

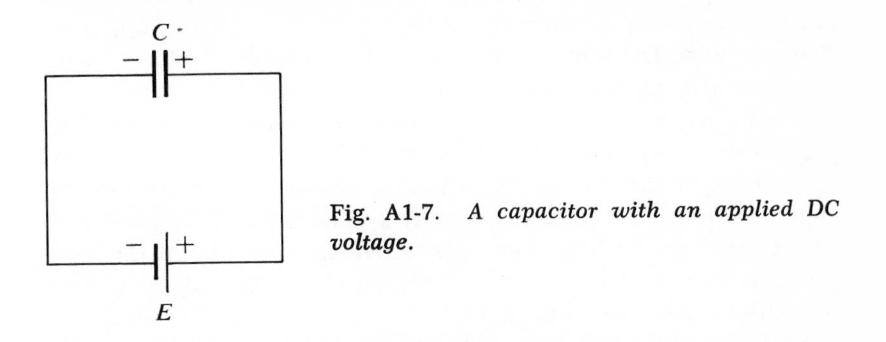

Fig. A1-7. *A capacitor with an applied DC voltage.*

voltage of the applied source. If the applied voltage is a constant or DC source, no more current can flow in the circuit once the capacitor has charged. For this reason, capacitors can be considered to have infinite resistance to DC voltages once the initial charging transients are complete.

On the other hand, AC voltages, which periodically reverse their polarities, will charge a capacitor and then, because of the reversed polarity, will discharge it and recharge it in the opposite direction. As the electrons in this charging and discharging process flow back and forth in the circuit, the effect appears to be that AC current is passing through the capacitor. As a matter of fact, no electrons actually pass through the capacitor, but the charge forces of the electrons on one or the other side of the capacitor will influence electrons on the opposite side. It can be observed that the higher the frequency of the applied voltage, the less the impedance of the capacitor to the flow of current. The following equation defines the impedance or reactance of a capacitor as a function of the frequency of the applied voltage and the capacity of the element itself:

$$X_C = \frac{1}{2\pi f C} \tag{A1-18}$$

where X_C is the impedance of the circuit to current flow in ohms, f is the frequency of the applied voltage in cycles per second, and C is the capacity in farads. From this equation it can be seen that when the frequency of the voltage gets very low, the impedance gets very large. This is a formal expression of the fact that when DC voltages are applied to capacitors almost no current flows after the first rush of electrons charging the capacitor.

Because of their frequency sensitivity, capacitors can be used to provide pathways for the flow of AC currents while simultaneously prohibiting the flow of electrons produced by DC voltages. For example, amplifiers with capacitors in their input leads are insensitive to applied DC voltages; they are said to be AC coupled. Capacitors can also be used as short circuits or shunts to remove AC components from the voltage produced by a power supply. This process is called filtering because the AC voltage components are filtered out of the desired DC voltages. A little thought will clarify the fact that the storage of charge by a capacitor and the passing of AC voltages are both, in fact, alternative explanations of the same phenomenon. A circuit can be analyzed from either point of view and still be described adequately.

So far we have not considered the initial charging time of the capacitor as a major part of its usefulness in electronic circuits. But the events in this initial period are extremely important and can be used in a wide variety of ways to alter applied electronic signals. A critical property of the charging time of a capacitor is that it is determined by any series resistance, as well as by the capacitor. Thus for series circuits made up of a resistance and a capacitor (see Fig. A1-8), a new dimension has been defined which is called the RC (Resistance-Capacitance) *time constant*, T:

$$T = R \times C \tag{A1-19}$$

The resistor acts in this circuit to limit the amount of charge that can flow in any given time period, and the capacitor contributes to the time constant by determining how much charge is necessary to bring the voltage up to a certain point. *T*, the *RC* time constant, can be shown to be the time it takes the capacitor to charge to approximately 63 percent of its maximum value. Since the amount of current flowing, and therefore the charging rate, is a

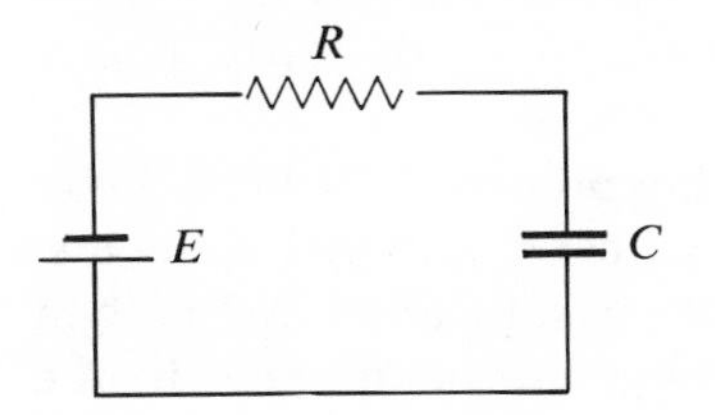

Fig. A1-8. *A series circuit made up of a resistor and a capacitor. The size of the resistor and the capacitor both determine the charging time of the capacitor.*

function of the difference in potential between the applied voltage and the charge on the capacitor at any given time, obviously the charging will occur more and more slowly as the capacitor becomes more fully charged. The charging curve approximates an exponential curve. The current through the circuit is described by the reciprocal of the charge curve with a heavy initial current and a gradual diminution as the capacitor is charged, as shown in Figure A1-9. For this reason, the circuit can be considered to be acting as a differentiator (in the sense of the differential calculus) for current. A voltage will exist across the resistor (recall Ohm's law) only when the current flows at the initial application of the voltage. This differentiation property is often used to convert voltage level shifts to brief voltage pulses necessary for some subsequent electronic application.

However, during the early part of the charge curve, which is

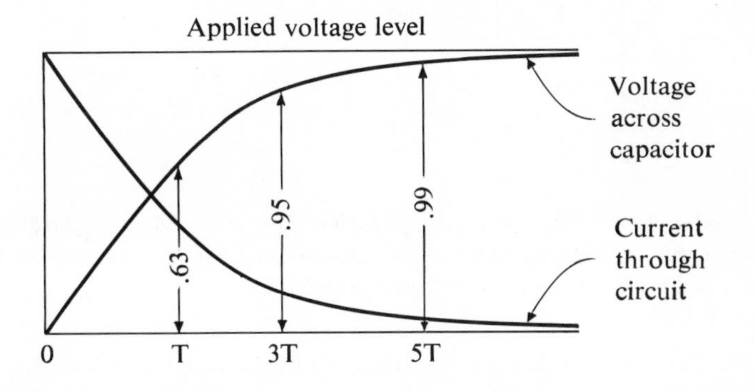

Fig. A1-9. *Charging curves for a series R-C circuit showing both the voltage across the capacitor (increasing in time) and the current through the circuit (decreasing in time).*

approximately linear, the voltage across the capacitor is very close to the integral of the constant voltage that has been applied to its input. Thus integration (in the sense of the integral calculus) can also be accomplished by monitoring the voltage across the resistor. In practice, capacitors to be used as integrators usually have high-gain amplifiers associated with them so that only the early, nearly linear portion of the charge curve is used.

Both the differentiating and integrating properties of RC circuits are widely used in analog computers as computational elements. In digital computers, these properties are usually employed only to sharpen a pulse or to perform some other useful function in the logical circuitry, but not as computational tools.

Capacitors, like resistors, may be combined into series and parallel circuits, but the rules of combination are somewhat different. Since the capacity of a parallel plate capacitor is directly proportional to the area of the plates, it is intuitively obvious that the rule for combining capacitors in parallel is an additive one. Thus for a parallel circuit, such as that illustrated in Figure A1-10*a*, the rule for combination is:

$$C_t = C_1 + C_2 + C_3 \qquad \text{(A1-20)}$$

On the other hand, since the amount of charge on each capacitor in a series circuit must be equal to the amount on all others (otherwise

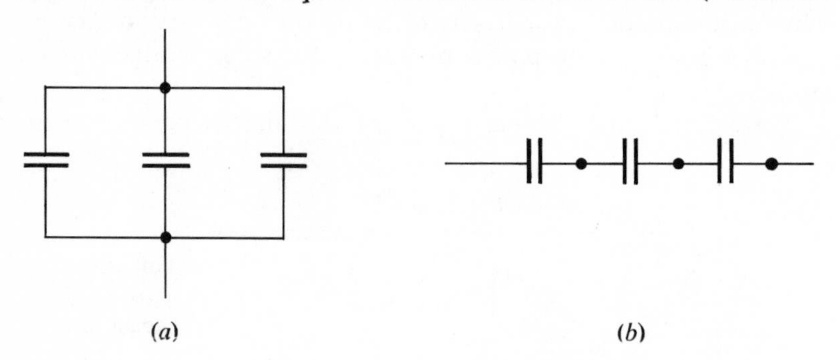

Fig. A1-10. (a) *Capacitors in parallel. The effect of this circuit is to increase the total capacitance.* (b) *Capacitors in series. The effect of this circuit is to decrease the total capacitance.*

we would have a violation of Kirchhoff's first law), the rule for series combinations of capacitors such as that illustrated in Figure A1-10*b* can be shown to be a reciprocal law:

$$\frac{1}{C_t} = \frac{1}{C_1} + \frac{1}{C_2} + \frac{1}{C_3} \qquad \text{(A1-21)}$$

Capacitors, thus, have a number of practical uses in electronic circuits. Because of their ability to selectively impede the flow of different frequency currents they can be used to filter one frequency signal from another. In combination with resistors, they can be used to time circuit operations owing to the flexible way the RC time constant can be varied. Because they differentiate changes in voltage level, they can be used as a means of sharpening pulses or converting level changes to pulses.

In summary, all of these applications and the many others we have not mentioned are due to the ability of the capacitor to store charge. It is important to distinguish between the capacitance of a capacitor as a measure of its charge-holding capability and the impedance of a capacitor to the flow of current. Practical capacitors also have limitations on the voltage range within which they can work. The design of capacitive circuits should always include consideration of this factor, just as resistors must be selected for their power-handling capability.

INDUCTIVE IMPEDANCE

We mentioned that when a current passes through a wire a magnetic field is formed around the wire. If the wire is coiled into a loop, the magnetic fields tend to build up voltages in the wire in the direction opposite that of the applied voltages. The opposing voltages tend to inhibit the flow of current, just as the opposing voltages of a charged capacitor tended to inhibit the flow of current in a capacitive circuit. Devices that exhibit impedance to current flow because of the induced electromagnetic fields are called *inductors*. As with capacitance, the inductance and therefore the inductive impedance of the circuit are functions of both the geometry of the coiled wire and the frequency characteristics of the applied voltage.

The inductance of a coil can be calculated by means of the following formula:

$$L = \frac{4\pi N^2 \mu A\, 10^{-9}}{l} \qquad \text{(A1-22)}$$

where L is the *inductance* of a coil on itself (the *self-inductance*) in henrys, N is the number of turns of wire in the coil, A is the cross-sectional area of the coil, and l is its length. μ is a constant called the *magnetic permeability* of the material in which the coil is embedded. This constant, μ, is nearly 1 for most common materials, such as air. From the equation we can see that, as with a capacitor, the geometry of the coil is the primary determinant of its inductance.

Once again it should be emphasized that this measure of inductance is not a measure of the impedance the circuit element will exhibit to the flow of current; rather, it is a measure of the coil's tendency to build up in itself an opposing voltage to the applied voltage. Henrys also turn out to be very large units, and millihenrys are more commonly used as measures of practical inductance.

Now let us look at a subtle point that many novices in the field find difficult to understand. For capacitors we pointed out in equation A1-16 that:

$$C = \frac{Q}{V}$$

Rearranging the formula we see that:

$$V = \frac{Q}{C} \qquad \text{(A1-23)}$$

In other words, the voltage across a capacitor is proportional to the charge on the capacitor. The constant of proportionality in this case is defined as the capacitance. For an inductor, however, repeated observations have shown that the reverse voltage ($-V$) generated by a current is:

$$-V = L\frac{dI}{dt} \qquad \text{(A1-24)}$$

The voltage is proportional to the rate of change of current with respect to time dI/dt:[4] In this case the constant of proportionality is the inductance L of the circuit defined above by the physical geometry of the coil.

Equation A1-11 states that $V = IR$. In this case the voltage across a resistance is proportional to the current, with a constant of proportionality called resistance. But I (current) is equal to the rate of movement of charge Q with respect to time; i.e.,

$$I = \frac{dQ}{dt} \qquad \text{(A1-25)}$$

Therefore, we can now summarize by pointing out that the three impedance characteristics of conducting circuit elements represent three different ways of generating a voltage. One of these properties

[4] For readers not familiar with the notation of the differential calculus, the term dI/dt may be considered simply as the rate of change of current at an instant in time rather than the average rate of change of current. Similarly, dQ/dt may be considered as the instantaneous rate of change of charge.

is sensitive to the amount of charge present and is called capacitance. The second is sensitive to the rate of change of charge and is called resistance. The third is sensitive to the rate of change of current (the second derivative of charge with respect to time) and is called inductance.

Reconsidering equation A1-24, we see that the inverse voltage produced by a current is larger for a current that is rapidly changing—a high-frequency voltage. If the current is not changing very rapidly or is a DC the inverse voltage is very small and little impedance to current flow is exhibited. This intuitive description can be formalized by the following expression for the impedance of an inductor to the flow of current:

$$X_L = 2\pi fL \qquad \text{(A1-26)}$$

where X_L is the impedance of the inductor in ohms, f is the frequency of the applied voltage, and L is the inductance of the coil. Thus a current produced by DC voltage passes through a coil as if it were a straight piece of wire of equivalent length, while a high-frequency signal can generate only a modest amount of current in such a coil owing to inductive impedance.

An inductor is, therefore, a frequency-sensitive device just as a capacitor is, but, contrary to capacitive action, it tends to pass low-frequency signals while inhibiting high-frequency signals. Inductors placed in a series circuit to block the passage of high-frequency signals are called chokes.

Inductors can be combined in series and in parallel. Figure A1-11*a* shows a series inductive circuit using the standard symbol for

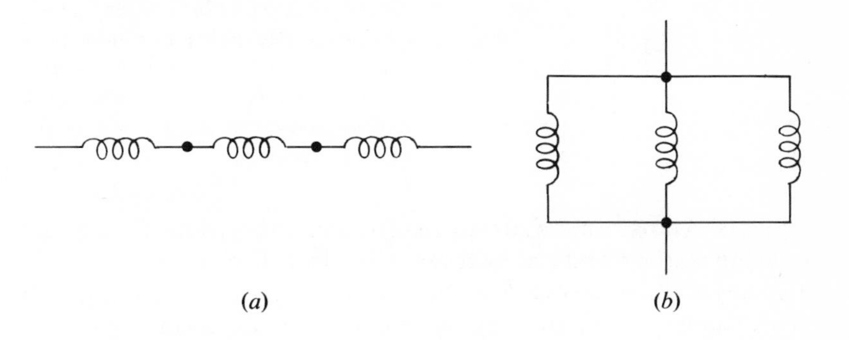

Fig. A1-11. (a) *Inductors in series. The effect of this circuit is to increase the total inductance.* (b) *Inductors in parallel. The effect of this circuit is to decrease the total inductance. However, great care must be used to avoid interaction of the magnetic fields of adjacent inductors. Otherwise the inductance of the combined circuit is not easily defined.*

an inductor. Figure A1-11*b* is a parallel inductive circuit. Series inductive circuits can be shown to be combined like series resistive circuits according to the following rule:

$$L_t = L_1 + L_2 + L_3 \qquad \text{(A1-27)}$$

Similarly, parallel inductive circuits can be shown to be combined by means of the same rule as parallel resistive circuits, namely,

$$\frac{1}{L_t} = \frac{1}{L_1} + \frac{1}{L_2} + \frac{1}{L_3} \qquad \text{(A1-28)}$$

Both rules, however, depend upon one further restriction. Inductances work because their own magnetic fields generate inverse voltages within and around the inductor itself. Thus, for either rule to be an accurate representation of the total inductance, the magnetic field of each of the individual inductances must be isolated from that of each of the others. If two inductors do not meet this criterion, voltages tend to be generated in one when a changing current is run through the other. This process is taken advantage of to form a *transformer,* which is used to vary AC voltages between different parts of a circuit intentionally. We have until now been speaking of the effects of a magnetic field generated in a coil on itself (self-inductance.) If a coil is placed in the magnetic field of another coil, the problem becomes one of *mutual inductance.*

Figure A1-12 is a diagram of a typical transformer, which works on the basis of the latter form of interaction between two inductive

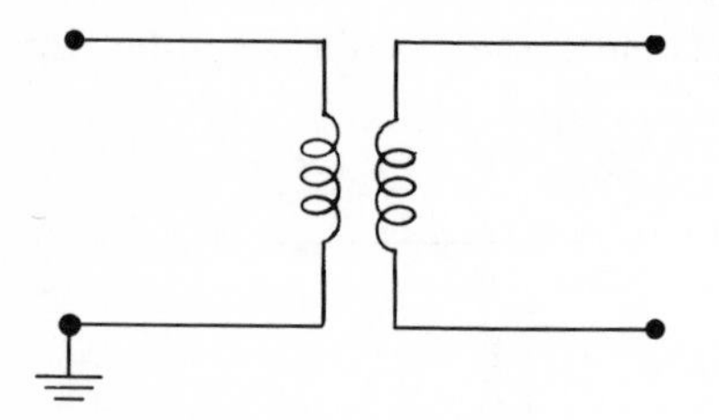

Fig. A1-12. *A transformer composed of two inductors in which the magnetic fields are intentionally designed to interact. The transformer can be used for changing voltage levels of AC signals or for voltage isolation.*

elements. Transformers are in reality miniature transmitting and receiving stations and are used very effectively to change the voltage of an alternating current. For tightly coupled transformer coils, with other factors equal, the voltage induced in the second coil will generally be related to the voltage applied to the first coil in proportion to the ratio of the number of turns in the second coil to the number of turns in the first. An increase in voltage, however, is paid for with a corresponding decrease in the available supply of current, as well as with some loss through heating of the two coils.

Nevertheless transformer action is a simple and efficient means of changing voltage levels in AC circuits. Transformers are also often used, not to increase or decrease the voltage level, but to alter the reference with which the voltage is being compared. Thus in Figure A1-12 the first or *primary coil* has an applied voltage that is referenced to ground. The voltage across the second or *secondary coil,* while perhaps still the same amplitude, is now said to be floating, since the effects of that voltage may be felt only across the two terminals of the coil and would not be felt between one side of the coil and ground.

PRACTICAL PASSIVE ELECTRICAL ELEMENTS

We have spoken of resistance, capacitance, and inductance as if they were completely separate and ideal circuit elements. In fact, most practical circuit elements actually have all three properties to a greater or lesser degree. A given inductor, while primarily an inductive element, is made of a coil of wire and thus has a certain resistive impedance associated with it. Capacitors generally leak small amounts of direct current and therefore also have resistive properties. In general, these small "parasitic" sources of potential are too small to matter, but in some special cases they can be of serious concern. One special case may be encountered when a resistive element (or even a piece of wire) is carrying a high-frequency signal. There is a small but measurable capacity between different parts of a given circuit, and if the frequency of the applied signal is high enough, the circuit may, by capacitive coupling, actually pass signals from one wire to the next. Care must be taken, by keeping leads short and in straight lines between connecting points, to avoid the apparently mysterious injection of these unwanted electrical signals into computer circuitry.

Another issue that should be briefly mentioned is the problem of phase shifting of signals passing through capacitors and inductors. For most practical purposes, there is no need to concern ourselves with this particular problem when dealing with the pulses and levels of digital computer circuits. It should be noted, though, that currents can be made to lag behind or even to lead the applied voltage as they pass through capacitive and inductive circuits.

Now that we have introduced passive electrical circuit elements, we can turn to a discussion of circuit elements that actively alter the nature of the electrical signals applied to them.

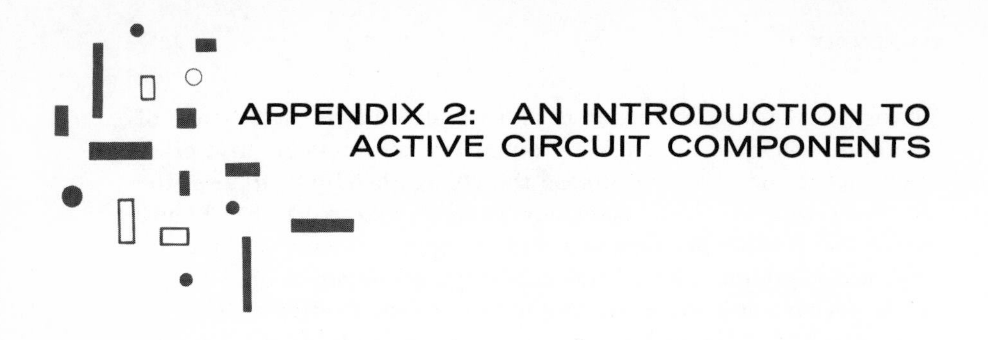

APPENDIX 2: AN INTRODUCTION TO ACTIVE CIRCUIT COMPONENTS

The atomic model of semiconductor action

As mentioned in Appendix 1, the several possible orbits surrounding an atomic nucleus can contain only certain numbers of electrons. These numbers are specific for each of the elements. But one important overall limitation is that the outermost orbit can contain no more than eight electrons. It is the outermost orbital electrons that determine the electrical properties of materials at ordinary room temperatures, and it is only the outermost orbit that concerns us in the following discussion of electrical conductivity.

For emphasis, let us review some of the basic facts of electrical conductance. Materials having only 1 or 2 electrons in the outer orbit are always good conductors because these few electrons are weakly bound into the orbital structure and can easily break loose to serve as carriers of electrical current. Metals like copper and silver have an easily detached single electron available to act as part of a current.

On the other hand, there are many atomic structures in which the outer orbit has the maximum 8 electrons. Not only are such materials generally poor conductors, but their electrons are so strongly bound to the atom that they only weakly participate in chemical reactions. The tendency for the outermost or *valence* orbits with 8 electrons to be very stable is called the *octet rule*.

Semiconductors are in an intermediate position betweeen the insulators and the conductors. They generally have three, four, or five valence electrons, which can, with moderate amounts of energy, be disengaged from their orbits to participate in electrical conduction.

Two important new ideas are to be introduced here. First, many materials that are semiconductors have also been found to be crystalline in structure. (A crystalline structure is one in which the composite atoms tend to be regularly arranged with very highly specified geometry.) Second—and dealing directly with interactions among the electrons themselves and with the octet rule—it is possible, in a well-ordered array, for the outer valence electrons of 2 atoms to be shared so that each atom appears to have a full octet of electrons in its outer orbit, even though only eight electrons are actually orbiting the two nuclei. In this case the electrons of both atoms tend to be tightly bound in their respective orbits since they are effectively satisfying the octet rule. The two atomic structures themselves also tend to be tightly bonded together because of this sharing of electrons. The bond between adjacent atoms is said to be *covalent*, an abbreviation of the term *cooperative valence*.

Covalent bonding is so strong that if the crystalline structures were perfect, and if each atom of a normally four-valence electron element shared eight electrons with the surrounding atoms, these materials would be perfect insulators. Inasmuch as there are, however, always imperfections in the geometry of a crystal and impurities of other atomic elements, usually an intermediate degree of conductivity exists.

Techniques of melting and recrystallization have been developed to increase the purity and crystalline order of materials such as silicon and germanium, the two most commonly used semiconductors. In one technique—*zone refining*—a radio-frequency induction heater is used to melt a zone or band of a crystal ingot. The radio-frequency heater is then physically moved along the ingot, moving the melted band with it. Since impurities tend to remain in the melted portion of the ingot, they can be cleared to the end toward which the heater is moving. This end is then cut off and discarded, disposing of the major portion of the included impurities. The precise and controlled cooling of the ingot increases the order of its crystalline structure and, along with the removal of the impurities, makes for a much more resistive material than that of which the raw ingot was composed. For example, highly purified germanium may have a resistance of 50 to 60 ohms per cubic centimeter, while highly purified silicon is typically found to have a resistance of 50,000 to 60,000 ohms per cubic centimeter.

The imperfections or impurities of which we spoke decreased the resistance by providing electrons that can participate as *carriers* in the flow of electrical current. Furthermore, it is important to realize that a deficiency of an electron—a "hole"—may also be a carrier. The hole effectively participates in the same way as a moving electron by providing a sink into which an electron can drop at a given instant. The hole can be treated theoretically as a carrier with a positive charge to explain current flow.

The conductance of a material can, therefore, be increased by adding available electrons or available holes to the semiconductor material. This is accomplished by putting accurately controlled amounts of certain impurities into the highly refined semiconductor materials produced as described above. The procedure of adding controlled amounts of impurities is called *doping* and is really an alloying process in which the constituent metals are mixed together in very precise proportions.

Let us consider how doping affects the conductivity of a semiconductor. Silicon and germanium have four electrons in their outer orbits. When a pure crystal is formed, adjacent atoms tend to share orbital electrons with each other by covalent bonding so

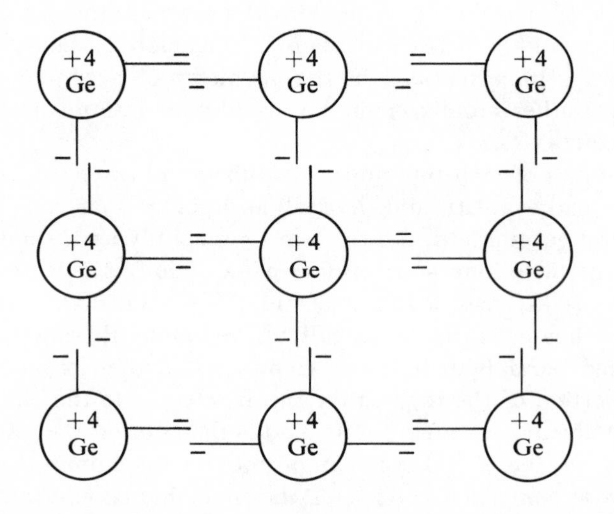

Fig. A2-1. *A schematic drawing of the very pure and high resistance crystalline structure of pure germanium, showing the sharing of electrons through covalent bonding.*

that each atom effectively has an octet of electrons rotating around it. The result is a stable crystalline structure with no excess or deficiency of electrons. Figure A2-1 is a diagram of such an arrangement for a pure crystal of germanium.

However, if we put into the germanium a small amount of antimony or arsenic, each of which has five electrons in its outer orbit, a different situation obtains. As before, there is the tendency for each atom to share the electrons of the others so as to form an octet about each atom. But this accounts for only four of the orbital electrons of the antimony or the arsenic atom. The other orbital electron is surplus above the octet needs, and it can move about just as easily as the single electron in the outer orbit of copper. It could participate as a carrier and would therefore be a means of conveying current in the semiconductor. The actual reduction in the resistivity would be a direct function of how much of the impurity was alloyed with the germanium. Figure A2-2 is a diagram of the situation which is obtained when germanium is doped with

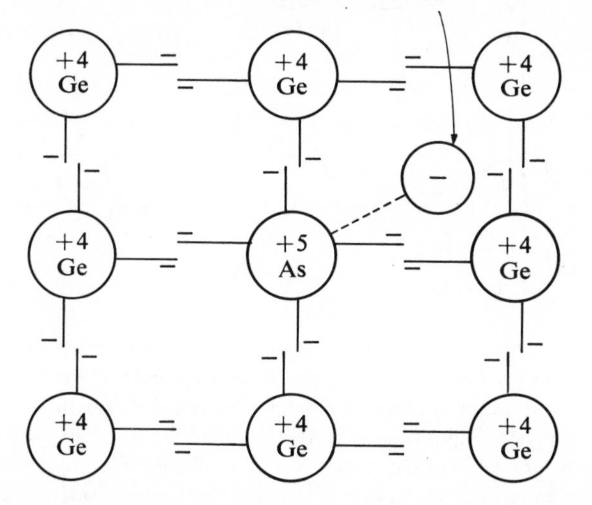

Fig. A2-2. *Doping a germanium crystal with arsenic with five outer valence electrons leads to the release of the extra electron as a carrier of electrical current. Such a material is called an N-type semiconductor.*

arsenic. A material with such a surplus of electrons is called an *N-type* semiconductor. The *N* stands for the fact that the available carriers in this material are *n*egatively charged electrons.

What would happen if we doped the germanium with indium, which has an outer valence orbit consisting of three electrons?

Figure A2-3 is a diagram of this situation. Since indium has only three electrons, it creates unfilled orbits (with only seven instead of eight electrons) when it shares electrons with surrounding germanium atoms. There is, therefore, on the average, a deficiency of electrons for the formation of stable octets, and it is expressed as the positively charged entity we called a hole. Any free electron moving near a hole will be likely to be attached to the valence electrons to complete the octet. It may even be that some electrons from nearby filled octets will be detached from their original positions and will join the orbital electrons around the indium atoms. Thus, a hole near the indium atoms may capture an electron, but in doing

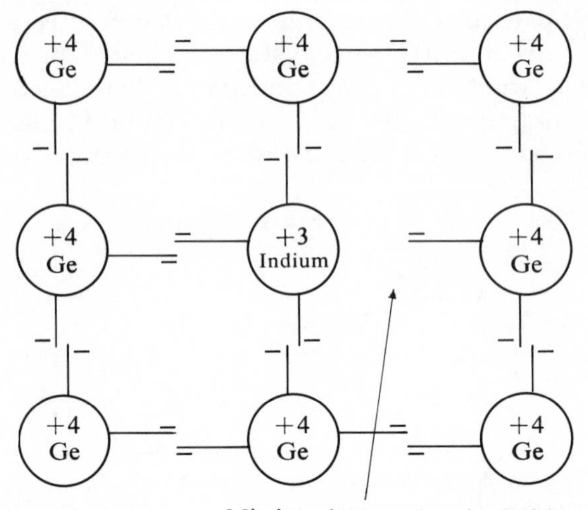

Fig. A2-3. *Doping a germanium crystal with indium with only three valence electrons leads to a deficiency of an electron for the formation of the complete octet of shared electrons. This deficiency is in the form of a potential hole, which is very likely to pick up a free electron. Thus the hole can act as a positive carrier just as the free electron acts as a negative carrier. Such a material is called a P-type semiconductor.*

so it produces a hole elsewhere. In this fashion a hole may tend to move, just as an electron does, from position to position. The drift of a hole is a current in the same way as the drift of electrons is. Semiconductor materials with excess numbers of holes (a deficiency of electrons) are called *P-type* semiconductors because their carriers are positively charged, relative to the surrounding environment. Table A2-1 is a list of some of the elements used in semiconductor doping.

Element (symbol)	Number valence electrons	Applications in semiconductor devices
Boron (B) Aluminum (Al) Gallium (Ga) Indium (In)	3	Doping materials used to create *P*-type semiconductors
Germanium (Ge) Silicon (Si)	4	The basic semiconductor materials
Phosphorus (P) Arsenic (As) Antimony (Sb)	5	Doping materials used to create *N*-type semiconductors

Table A2-1. *The elements involved in semiconductor manufacturing and their valence characteristics. (Modified from* General Electric Transistor Manual, *Semiconductor Products Department, General Electric Company, 1964, p. 12.)*

For both the *N*- and the *P*-type semiconductor materials we have described, a majority of the carriers are of the kind produced by doping. However, in both materials the oppositely charged kind of carrier is also present, but in smaller amounts. The presence of the *minority carriers* (holes for *N*-type materials and electrons for *P*-type materials) is due to the residual imperfections and impurities in the germanium or silicon crystal. Minority and majority carriers can also be produced by thermal agitation. Even ordinary room temperature is sometimes able to dislodge an electron from a filled orbit of eight electrons. Thus, there are many sources of minority carriers. Minority carrier current is very important, and later we shall see how it is the basis of transistor action. Table A2-2 summarizes the majority and minority carrier systems for *N*- and *P*-type materials.

If a voltage is applied to an *N*- or *P*-type material, electrons tend to drift from the negative pole to the positive pole. In both cases,

Type	Majority carrier	Minority carrier
N	Electron	Hole
P	Hole	Electron

Table A2-2. *A summary of the majority and minority carriers for N- and P-type semiconductor materials.*

however, as far as the external circuit is concerned, there appears to be an injection of electrons at the negative pole and an emission of electrons at the positive pole. Since the average lifetime of a hole or an electron is short—less than the time it takes to migrate across the semiconductor material—the electrons that are injected into the semiconductor material are not the same as the electrons that are emitted from it. Electrons are inclined to recombine with holes, releasing other electrons to continue the recombination process. Holes recombine with electrons, releasing other holes. The process of majority and minority carriers, though best described in terms of the drift of specific electrons and holes, is truly a statistical process of combination, release, and recombination.

The diode

If a block of *P*-type semiconductor is joined to a block of *N*-type semiconductor, a number of internal charge rearrangements occur that lead to the development of certain unique properties. Such a combination of semiconductors is called a *diode*, indicating that it is a device with two electrodes. Diodes, along with other properties, have the important capability of having different resistances, depending upon the direction in which voltage is applied. Diodes are therefore said to be *rectifiers*, since current can pass in one direction very easily but is strongly impeded in the opposite direction. Most applications of diodes depend upon this capacity for directional sensitivity to the flow of current.

Figure A2-4*a* is a schematic diagram of a diode composed of a *P*-type semiconductor butted against an *N*-type semiconductor. The majority carriers in each material have been indicated by their appropriate charge. Prior to the formation of the interface or junction, the holes in the *P* material and the electrons in the *N* material are equally dispersed throughout the two blocks of semiconductor. The moment they are joined, however, a certain amount of recombination of some of the holes and some of the electrons takes place at the region around the junction. Since the excess electrons from the *N* material are no longer present, the region near the junction tends to be positively charged with respect to the other parts of the diode. The charge is positive because the atoms that have given up electrons have become charged ions. Before the formation of the junction the average charge of the region was zero, for the potential of the positively charged ions was balanced by the free electrons in that general area. Similarly, on the *P* semiconductor side of the diode, holes are depleted as they combine with the electrons from

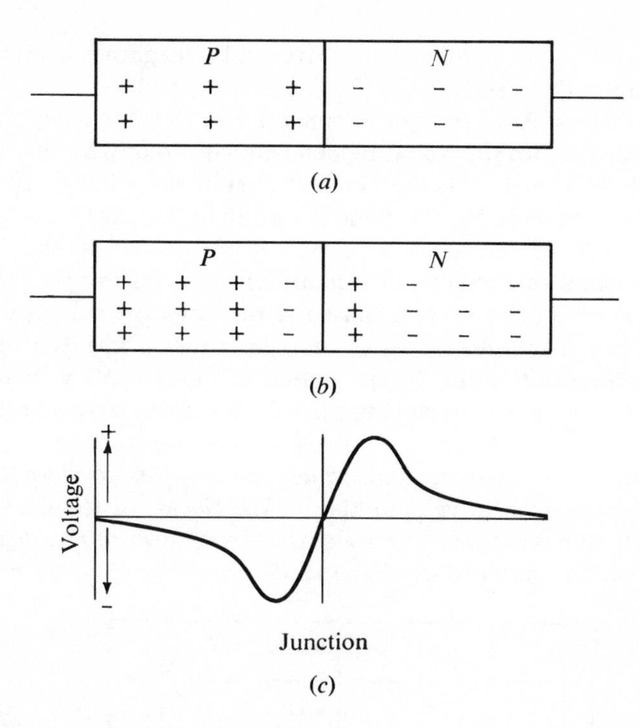

Fig. A2-4. (a) *A diode made up of a block of N-type material butted up against a block of P-type material. The charge distribution is shown before the holes and electrons have had a chance to recombine.* (b) *After the recombination, a depletion region is formed near the junction generating a barrier potential.* (c) *The internal voltages within different parts of a diode are shown in this figure. This internal voltage cannot be detected from the outside since they are equal and opposite voltages being added together.*

the other side, and a group of negatively charged ions is created. Figure A2-4*b* depicts the charge distribution in the *depletion region* (the depletion region being the volume on either side of the junction from which electrons and holes have been effectively removed by recombination).

The potential created at the junction by the depletion of holes and electrons is called the *barrier potential,* and the rectifying action of a diode is easily explained on the basis of this potential. Figure A2-4*c* is a plot of the voltage that would be measured if we were able to probe the potential difference between various points of the crystal lattice. However, if we measured the voltage between the two ends of the material, we would of course see no potential difference because there is a positive and a negative potential of equal amplitude in series.

Nevertheless, if we tried to force a current through such a diode, the amount of current would be determined directly by the barrier potential. To explain this further, we must define what is meant by *forward and reverse bias*. A diode is said to be forward biased if the negative pole of the applied voltage is connected to the *N*-type material while the positive pole is attached to the *P*-type material. A diode is said to be reverse biased if the negative pole of the applied voltage is connected to the *P*-type material and the positive pole is connected to the *N*-type material. Figures A2-5*a* depicts a forward-biased diode while Figure A2-5*b* depicts a reverse-biased one.

Consider now what happens when the diode is forward biased. Since there is a negative potential on the *N* side of the diode, and since like charges repel, electrons are forced toward the depletion region. On the other side of the diode, holes tend to be repelled

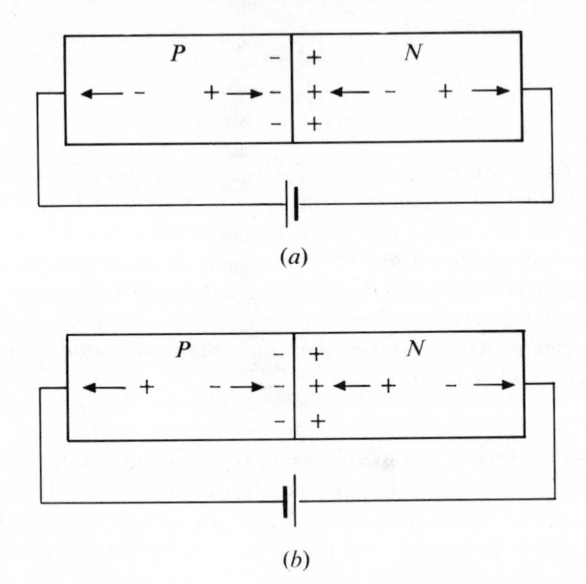

Fig. A2-5. (a) *A forward-biased diode. Electrons in this case are forced by the applied voltage toward the positively charged barrier and holes are forced toward the negatively charged barrier. Since these opposites will recombine with the appropriate part of the barrier potential, the barrier potential is reduced and the effective resistance of the diode is low.* (b) *A reverse-biased diode. The barrier potential in this case is increased and therefore the resistance of a reverse-biased diode is quite high.*

from the positive pole of the voltage source, also toward the depletion region. In each case the effect is to bring the charge necessary to reduce the barrier potential into the depletion region. Thus, the barrier potential tends to be reduced to zero. Electrons are then free to move across the junction where they had previously been inhibited by the presence of the barrier potential. The diminution of the barrier potential results in a relatively unimpeded flow of electrons. Such a forward flow of current can be relatively large, for the applied voltage is acting on a semiconductor so that it can dislodge as many electrons as necessary to keep up the applied current.

Reverse bias, on the other hand, increases the magnitude of the barrier potential. Figure A2-5*b* shows that the negative pole is connected to the *P*-type semiconductor region. Thus minority electrons are repelled toward the junction, where they add to the total negative charge of this part of the barrier potential. Similarly, the minority holes repelled by the positive pole of the applied voltage that is connected to the *N* region tend to drive other holes toward the positive part of the barrier potential. The net result is that the barrier potential is increased, and the effective resistance of the diode in this reverse direction becomes very large. The reason is that electrons forced toward the negatively charged barrier potential in the *P*-type depletion regions and holes forced toward the positively charged depletion region of the *N*-type material tend to be repelled by the barrier potentials.

Another significant difference between forward and reverse current is that the small current flow in the reverse direction is purely a function of the available minority carriers produced by thermal disassociation. This small current that flows through the diode is actually *independent of the applied voltage*. In other words, a constant current flows, regardless of the voltage of the applied voltage. There is, of course, an upper limit to this generalization, for voltages higher than a certain value tend to cause a breakdown in the resistance of the diode, resulting in an extremely large flow of current, just like a forward-biased diode. Figure A2-6 is a plot showing the relationship of voltage and current for a diode. Forward bias (to the right of the vertical coordinate) can be seen to produce large currents dependent upon the amplitude of the forward voltage; reverse biases (to the left of the vertical coordinate) tend to produce small currents independent of the applied voltage until the breakdown occurs, when a very large reverse current results.

Figure A2-7 is the usual symbol for the diode. The triangle indicates the anode (the *P*-type material), while the straight line

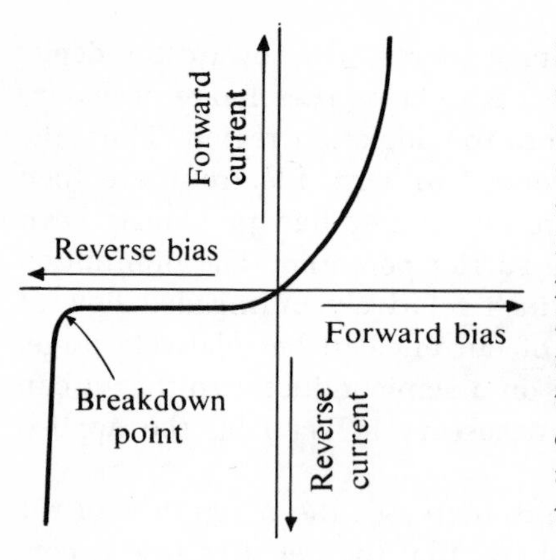

Fig. A2-6. *The relation of a current and voltage in a diode. For forward biases the current increases significantly with increases in the applied voltage. For reverse biases the current, however, is dependent mainly upon the availability of minority carriers and is therefore relatively constant over wide ranges of bias. Finally, however, a point is reached at which the diode breaks down and there is very heavy inverse current.*

indicates the cathode (the *N*-type material). Diodes can be used to rectify current, allowing electrons to flow only when forward biased. Applying an alternating voltage to a diode so that the polarity across the diode is reversed every half-cycle causes only the half current associated with the forward direction to be passed because the diode is able to keep up with the oscillation of the voltage, even at very high frequencies. Diodes may also be used to

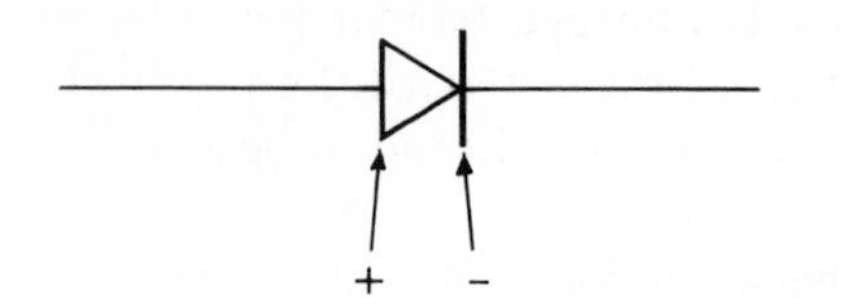

Fig. A2-7. *The standard symbol for a diode.*

short-circuit negative (or positive) voltages above a certain level, thus *clipping* or constraining the amplitude of the voltage fluctuations.

The transistor— An active three-element semiconductor device

Diodes, although extremely useful, can only selectively pass current in one direction and inhibit its flow in the other direction. They are not able to amplify the signals fed into them or in any other way alter the characteristics of the signals in the various circuits comprising a complicated electronic system. By combining additional blocks of semiconductors it is possible to arrive at configurations of semiconductor materials that can be used to affect drastically the signals circulating in electronic circuits. Currently, the most common active semiconductor device is a combination of three blocks of semiconductors called a *transistor*. It is rapidly replacing all the earlier technologies as the basis of modern electronics. Transistor action depends upon minority carrier current across a reverse-biased junction. From the previous section, recall that the amount of current across a reverse-biased diode is independent of the applied voltage up to relatively high voltage levels. The current is dependent upon the availability of minority carriers, which for a diode are produced mainly by thermal disassociation. If, however, there were a way of injecting minority carriers into the diode, the amount of current passing through the diode could be regulated. Suppose that we had some magical technique for inserting electrons into the *P* side of a diode, as depicted in Figure A2-8*a*. For a constant reverse bias such as that shown, we would generate a family of curves (Fig. A2-8*b*) for the reverse minority current as a function of the amount of electrons available. This family of curves is really the reverse bias portion of Figure A2-6 for several different values of minority carrier availability. In this case we have not drawn the forward-biased or the breakdown portion of the curves.

Such a hypothetical injection system can actually be realized. Consider what would happen if another block of *N* material were connected to the block of *P* material and were forward-biased with regard to the block of *P* material. Looking at the forward-biased portion of the diode curve (Fig. A2-6), we see that the amount of

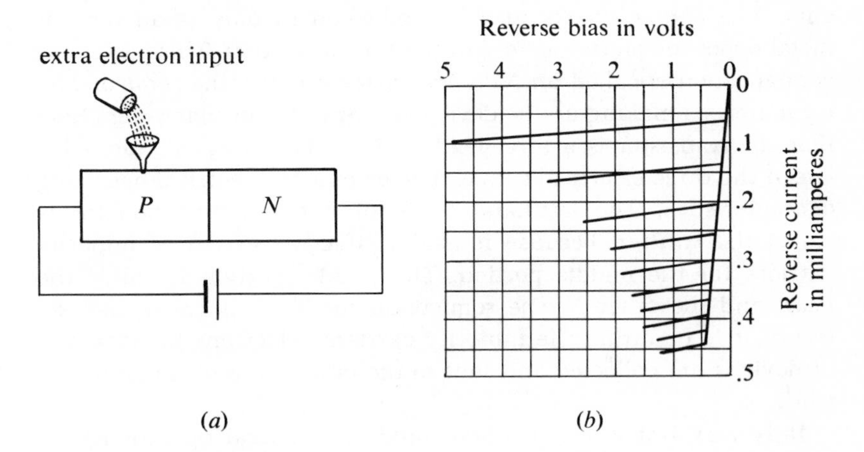

Fig. A2-8. *If we had a magic way of adding minority carriers (electrons) into the P region of a diode, then the reverse current would be controllable.* (a) *A picture of a hypothetical magic inserter of minority carriers.* (b) *The inverse current shown as a function of applied voltage but for various amounts of minority carriers. The forward-biased portion of the curve has not been shown.*

current that will flow from the *N* block into the *P* block is approximately proportional to the applied forward voltage. This current will be in the form of electrons that are therefore being injected into the *P* block, where they serve as minority carriers and accomplish the injection process we desired. Figure A2-9 is a diagram of the three-element semiconductor just described, showing the for-

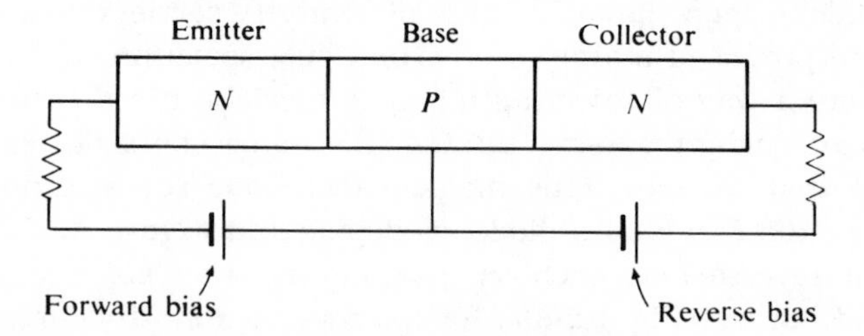

Fig. A2-9. *The NPN transistor—a three-element semiconductor device. The additional block of forward-biased semiconductor material provides varying amounts of carriers to the central block just as our magical funnel in Fig. A2-8a did.*

ward-biased *NP* portion and the reverse-biased *PN* portion as they are conventionally drawn. In fact the actual physical structure of a typical transistor looks quite different. The middle *P*-type section is usually very large physically, compared to the other two components. The *N*-type blocks may be embodied in only small dots of metal deposited on the surface of the central section. This particular configuration is called an *NPN* transistor because the semiconductor materials making up the device are arranged in that order. Note that the transistor is a three-lead device. The voltage relations between the three electrical contacts determine its electrical operating characteristics. The left-hand block of *N*-type semiconductor is called the *emitter*, because it is the effective source of minority carriers for the middle portion. The middle portion is called the *base*, and the other *N*-type semiconductor block is called the *collector*. It is here that the minority carriers (electrons for this type of device) are collected and sent to the outside circuit to do useful work.

It is very important to understand the general operation of a transistor in order to appreciate fully the actions of a modern digital computer. The following outline summarizes the general principles of operation of an *NPN* transistor:

1. The *NPN* transistor is a three-part semiconductor device.
2. A forward-biased voltage applied between the emitter and the

base regulates the number of electrons that are injected into the base.

3. The number of electrons in the base (minority carriers for the *P*-type material) regulates the amount of reverse current that will flow when a reverse voltage is applied across the collector and the base.
4. The current of electrons that flows in the external circuit will be almost independent of the voltage and resistance in the circuit up to the limits of Ohm's law.

For a transistor wired as shown in Figure A2-9, the amount of current flowing in the emitter-base circuit is approximately equal to the amount of current flowing in the collector-base circuit. Thus, if there is a larger resistance in the collector-base circuit than in the emitter-base circuit, a small voltage applied to the emitter-base circuit (the input) will cause a large voltage to be measured across a resistor in the collector-base circuit (the output). (This can be shown by applying Ohm's law to the two nearly equal currents.) By using this device, then, we can amplify voltages. A smaller voltage applied to the input results in a larger voltage across the output. Such a gain in voltage is entirely due to the fact that the base-collector circuit is a constant-current device for reverse biases.

We can also make a useful transistor with two *P*-type blocks of semiconductor and one *N*-type. It would be organized in the fashion shown in Figure A2-10. The explanation for its operation is the

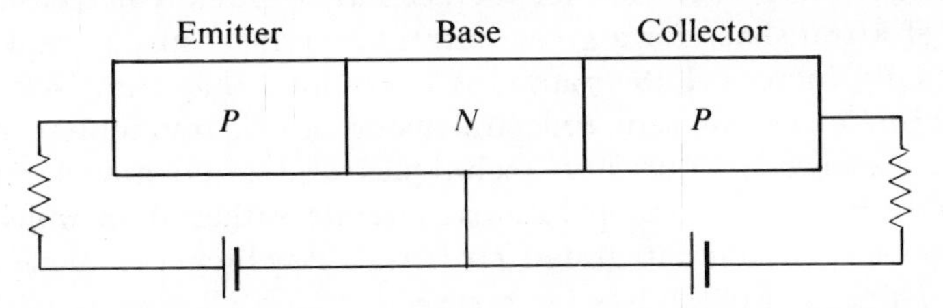

Fig. A2-10. *An PNP transistor. The forward and reverse biases now have to be of the opposite polarity as in the NPN case.*

same, except that we now must phrase our discussion in terms of the alternate minority carrier, holes, and therefore the reverse biases are of opposite polarity. The general idea is, however, identical in every respect to that of the *NPN* transistor. The following outline describes the sequence of operations of the *PNP* transistor:

1. The *PNP* transistor is a three-part semiconductor device.
2. A forward-biased voltage (in this case the emitter is positive

with respect to the base) applied between the emitter and the base regulates the number of *holes* that are injected into the base.

3. The number of holes in the base (in this case minority carriers for the *N*-type material) regulates the amount of reverse current that will flow when a reverse bias (in this case the collector is negative with respect to the base) is applied across the collector and the base.
4. The reverse current of electrons that flows in the external circuit will be almost independent of the resistance and the applied voltage up to the limits of Ohm's law. It will, however, be in the opposite direction to the collector-base current in the *NPN* transistor.

Many technical specifications determine which transistor is to be used in a given application. Transistors may vary in their gain characteristics as well as in their current-carrying capacities. Other specific features, such as the maximum frequency signal that can be carried and the delay of a signal passing through a transistor, become important considerations in very fast applications. Similarly, the semiconductor material of which the transistor is composed is a major practical factor in the choice of the system. In general, silicon is superior to germanium because it can withstand wide temperature variations better and thus, in the long run, is more reliable.

Modern manufacturing techniques have gradually decreased the size of a transistor for a given current-carrying capacity and have gradually increased the range of operations that transistors can perform. At the present time transistors are manufactured by almost completely automatic techniques and often are assembled directly into complete operational circuits rather than individual components. Such integrated circuitry, in which the diodes and transistors as well as passive components are all formed within a single encapsulation, is unusually reliable, since less additional external wiring is needed than in ordinary transistor circuitry. It should be remembered, however, that, even though the manufacturing techniques differ, the theory of the operation of the transistor remains the same.

For diagramming circuits, a standardized symbol has been created for both types of transistors. Figure A2-11 depicts the symbols for both the *NPN* and the *PNP* transistor. The emitter is always the connector indicated by the arrow. The collector is the other connection coming off the base. The direction of the arrow

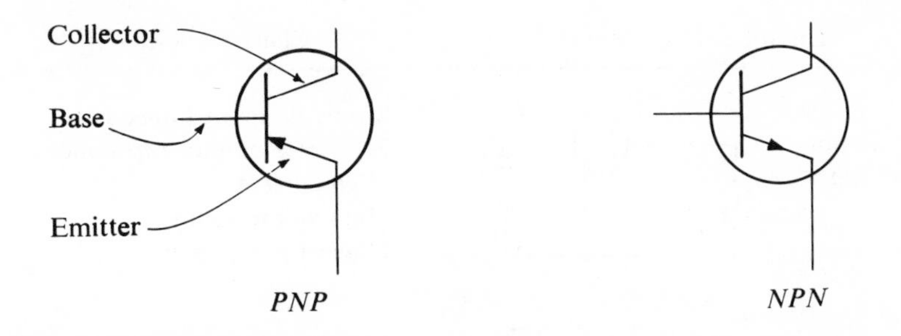

Fig. A2-11. *The standard symbols for the PNP and the NPN transistors. The arrows on the emitter lead identify the two types. In each case the arrow points in the opposite direction to electron flow.*

shows which of the two types of devices is being used. The direction the arrow points has by convention been the direction of the flow of current in the classic sense and is thus in the direction opposite the flow of electrons.

Although transistors can accomplish an almost endless variety of functions in electronic circuitry, they are generally connected in one of three different modes. This classification is determined by which of the three connections—the base, the emitter, or the collector—is used as the common reference for the voltages applied to the other two connections. So far we have been talking about the common-base situation, in which the voltages applied to the emitter and the collector are referenced to the base. But transistors can be used in two other configurations: the emitter may be common to both of the applied voltages, or the collector may be common. Figure A2-12 diagrams the three types of transistor configurations and defines their advantages.

Each of the three basic arrangements is suitable for performing special kinds of tasks. The common-emitter arrangement, for example, permits large gains in the amount of current, since the injection of a small amount of current into the base results in the flow of larger amounts of current between the emitter and the collector. Voltage gains are therefore easily accomplished by selecting the appropriate load resistor in the output circuit. However, since the resistor in the output circuit must be fairly large to produce a given voltage change relative to the input, the ability of this circuit to drive heavy loads is restricted. A heavy load (a small resistance in parallel with the output) would tend to reduce the output voltage by reducing the output resistance for the constant current. Nevertheless, the gain characteristics of the grounded emitter circuit make it the most generally useful of the three configurations.

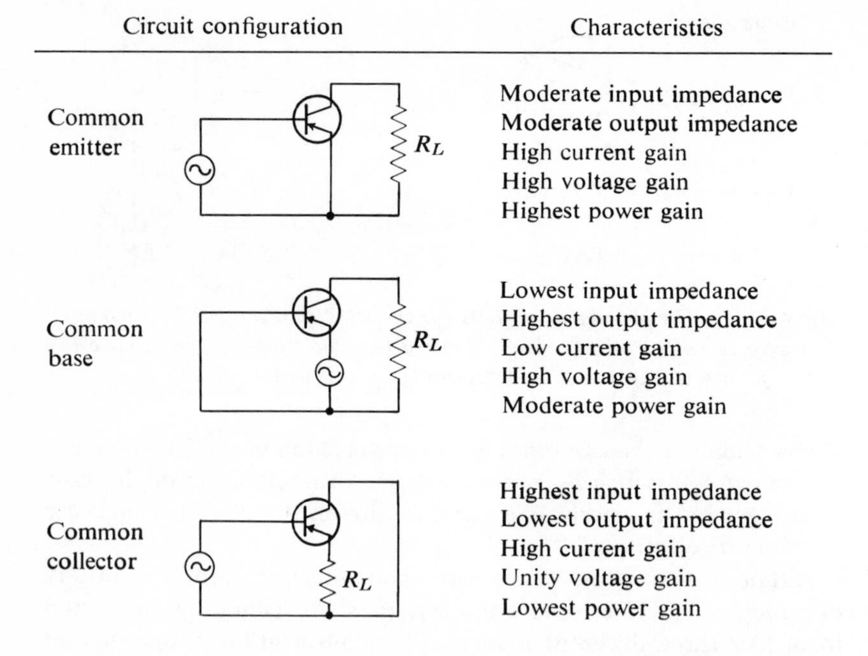

Fig. A2-12. *The three different standard configurations of transistor usage and their advantages and attributes. (Modified from* General Electric Transistor Manual, *Semiconductor Products Department, General Electric Company, 1964, p. 28.)*

The common-base circuit has little current gain, and, in fact, it has a slight loss of current from input to output. The voltage gain indicated is accomplished by making the input resistor smaller than the output resistor. Since the functions of the common-base circuit can be handled by common-emitter circuits with the additional advantages of current gain, common-base transistors are infrequently used in computer circuits.

Common-collector circuits have the capability of extremely high current gain. A small current in the input will produce the largest current output of the three circuit configurations. But more important is the fact that, although the input impedance is very high and requires only a small amount of current to accomplish its function, the output impedance can be made very low. Thus, a common-collector circuit can have a heavy load placed on its output without seriously distorting the output voltage. Such circuits are ordinarily called *emitter followers* and are used to take a driving voltage with only a small current capacity and convert it into an equal (or slightly lowered) voltage with a much enlarged current-driving capacity.

One other feature relevant to the use of transistors is *polarity reversal* or *inversion.* Inversion refers to the capability of a transistor to change a positive going signal into a negative going signal or vice versa. It should be apparent, when one studies the current flow in a common-emitter transistor, that a transistor connected in this manner acts to invert the polarity of the signal. On the other hand, common-base and common-collector circuits do not invert. The requirement for inversion capability, therefore, adds another argument for the principal use of the common-emitter circuit configuration in digital computer circuits.

The amplitude of transistor output signals can be made to vary continuously by applying continuously varying input signals. Such circuits are used in audio and other amplifier applications in which it is desirable to represent a continuous series of signal amplitudes. In digital circuits, however, one need only represent two states to encode the 1 and 0 conditions. These two states can be adequately represented by two special conditions of transistor operation. In the first, no minority carriers are being injected into the base; only the very smallest amount of current will be flowing between the emitter and the base. This is the condition known as *cutoff*. In the second condition the number of minority carriers corresponds to the maximum current-carrying capability of the transistor. This is the condition called *saturation,* for the transistor is conducting as heavily as it possibly can; no further injection of minority carriers will increase the current. These two conditions correspond to the open and closed positions of an electromechanical switch. The saturated state corresponds to the closed position of the switch, with current flowing through the unit at the maximum rate. The cutoff state corresponds to an open switch.

In addition to the junction type of transistors and diodes described earlier, many other semiconductor devices are becoming available that may have applications for computer circuitry and research problems in the life and social sciences.

Photosensitive diodes have been developed that change their resistance as light falls upon them. Such units can be placed in a circuit and behave very much like a transistor, except that the minority carriers are made available by photoelectric emission rather than by carrier injection from a second diode junction. Light-emitting semiconductors have also been developed that can produce a wavelength appropriate for the stimulation of photosensitive devices.

Conventional transistors require that the input be maintained during the entire time the output is desired. There is, however, a class of four-terminal semiconductor devices, called *silicon control-*

led rectifiers, that can be pulsed through either one of two inputs and then maintain a conducting or a nonconducting state through the other two terminals, even though the input signal is no longer present. They exhibit memory, therefore, and could be used instead of some of the more elaborate multivibrator circuits. Zener diodes are used for regulating voltages because of their ability to break down at a precisely defined voltage. The breakdown acts to limit the voltage applied to a given circuit to that very specific breakdown voltage. Field-effect transistors operate much as did the older vacuum tubes (see below) and have the advantage of enormously high input impedances. This allows them to sense signals from sources which themselves are of very high impedance output levels without distorting or reducing the amplitude of the signal.

The list can go on and on, for the semiconductor research field is at present very active. The properties of semiconductors make them extremely useful for a wide variety of applications at high speeds and power capacities.

Electromechanical switches

Although transistors exhibit powerful control properties for small and moderate power levels, it is often necessary or desirable to control electrical functions with the slower-acting but generally higher-powered electromechanical contact. As a matter of fact, the earliest computers were made almost entirely of *relays*—the generic name for electromagnetically operated switches. The logical properties of saturated transistors are identical to those of the closed switch, although the transistor can, of course, operate at much higher speeds. Figure A2-13 is a diagram of a typical relay, showing the electromagnetic control coil and the contacts. In addition, other mechanical attachments (typically coil springs) provide restoring forces that return the contacts to their unactivated position as soon as the coil is de-energized.

The coil is activated by passing a current through it. The current produces an electromagnetic force that is concentrated in a soft iron core within the coil. This force magnetically attracts the upper arm, on which the common contacts are mounted during the time the coil is activated. When the coil is deactivated, a spring pulls the common arm back to its original, normally open, position. Connections may be made from the common contact to the other contacts during both of the two states—the normally open and the normally closed.

Besides carrying heavy currents, relays can be constructed with

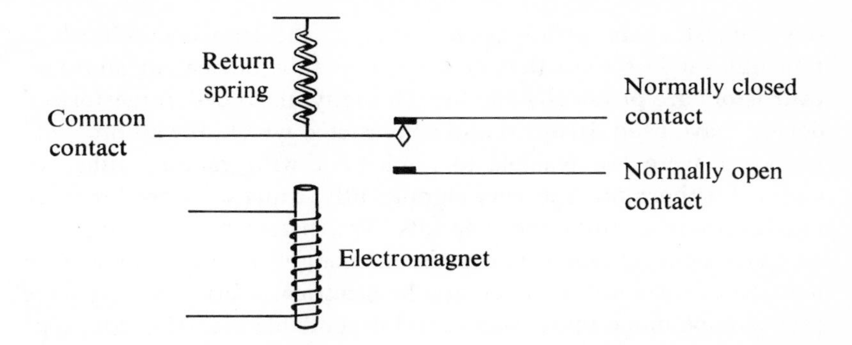

Fig. A2-13. *A schematic diagram of an electromagnetic relay showing the coil, the moving arm, and the restoring spring as well as the contact arrangement.*

multiple poles or contacts. Thus, many circuits may be simultaneously switched while maintaining electrical isolation from one another.

Devices of even higher power capability have been designed and actually do useful mechanical work. They are grouped under the generic name *solenoid.* Instead of simply closing a set of switches, as in the relay operation, the solenoid can perform some heavier mechanical action, such as releasing a clutch in a typewriter or opening a shutter in a visual experiment.

A historical note

We mentioned that relays were used as logical elements in the earliest computers. In the so-called second generation of computers electronic vacuum tube circuitry was used. Vacuum tube circuitry was encumbered by the tremendous amount of power used for nonlogical operations, which had to be dissipated as heat. Most of this power was used to heat the filaments of the vacuum tubes so that electrons could be boiled off thermally. The free electrons then served as the carriers of current. The filament in a typical vacuum tube glowed cherry red, indicating that much energy was being wasted as visible light. It also felt hot to the touch, indicating that much energy was being wasted as heat. All vacuum tube computers, therefore, required extensive air conditioning systems to keep their enviroments inhabitable for their users and themselves.

Transistors, on the other hand, do not have to be heated. Their carriers can be injected in sufficient numbers by the simple application of a low voltage. Although there is, of course, some heating in the transistor, the entire power level of the transistor circuit is typically far less than that of a vacuum tube device; in addition, transistors are physically smaller. In many instances transistorized devices have been designed and constructed which, for all practical purposes, were not feasible to implement with vacuum tube circuitry. Furthermore and very significantly, transistors are far more reliable than vacuum tube circuits. Transistors are, in fact, only simple blocks of solid materials. Although they are subject to damage by mechanical shock and by electrical overloads, they have proved to be much more rugged and dependable than the older type of circuits.

Such practical considerations have led to the almost universal adoption of transistors in computer circuitry, but in all cases the logical functions performed by the specific devices are the same.

BIBLIOGRAPHY AND INDEX

Adams, J. A., & Humes, J. M. Monitoring of complex visual displays: IV. Training for vigilance. *Hum. Factors,* 1963, *5,* 147–153.

Adey, W. R., Dunlop, C. W., & Hendrix, C. E. Hippocampal slow waves; distribution and phase relationships in the course of approach learning. *A.M.A. Arch. Neurol.,* 1960, *3,* 74–90.

Babbage, C. In P. Morrison & E. Morrison (Eds.), *Charles Babbage and his calculating engines: Selected writings by Charles Babbage and others.* New York: Dover, 1961.

Barlow, J. S., & Brown, R. M. An analog correlator system for brain potentials. *Tech. Rep. 300,* Res. Lab. Electron., Mass. Inst. Technol., 1955.

Bickford, R. G. An automatic recognition system for spike-and-wave with simultaneous testing of motor response. *EEG clin. Neurophysiol.,* 1959, *11,* 397–398. (Abstract)

Bickford, R. G., Jacobson, J. L., & Cody, D. T. R. Nature of average evoked potentials to sound and other stimuli in man. *Ann. N.Y. Acad. Sci.,* 1964, *112,* 204–223.

Brazier, M. A. B. (Ed.) Computer techniques in EEG analysis. *EEG clin. Neurophysiol.,* Suppl. 20, 1961.

Brazier, M. A. B. The problem of periodicity in the electroencephalogram: Studies in the cat. *EEG clin. Neurophysiol.,* 1963, *15,* 287–298.

Brazier, M. A. B. Evoked responses recorded from the depths of the human brain. *Ann. N.Y. Acad. Sci.,* 1964, *112,* 33–59.

Buiten, R., & Lane, H. S. Experimental system gives language student instant error feedback. *Digital Equipment Corp. Computer Application Note.* Maynard, Mass., 1965.

Bullock, T. H. Neuron doctrine and electrophysiology. *Science,* 1959, *129,* 997–1002.

Burks, A. W., Goldstine, H. H., & von Neumann, J. *Preliminary discussion of the logical design of an electronic computing instrument.* Part I, Vol. I. Princeton, N.J.: Inst. for Advanced Study, 1947.

Casby, J. U., Siminoff, R., & Houseknecht, T. R. An analogue cross-correlator to study naturally induced activity in intact nerve trunks. *J. Neurophysiol.,* 1963, *26,* 432–448.

Clapp, L. C., & Kain, R. Y. A computer aid for symbolic mathematics. *AFIPS Conf. Proc.,* 1963, *24,* 509–518.

Communications Biophysics Group of Research Laboratory of Electronics, & Siebert, W. M. Processing neuroelectric data. *Tech. Rep. 351,* Mass. Inst. Technol., 1959.

Coulson, J. E. (Ed.) *Programmed learning and computer-based instruction: Proceedings of the Conference on Application of Digital Computers to Automated Instruction, Oct. 10–12, 1961.* New York: Wiley, 1962.

Cox, D. R., & Smith, W. L. On the superposition of renewal processes. *Biometrika,* 1954, *41,* 91–99.

Crowder, N. A. Automatic tutoring by means of intrinsic programming. In E. Galanter (Ed.), *Automatic teaching: The state of the art.* New York: Wiley, 1959. Pp. 109–116.

Davis, M. R., & Ellis, T. O. The RAND tablet: A man-machine graphical communication device. *AFIPS Conf. Proc.,* 1964, *26,* 325–331.

Dawson, G. D. Cerebral responses to electrical stimulation of peripheral nerve in man. *J. Neurol. Neurosurg. Psychiat.,* 1947, *10,* 137–140.

Dawson, G. D. Cerebral responses to nerve stimulation in man. *British Medical Bulletin,* 1950, *6,* 326–329.

Dawson, G. D. A summation technique for the detection of small evoked potentials. *EEG clin. Neurophysiol.,* 1954, *6,* 65–84.

de Grazia, S. *Of time, work and leisure.* New York: Twentieth Century Fund, 1962.

Domino, E., & Corssen, G. Visually evoked response in anesthetized man with and without induced muscle paralysis. *Ann. N.Y. Acad. Sci.,* 1964, *112,* 226–237.

Domino, E., Matsuoka, S., Waltz, J., & Cooper, I. Simultaneous recordings of scalp and epidural somatosensory-evoked responses in man. *Science,* 1964, *145,* 1199–1200.

Edwards, W. Men and computers. In R. M. Gagné (Ed.), *Psychological Principles in system development.* New York: Holt, Rinehart & Winston, 1962. Pp. 75–113.

Edwards, W. Probabilistic information processing in command and control systems. *Tech. Doc. Rep.* No. ESD–TDR–62–345, University of Michigan, Institute of Science and Technology, March, 1963.

Edwards, W. Non-conservative probabilistic information processing systems. *Tech. Doc. Rep.* No. ESD–TDR–66–404, University of Michigan, Institute of Science and Technology, December, 1966.

Farley, B. G., Frishkopf, L. S., Clark, W. A., Jr., & Gilmore, J. T., Jr. Computer techniques for the study of patterns in the electroencephalogram. *IRE Trans.,* 1962, *BME-9,* 4–12.

Fox, S. S., & O'Brien, J. H. Duplication of evoked potential waveform by curve of probability of firing of a single cell. *Science,* 1965, *147,* 888–890.

Galton, F. *Inquiries into human faculty and its development.* London: Macmillan, 1883.

Gasser, H. S., & Erlanger, J. *Electrical signs of nervous activity.* Philadelphia: Univer. of Pennsylvania Press, 1937.

General Electric Transistor Manual, General Electric Company, 1964.

Grabbe, E. M., Ramo, S., & Wooldridge, D. E. (Eds.) *Handbook of automation, computation, and control.* New York: Wiley, 1958–1961.

Grass, A. M., & Gibbs, F. A. A Fourier transform of the electroencephalogram. *J. Neurophysiol.,* 1938, *1,* 521–526.

Green, B. F. *Digital computers in research.* New York: McGraw-Hill, 1963.

Haber, R. N., Hershenson, M., & Schroeder, D. Apparatus note: Use of an IBM 024 or 026 card punch for simultaneous stimulus programming and response recording. *Percept. mot. Skills,* 1962, *15,* 627–630.

Holland, J. H. A universal computer capable of executing an arbitrary number of sub-programs simultaneously. *Proc. E. Joint Comp. Conf.,* 1959, 108–113.

Hughes, R. R. *An introduction to clinical electro-encephalography.* Bristol, England: John Wright & Sons, 1961.

Huskey, H. D. Automatic computers and teaching machines. In J. E. Coulson (Ed.), *Programmed learning and computer-based instruction.* New York: Wiley, 1962. Pp. 257–272.

Julesz, B. Binocular depth perception of computer generated patterns. *Bell System Tech. J.*, 1960, *39*, 1125–1162.

Katzman, R. (Ed.) Sensory evoked response in man. *Ann. N.Y. Acad. Sci.*, 1964, *112*, 1–546.

Lee, Y. W. *Statistical theory of communication.* New York: Wiley, 1960.

Licklider, J. C. R. Man-computer symbiosis. *IRE Trans.*, 1960, *HFE-9*, 4–11.

Licklider, J. C. R. Preliminary experiments in computer-aided teaching. In J. E. Coulson (Ed.), *Programmed learning and computer-based instruction.* New York: Wiley, 1962. Pp. 217–239.

McConnell, D., Polidora, V. J., Friedman, M. P., & Meyer, D. R. Automatic reading and recording of digital data in the analysis of primitive behavior. Paper read at 11th Annual Conf. on Electrical Techniques in Medicine and Biology, Minneapolis, November, 1958.

Miller, G. A. The magical number seven-plus-or-minus two. *Psychol. Rev.*, 1956, *63*, 81–97.

Miller, G. A., Bregman, A. S., & Norman, D. A. The computer as a general purpose device for the control of psychological experiments. In R. W. Stacy & B. D. Waxman (Eds.), *Computers in biomedical research.* (Vol. I.) New York: Academic Press, 1965. Pp. 467–490.

Nickerson, R. S. The computer as a control device for psychological experimentation. (Informal note.) Decision Sci. Lab., ESD, AFSC, Bedford, Mass., 1964.

Norman, D. A. Acquisition and retention in short term memory. *J. exp. Psychol.*, 1966, 72, 369–381.

Okajima, M., Stark, L., Whipple, G., & Yasui, S. Computer pattern recognition techniques: Some results with real electrocardiographic data. *IEEE Trans.*, 1963, *BME-10*, 106–114.

Penfield, W., & Roberts, L. *Speech and brain-mechanisms.* Princeton, N.J.: Princeton Univer. Press, 1959.

Pollack, I., & Headly, P. Methodological study of PEST procedure. Personal communication, 1967.

Pressey, S. L. Certain major psycho-educational issues appearing in the Conference on Teaching Machines. In E. Galanter (Ed.), *Automatic teaching: The state of the art.* New York: Wiley, 1959. Pp. 187–198.

Presti, A. J. High speed sound spectrograph. *J. Acoust. Soc. Amer.*, 1966, *40*, 628–634.

Rapoport, Amnon. Sequential decision-making in a computer-controlled task. *J. math. Psychol.*, 1964, *1*, 351–374.

Reitman, W. *Cognition and thought: An information processing approach.* New York: Wiley, 1965.

Rémond, A. Level of organization of evoked responses in man. *Ann. N.Y. Acad. Sci.*, 1964, *112*, 143–159.

Ruchkin, D. S., Villegas, J., & John, E. R. An analysis of average evoked potentials making use of least mean square techniques. *Ann. N.Y. Acad. Sci.*, 1964, *115*, 799–826.

Schmitt, O. H. Averaging techniques employing several simultaneous physiological variables. *Ann. N.Y. Acad. Sci.*, 1964, *115*, 952–975.

Schoenfeld, R. L. The role of a digital computer as a biological instrument. *Ann. N.Y. Acad. Sci.*, 1964, *115*, 915–942.

Shuford, E. H., Jr. The decision sciences laboratory program of techniques and facilities for automating research. *Tech. Doc. Rep.* No. ESD–TDR–64–553, 1964.

Siminoff, R. Cutaneous nerve activity in response to noxious stimuli. *Exp. Neurol.*, 1965, *11*, 288–297.

Skinner, B. F. Teaching machines. *Science*, 1958, *128*, 969–977.

Smith, J. E. K. Stimulus programming in psychophysics. *Psychometrika*, 1961, *26*, 27–33.

Sokolnikoff, I. S., & Sokolnikoff, G. S. *Higher mathematics for engineers and physicists.* New York: McGraw-Hill, 1941.

Stacy, R. W., & Waxman, B. D. (Eds.) *Computers in biomedical research.* New York: Academic Press, 1965. 2 vols.

Sutherland, I. E. Sketchpad, A Man-machine graphical communication system. *AFIPS Conf. Proc.*, Spring Joint Computer Conf. New York: Spartan Books, 1963.

Swets, J. A., & Feurzeig, W. Computer-aided instruction. *Science*, 1965, *150*, 572–576.

Swets, J. A., Millman, S. H., Fletcher, Wm. E., & Green, D. M. Learning to identify non-verbal sounds: An application of a computer as a teaching machine. *J. acoust. Soc. Amer.*, 1962, *34*, 928–935.

Taylor, M. M., & Creelman, C. D. PEST: Efficient Estimates on Probability Functions. University of Toronto preprint, 1965.

Teager, H. M. Systems considerations in real-time computer usage. In J. E. Coulson (Ed.), *Programmed learning and computer-based instruction.* New York: Wiley, 1962. Pp. 273–280.

Tolles, W. E. (Ed.) Computers in medicine and biology. *Ann. N.Y. Acad. Sci.*, 1964, *115*, 543–1140.

Turing, A. M. Computing machinery and intelligence. *Mind*, 1950, *59*, 433–460.

Uhr, L. The compilation of natural language text into teaching machine programs. *AFIPS Conf. Proc.*, 1964, *26*, 35–44.

Uhr, L. The automatic generation of teaching machine programs. Unpublished report, Aug. 13, 1965. Available from the author, Computer Sciences Dept., Univer. of Wisconsin, Madison, Wis.

Uttal, W. R. My teacher has three arms! ! ! *IBM Res. Rep., RC* 788. IBM Research Center, Yorktown Heights, N.Y., September, 1962. (*a*)

Uttal, W. R. On conversational interaction. In J. E. Coulson (Ed.), *Programmed learning and computer-based instruction.* New York: Wiley, 1962. Pp. 171–190. (*b*)

Uttal, W. R. Apparatus note: The use of a summary card-punch to generate stimuli and to collect data simultaneously. *Amer. J. Psychol.*, 1962, *75*, 150–151. (*c*)

Uttal, W. R., & Kasprzak, H. The caudal photoreceptor of the crayfish: Quantitative study of responses to intensity, temporal and wavelength variables. *AFIPS Conf. Proc.*, 1962, *21*, 159–169.

Uttal, W. R., & Krissoff, M. Effect of stimulus pattern on temporal acuity in the somatosensory system. *J. exp. Psychol.*, 1966, *71*, 878–883.

von Neumann, J., *et al.* See Burks, Goldstine, & von Neumann.

Wald, A. *Sequential Analysis.* New York: Wiley, 1947.

Weinberg, G. M. Experiments in problem solving. Unpublished doctoral dissertation, Univer. of Michigan, 1965.

Weiss, B., & Laties, V. G. Reinforcement schedule generated by an on-line digital computer. *Science,* 1965, *148,* 658–661.

Weizenbaum, J. ELIZA—a computer program for the study of natural language communication between man and machine. *Communications of the ACM,* 1966, *9,* 36–45.

White, B. W. Computer applications to psychological research: Studies in perception. *Behav. Sci.,* 1962, *7,* 396–401.

Yntema, D. B., Wozencraft, F. T., & Klem, L. Immediate recall of digits presented at very high rates. Paper presented at Psychonomic Society, Niagara Falls, Ontario, 1964.

68 69 70 7 6 5 4 3 2 1